THE AWESOME LIFE FORCE

The Hermetic Laws of the Universe as Applied to All Phenomena

JOSEPH H. CATER

Health Research
P.O. Box 850
Pomeroy, WA 99347

Second Revised Edition With New Material
and Added Diagrams, Appendix

Library of Congress Card No. 84-081389

Printed in the United States of America

PUBLISHER'S FOREWORD

The author presents surprising facts concerning our planet. These facts are in variance with conventional science and preconceived opinions of the average individual. However, a careful study of this unusual book should convince the orthodox reader that there are new ideas under the sun.

The study of history will show many examples of how orthodox views gave way to new knowledge. Most of these did not take place overnight. In this new age many former scientific theories will be discarded or improved upon. Truth will not contradict truth.

Joseph H. Cater, B.A. in physics (U.S.C. 1948), decided to abandon an academic career in science when he began to sense that there were things drastically wrong with conventional science. At that time he resolved to develop a better approach to science and find a unifying principle that linked metaphysics, the occult, mathematics and the physical sciences.

Mr. Cater has spent some seven years in preparation of this final revised edition. The previous edition was badly edited by the former publisher, paragraphs were placed in wrong positions, many words were misspelled, words were added into sentences — words were left out. This created embarrassment to the author. This second, revised edition was promised in late 1983 by the publisher. However, after many delays, excuses and complete lack of communication, the author gave up. He turned the copyright and publication over to Health Research.

This book is probably the most unusual we have had the opportunity to publish. Soft Particle Physics is a modernization and logical update based upon the concepts of ether. In physics, some seventy years ago, the concept of the ether was commonly accepted. The scope of Sciencegate is beyond rational comprehension. With the Establishment acceptance of the erroneous Theory of Relativity, all concepts of ether disappeared from the physics texts and research.

If one refuses to accept the false dogmas as truth, he will not receive a diploma and will be excluded from prestigious and lucrative positions. The author was born ahead of his time. He is a keen analyst and is endowed with wisdom from the *Universal Mind.* Free energy is no longer a dream or a myth — it is now a hard reality. Roy J. Myers, Harry E. Perrigo and others furnished working models to the U.S. patent office showing that electricity as free as air is possible. *They were refused patents!*

Newspapers described the Perrigo invention as a hoax. Mr. Perrigo's health finally gave way to the barrage of skepticism. (Kansas City Star, January 15, 1922.) Numerous amazing inventions are suppressed by the power elite. Many have not published their findings because of the feelings of the academic community. Some inventors are afraid of public ridicule. Joseph H. Cater has had several magazine articles sabotaged through editing.

The author has corrected many pages of the former title, *The Awesome Life Force.* He has rewritten chapter eight — additional pages have been added to chapters twenty-two and thirty-two. Many pages of the text have been entirely rewritten. He has added additional diagrams and ten new pages of appendix. The content pages have been expanded into more detail.

The word "impossible" is one of the most dangerous in the English language. It's generally the fellow who doesn't know any better who does the thing that can't be done. You see, he doesn't know it is impossible (can't be done), so he goes ahead and does it! Several new inventions are the direct result of reading Mr. Cater's writings.

TRUTH is such a rare quality, a stranger so seldom met in this civilization of fraud, that it is never received freely, but must always fight its way into the world. This is true in the case of this title.

Health Research
P.O. Box 850
Pomeroy, WA 99347

Acknowledgements

The author is indebted to those he has encountered in the past who have channeled or triggered thought processes that have led to fruitful revelations, many of which appeared in an earlier version of this book, entitled *"The Awesome Force"*. This includes such individuals as Jesse Wilson, Irving Dyatt and more recently, friend and associate Marvin Brouillet and Walter Kirshenman. He is also thankful for valuable criticism and suggestions that have been instrumental in making this a better book than the original version.

CONTENTS

PART IV

INTRODUCTION

The deeper mysteries of the universe have always been considered beyond human understanding. There is one important and almost self-evident principle such believers, who make up all but a few of the world's thinkers, seem to overlook. Everything in the process of creation proceeds from the simple to the more complex. Every mechanical or electronic device, regardless of its complexity, operates according to a very few simple and easily understood principles. It follows that the universe should also comply with the same pattern, regardless of its near infinite complexity. This will be proven during the course of this treatise. Such a statement may seem overly optimistic and even blasphemous to many.

The test for the validity of a theory or concept is its ability to explain and even predict a wide range of phenomena. The wider the range, the more likely it is to be correct. The principles and concepts introduced in this treatise more than live up to this standard. In fact, there is no known phenomenon not taken in stride by these new ideas. This reduces the probability to the vanishing point that they do not have validity. The power of the concepts presented is often demonstrated by the fact that some of the most baffling phenomena known, merely serve as confirmations of the truth contained in these ideas.

It is to be expected that such revelations would make a shambles of currently popular, and universally accepted ideas of conventional science. The trend of orthodox scientific thinking is diametrically opposed to reality. It seems to be the consensus that ever greater complexities will be encountered, the deeper one probes into fundamental causes. In any event, orthodox, theoretical physics is in a deplorable state of confusion. It has become a hodgepodge of mathematical monstrosities. Profundity has usually been associated with complexity. In general, the latter is merely an indication of a perplexed state of mind with a very limited degree of comprehension. This describes the mind of the typical academic scientist.

The author is not likely to endear himself with the scientific community at large, and it is equally improbable that he will experience any remorse or guilt complex over any unfriendly attitudes this treatise may engender. Fortunately, the members of the scientific community constitute only a minute percentage of the population. There are still many people whose minds have not been scrambled and ossified by institutions of "higher learning," and who have some degree of intelligence and common sense. Such individuals can find much of interest and value in this treatise, despite the fact only a very small minority could likely gain a complete understanding of all the ideas presented.

For the first time in the history of this civilization, or perhaps any other, the seemingly impossible has been achieved. The physical sciences, the occult, metaphysics, and even philosophy have all been combined into a unified whole with no sharp lines separating them. This makes possible a far deeper insight into each of these subjects than was available before. Such a presentation, within one volume, renders this book unique among all the others. As such, it cannot be categorized. Therefore, it should create a dilemma for librarians with their present system of classification.

It will be noted that the author has not been able to always supply the exact date and name of the publication from which certain information has been extracted. In such cases he was faced with the option of either omitting or mentioning it. He always chose the latter. This, of course, is contrary to standard procedure and the rigid and unimaginative thinking of academic researchers. The reader can be assured that such information exists in some publication even if its author at the present time cannot put his finger on it. Inclusion of such information has added to the book and not detracted from it.

The author has also been criticized for treating speculation and theory as though they are facts. To put it bluntly this is a reflection of a mind of very limited comprehension steeped in the inflexible rules of the academic tradition. It is true that every procedure designed to expand one's understanding of the universe starts out with a speculation as was done extensively during the development of the new science revealed in the following pages. However, if such "speculations" turn out to be as fruitful as those introduced in this treatise, then it is safe to remove them from the realm of mere speculation and consider them facts. It has been found that as more new "facts" are uncovered, more support is given to these "speculations". The continual reminding of the reader that the material is based on speculation by the continual use of such words as probable, perhaps, likely, etc., is not only poor writing style, but an insult to the intelligence of the reader. It is also an indication the author does not have a firm grasp of the subject matter.

Despite the vast wealth of incontrovertible evidence which supports the ideas presented in this treatise, the new science outlined in the pages to follow will never be accepted by a significant portion of the scientific community. It is difficult for a rational person to believe that minds exist which can mutually accept two contradictory ideas simultaneously and repeatedly reject undeniable facts which are contrary to accepted beliefs. It is even more inconceivable that there are many such minds among the so called intelligentsia of the population. Nevertheless it is true. It has been the author's misfortune to encounter such individuals. Hopefully such experiences can be kept to a minimum in the future.

INTRODUCTION TO PART I

The image of the scientific community has been somewhat tarnished in the eyes of many thinking people during the past few decades. This is completely justified. Orthodox scientists, as a whole, are always the last to recognize or accept (if they ever do) any unusual fact or reality that does not fit comfortably into the picture of the universe as they see it. This is the case, regardless of any proof or evidence made available to them. A typical example is the much publicized Sasquatch. The proof of its existence is beyond question, as far as rational minds are concerned. In fact, it would be difficult to find anyone outside the scientific community who is not convinced of its reality. The evidence is too overwhelming. Yet the scientific world is still doubtful. One commentator stated that the attitude of the scientists in this matter is more amazing than the Sasquatch itself. If this individual had investigated the record of the scientific community, he wouldn't have found this behavior so unusual. For ages the vanguard of the status quo of science has ruthlessly persecuted any legitimate pioneer who has tried to introduce a new idea, or made a discovery, which might question the validity of any established concept.

A present-day, innovative pioneer faces formidable odds in any attempt to present a revolutionary concept or discovery. He has not only the influential scientific community to contend with, but also its powerful allies behind the scenes who control the press, radio and television, From a financial standpoint it is to their advantage for things of a scientific and technological nature to remain as they are. Consequently, the old dogmas and fallacies of science still constitute the backbone of all school curriculum, textbooks, and encyclopedias where science is concerned.

Through such channels, the public is led to believe that many of the illogical speculations of orthodox scientists have been shown to be valid. For example, the existence of black holes and validity of Einstein's theories, which have allegedly changed our conception of the universe, are now supposedly confirmed facts. The ideas and concepts introduced in the pages to follow will destroy such cherished theories.

Part I will reveal some of the incredible flaws underlying the superstructure of modern, orthodox physics. Since there can be no fruitful coexistence of diametrically opposed concepts, this procedure is necessary to pave the way for the introduction of infinitely better ideas. After reading Part I, the reader will likely be surprised at how egregiously bad the logic underlying such theories as those of Einstein and others really is. He will wonder how such supposedly profound minds could commit so many blunders, and also why they had not been brought to light long before this book was written. The reasons will become apparent by the time he finishes this treatise.

INCREDIBLE FLAWS AND DISCREPANCIES OF ORTHODOX SCIENCE

CHAPTER 1

UNDENIABLE DISCREPANCIES IN CONVENTIONAL SCIENCE AS GATHERED FROM THE FINDINGS OF THE SPACE PROGRAM, THE RESEARCHES OF CHARLES FORT AND OTHERS

NASA as well as other interests has gone to great lengths to cover up the real findings of the space program. Such findings provide undeniable proof the most celebrated theories and concepts of conventional physics are completely erroneous. Despite all efforts to camouflage their program, leaks and slip-ups did occur. These leaks opened the door to many incredible revelations for any intelligent researcher with the necessary dedication and perseverence to take full advantage of the situation. Such findings will now be summarized. The following items are not mere speculation but are realities with a great wealth of factual evidence in conjunction with logical analysis to substantiate them.

1. The moon has a high surface gravity which rivals earth's gravity.
2. The moon has a dense atmosphere comparable to that of earth. In some of the low areas such as the mares, the atmosphere is actually denser than experienced any place on the earth!
3. Methods of propulsion of other than rockets were employed during critical stages of the Apollo missions. The space ships could not have carried sufficient fuel for the astronauts to reach the moon and return because of the moon's high gravity. The liftoff from the earth with rockets was part of the great NASA cover-up.

4. The earth (as all planets are) is hollow with a great egress, or entrance, into the earth's interior that is hundreds of miles across. It is located in the north polar regions just south of the north pole. Earlier satellite pictures of the earth show this entrance quite clearly. Subsequent pictures released by NASA were doctored to obliterate any evidence of such an entrance. Apparently, they neglected to do this with the earlier releases.
5. For years prior to the Apollo missions, NASA had space ships capable of interplanetary travel at its disposal. These ships employ fuelless propulsion systems similar to that of the highly publicized UFO (The principles will be analyzed later on in this treatise).
6. Gravity effects are produced by a highly penetrating radiation in the electromagnetic spectrum. It can be produced by mechanical means and used as levitating beams, as well as for a very effective method of propulsion. NASA has had such devices for many years. In fact, the U.S. Government sponsored experiments as early as 1958 that proved such devices feasible.

The moon's high gravity was in evidence during the telecasts, despite the efforts of NASA to give the illusion of a low gravity. One of the tricks was slowing down the rate of transmission to make objects appear to fall more slowly, and give the impression that the astronauts were careful in order to remain moonbound. Nevertheless, there was an occasion when an astronaut tried a spectacular leap that no doubt was not in the script. He did no better than he would have on the earth under the same conditions. Some photos refuted claims by NASA that the space suits included life-support systems weighing 185 pounds. For example, one of the astronauts was seen leaning over backwards with his supposedly heavy gear. If the weights were even a modest fraction of the claimed amount, he would have fallen over backwards. In order for him to have done this without falling over, the bulky pack he was carrying must have been empty. Evidence and research indicate that combined weight of suit and alleged life-support system did not weigh over 20 pounds. The earthlike conditions on the moon and its dense atmosphere obviated the space suits. It seems the space suits were a cover-up in more ways than one.

A photo of one of the "great" jumping exhibitions of an astronaut graced the front pages of some newspapers. A caption under it read "Astronaut John Young jumps high while saluting the flag on the moon oday." He did get all of about 16 inches off the ground while saluting the flag. However, some basketball players often get three feet and more off the ground in a similar manner. However, in deference to John Young, it should be mentioned that had they been wearing space suits, they probably couldn't have jumped much higher on the earth than did John Young on the moon.

The anemic jumping feats of the astronauts under alleged, one-sixth earth gravity, as shown on the telecasts, represent only part of the evidence of a high moon gravity. The consistent reports of the point where the space ships entered the gravitational influence of the moon indicated a moon gravity comparable to that of the earth. If the moon's surface gravity were only one-sixth earth gravity, this point of entry, or the point where the gravitational influence of the moon exceeds that of earth, would be approximately 22,000 miles from the moon. This can easily be confirmed by elementary mathematics and mechanics and will not be given here. The distance will vary slightly percentagewise because the moon's distance from the earth fluctuates. Since the advent of the Apollo missions, the distance reported for this point of entry has been consistently much greater than 22,000 miles. The distances claimed by various writers, as well as the media, have varied from about 39,000 to nearly 44,000 miles.

This is, indeed, incredible since it contradicts the consistent claims of a low moon gravity. Interestingly enough, prior to the space program this distance was always given in the 20,000 to 22,000 range, corresponding to one-sixth earth gravity for the moon. It can be found in a number of earlier textbooks, including Encyclopedia Britannica. Yet, the later editions of Encyclopedia Britannica put this distance at about the 40,000-mile range. There are many other indications of a high moon gravity.

On many occasions, the astronauts had difficulty in handling or moving weights that under one-sixth gravity should have been child's play. This was emphasized in one notable case. The astronauts became exhausted during a rock-gathering trek while climbing a hill. They failed to reach their destination.

During one of the Apollo missions an astronaut stumbled and fell on his face on more than one occasion. Under one-sixth gravity even a dotard with too much to drink could avoid doing this, even on one of his off days, and NASA doesn't pick stumblebums for astronaut material.

After this fiasco, a land rover was employed in subsequent missions. Interestingly enough, any mechanical engineer should have noticed it was designed for high gravity conditions instead of the low gravity the moon is supposed to have. The rover was about 10 feet long and four feet high, with a 7.5 foot wheelbase and 6 foot tread width. The wheels were 32 inches in diameter. Each wheel had a one-quarter horsepower motor, which gave it a top speed of 10.5 miles per hour. It had an earth weight of 460 pounds which would be only 75 pounds under one-sixth gravity. It is significant that the astronauts had great difficulty unloading it from the Lunar Module.

Prior to the space program, the problems anticipated on the moon with surface vehicles was analyzed by experts. Stability would be a major problem because of weak gravity. Inertial properties would be the same as on Earth, but the wheels would have only one-sixth the traction. This means that sudden turns would be dangerous and braking problems would be colossal. It was determined that a minimum size vehicle would need a 20 foot wheelbase and a tread of 20 feet to give it any speed capability over rough terrain, and to keep the center of gravity within six feet of the surface. The long wheelbase would necessitate a higher center of gravity to give it reasonable clearance. This proposed design would insure that the vehicle would clear rocks and still maintain stability in gravity conditions that would easily overturn an Earth type vehicle such as the Rover.

Calculations show that the Rover, with a loaded Earth weight of about 1600 pounds, would need a turning radius of well over 80 feet to keep from turning over at 10 miles per hour under one-sixth gravity. Even at 5 miles per hour this radius would need to be over 20 feet. Its minimum stopping distance at 10 miles per hour would be more than 40 feet. It is apparent that descending steep hills without disaster would be an impossibility. Yet, the astronauts did descend steep hills and did some "Grand Prix" driving while making sharp turns at top speed. Photos of tracks made by the Rover indicate very sharp turns having been made at times. Even with the Rover, the astronauts had to stay within a six mile radius of the Module. This was the maximum walking distance back to the ship in the event of a breakdown.

One of the photos brought back from the Apollo 12 mission showed an astronaut carrying a barbell-like package of instruments with an earth weight of 190 pounds. The pronounced bow in the bar holding the weights was not consistent with the claims that it had a moon weight of only 30 pounds.

It is also interesting to note that the sky in this same photo showed unmistakable evidence of cloud formations.

Early in 1967 an unbelievable announcement came on a newscast. It was stated that moon probes showed the moon's gravity was very nearly the same as earth's. There were contradictions among astronauts concerning moon gravity. During an interview on radio shortly after the Apollo 11 mission, the author heard Neil Armstrong hint very strongly about the moon having considerably more gravity than formerly believed. Later, other astronauts went out of their way to harp on the low, gravity conditions on the moon. No doubt they were pressured to lie about their experiences. The various types of leaks mentioned above cause one to speculate whether such lapses were a result of deliberate attempts of some within the space program to sabotage the cover-up; or that they were victims of mind control by outerspace intelligences who might look with disfavor upon the mendacity of officials in the space program, or a combination of both.

There is considerable indirect evidence of a high-moon gravity. The most notable is the moon's atmosphere. The proof of a dense atmosphere on the moon is fully as convincing as that of the moon's high gravity. Many viewers were puzzled at the billowing flags, the drifting of dust kicked up by the astronauts, and the fluttering of ribbon-like material on some of the instruments during a few of the telecasts from the moon. Photos taken by the astronauts showed unquestionable light diffusion of the moon. One of the photos including the sun indicated diffusion so pronounced the sun's disc was obliterated and most of the sky illuminated. Light is not supposed to be diffused in the vacuum conditions said to exist on the moon. The diffusion was incongruous with the black sky that appeared in all of the photos released to the public, except for at least one notable case. This exception that NASA failed to doctor showed a sky similar to that usually seen on the earth during the day.

There was another interesting slip-up by NASA in the photo department. All the photos taken by the moon orbiter, except one, showed an absence of any atmospheric fringe on the moon's horizon. The exception looked like a picture taken from an earth satellite. A blue atmospheric fringe was very apparent along the far edge of the moon!

Perhaps the most obvious indication of a dense moon atmosphere is the soil and deep layers of loose dust on the moon's surface. Such conditions cannot exist in a vacuum or near vacuum. Air molecules tend to adhere to surfaces. This layer of air tends to counteract cohesive forces, and prevents solid surfaces from adhering together or becoming "sticky." This, of course, prevents dust particles from coalescing and forming a solid, rocklike mass. This principle has been demonstrated on numerous occsions by placing soil or dust in a chamber and evacuating it to produce a near vacuum inside.

The evidence of a moon atmosphere has by no means been exhausted. Much of it obtruded on the scientific world long before the space program. Considerable light refraction by stars being occulted by the moon has been observed on many occasions. Meteors have been seen disintegrating in the moon's upper atmosphere. In fact, evidence shows that the moon's surface has better protection from meteorites than the earth.

At this stage, it is interesting to refer to an article entitled, "How Dead is the Moon" that appeared in Natural History magazine for February, 1950, pages 62-65. It is extremely significant from several standpoints. There was a reference made concerning a scientist, Dr. Lincoln La Paz, in the 1930's, calculated that meteors weighing ten pounds or more falling on the dark side of the moon should disintegrate in a flash bright enough to be seen with the naked eye. This is, of course, assuming the moon has no atmosphere. Over 100 should occur every year, yet, only two or three such flashes have been seen in all human history. The conclusion was that the moon seems to be better protected from meteors than the earth.

In 1941, an astronomer, Walter Haas, and associates searched the dark side of the moon for 170 hours with a telescope in an attempt to detect meteors burning up in a moon atmosphere. During that time twelve bright moving specks which began and ended at points on the moon were visible under their telescope. During these observations, four or five of our own meteors crossed the telescope field. One or two of the lunar flashes may have been extremely faint, earthbound meteors coming along directly toward the observer, but the laws of probability show most of them occurred on the moon.

According to author of this article, it was assumed the density of the atmosphere at the moon's surface was 1/10,000th as dense as the earth's. On this basis and the belief that the moon had one-sixth earth gravity, scientists calculated that above 43 to 55 miles above the moon's surface, the atmosphere was denser than earth is at similar altitudes. This was supposed to account for the great protection the moon's atmosphere provides the surface from meteor impact. It seems scientific reasoning in those days was as infantile as it is now.

It is obvious, or at least should be, the amount of protection an atmosphere gives a planetary surface is dependent upon the quantity of atmosphere existing above a unit area of the surface, not just its depth. In other words, it is the number of air molecules the meteor encounters, not the distribution that is the governing factor. On the basis of one-sixth earth gravity and a density at the surface of 1/10,000 that experienced at the earth's surface, the moon has only 6/10,000 as much atmosphere per unit areas as the earth. This conclusion is based on the fact that the volume of a gas is directly proportional to the pressure exerted on it. The gravitational field of a planet compresses the atmosphere and the amount of compression is almost directly proportional to the surface gravity. There will be a slight deviation because of the finite size of a planet. According to the above figures, our earth would have about 1,666 times the atmosphere protecting its surface as does the moon. This means that a meteor would encounter 1,666 times as many gas molecules before it reaches the earth's surface than it would if it were to strike the moon. Yet, the evidence indicates that the moon's surface has better protection than the earth's.

To make matters worse, a given amount of atmosphere compressed to a thinner layer under high gravity would actually give better protection from meteors than would the same atmosphere subjected to a lower gravity and thus be distributed over a greater depth. In passing through the deeper atmosphere, the meteor would encounter fewer gas molecules per unit time and would have more time to dissipate the heat built up by friction. By passing through the same number of molecules in a shorter time, it would get hotter. The time interval, being several times greater in the former case, would more than offset the fact that heat is dissipated more rapidly at higher temperatures.

When the process forming an atmosphere is considered, it follows that the moon should have as much atmosphere per unit area as the earth. An atmosphere comes from gases discharged from material in the crust. Matter below a certain depth cannot contribute to an atmosphere. This is independent of the size of a planet but is dependent on the kind of material in the crust. The earth and moon have a similar composition.

Large areas of the moon facing us are considerably lower than the average elevation of the moon's surface. The mares on this side of the moon make up a high percentage of the area and it is apparent they were once ocean bottoms. If we were to lose our oceans, most of the atmosphere would settle in the deeper ocean beds. As a result, such areas would experience great air pressures. A deeper and more dense atmosphere in such areas would, indeed, provide better protection from meteors than other places.

The dense moon atmosphere is not as evident to viewers from earth for several reasons. The long days and nights, coupled with lack of any large bodies of water, mitigate the weather to the extent that strong winds and large cloud formations never occur. However, small clouds are seen occasionally drifting across the surface. Light diffusion is caused largely by suspended particles in the atmosphere. Due to the type of weather that exists on the moon, there is a paucity of dust particles in its atmosphere as compared to the earth's. Therefore, the moon's atmosphere, although as dense on the average as the earth's, will not diffuse light to the extent experienced on the earth. Consequently, the scientific community has been able to fool people with their claims of a practically non-existent moon atmosphere. This is certainly amazing in view of the fact that eclipses of the sun do show a substantial moon atmosphere despite its modest ability to diffuse light. An atmospheric fringe is clearly seen around the moon's periphery. It is entirely possible the moon has even a denser atmosphere on the average than the earth. This possibility will be discussed in chapter eighteen.

Other powerful evidence of a dense moon atmosphere came from statements made by astronauts during Apollo missions. The following case is a typical example. Prior to the publicized excursions to the moon, early astronauts had stated that the stars were not visible above the atmosphere. This is to be expected. There is little or no diffusion of light in outer space and, therefore, the only stars that could be seen would be those whose discs could be resolved. This could only be done with powerful telescopes. An atmosphere functions in a manner analogous to a lens. The light from a distant star is diffused and spread out. As a result stars are visible because of a greatly enlarged and distorted image of the disc caused by the atmosphere.

On the Apollo II mission shortly before reaching the moon, Armstrong stated that he could see the crater, Tycho, clearly and that he could see the sky all around the moon, even on the rim of it where there is no earthshine or sunshine. Collins then stated "Now we're able to see stars again and recognize constellations for the first time on the trip — the sky's full of stars — it looks like it's night side on Earth." This means that after leaving the Earth, the astronauts could not see any stars until they got close enough to the moon to view them through the moon's atmosphere!

An extensive moon atmosphere means the moon has a high gravity. Since the moon is a relatively small planet, a gravity as weak as that attributed to it would be unable to hold an atmosphere of any signficance. It is not difficult to see why the evidence of a substantial moon atmosphere has been cheerfully ignored by scientists past and present. A strong moon gravity, of course, is not compatible with orthodox physics.

Gravity effects are produced by a highly penetrating radiation in the electromagnetic spectrum. The frequency range is located between the lower portion of the infrared and the radar band. The frequency is approximately a trillion cycles per second. The author transmitted this information to various scientific groups in 1958. Goverment-sponsored experiments soon confirmed the validity of the concept. This created considerable excitement among scientists involved, and rumors circulated about the discovery of an anti-gravity device. One of the scientists told John W. Campbell about such an experiment he witnessed. Campbell at that time was editor of the well known science fiction magazine "Astounding" which later became known as "Analog." He promptly inserted this information in one of his editorials. In any event, Campbell's writing style suddenly changed. His editorials, which had been extremely speculative and thought provoking, now became relatively mundane and orthodox. The rumors also came to a grinding halt.

Many years later, a former associate of the author stumbled on to the same thing while experimenting with high frequency oscillators. His levitating heavy objects with his device soon brought CIA agents down on him. He was forced to abandon his experiments and dismantle his equipment. He has been hounded and his activities have been under close surveillance ever since. He is fortunate to still be alive.

The application of gravity-inducing radiations to space travel is not difficult to understand. Everything in the path of the radiation is accelerated in a direction opposite to the direction of propagation. This means a properly located device attached to a spaceship can give it almost unlimited velocity. The occupants as well as the ship are not subjected to stress during acceleration, since the gravity-radiations impart the same acceleration to everything in the path. It would be somewhat naive to assume that NASA or at least some segment or branch of it didn't make useof this principle early in the space program, even though the public didn't know about it. The anti-gravity principle has no doubt been one of the most jealously guarded of all government secrets. There are well-founded rumors that men were put on the moon as early as 1960. There is not the free exchange of information in the different parts of the military or the government that one might think. Money is not always channeled to the projects it was meant to subsidize. Each department has its own pet or secret project. It's a case of the right hand not knowing what the left hand is doing.

It follows that gravity radiation devices were employed to assure the success of the Apollo missions. Rockets were used for the liftoff from earth to preserve the secret of anti-gravity and to satisfy those responsible directly and indirectly for the financing of the project. It is quite significant that photos of the liftoff of the lunar module from the moon show no signs of an exhaust. The soft ground directly below it was in no way disturbed as it would have been had the crude rocket system been employed.

Films showing the complete liftoff sequence of the module are quite revealing. An initial blast from the rocket nozzle looked like a red plume extending from it. It stopped soon after the ascent stage separated from the descent stage. This initial display was no doubt staged to convince the public that rockets were the only means of propulsion. From this period on, the absence of a visible exhaust stream is quite evident. Those who might attempt to dismiss this evidence will likely assert that the exhaust would not be visible in a vacuum. This is very poor reasoning. Chemical rockets eject hot gasses of a temperature of thousands of degrees fahrenheit. As a consequence they will radiate light of a high intensity in an exhaust stream that extends a considerable distance beyond the exhaust nozzle. In fact, this exhaust stream would extend for a greater distance in a vacuum before dispersing than in an atmosphere. Collisions of ejected gases with air molecules would tend to produce rapid scattering. Since the greatest light intensity is in the exhaust stream itself, the exhaust would actually be more apparent in a vacuum than in an atmosphere. The exhaust gases and other products of combustion produce their own light. A typical academic "scientist" whom the author knows quite well argued that the ground below the rocket was not disturbed, because in a vacuum the exhaust products would be rapidly dispersed as soon as they left the nozzle!

Another aspect of the module which indicated rockets were not used for the liftoff was its aerodynamics. At high velocities it would have been very unstable. NASA stressed that this was no concern because of vacuum conditions on the Moon. Since the Moon has a dense atmosphere, the velocity of the module had to be kept relatively low. This cannot be done with rockets because the fuel requirements become prohibitive at low velocities. This is consistent with the fact that the astronauts were standing up during ascent and descent. No appreciable deceleration or acceleration could have been tolerated by the astronauts under such a condition.

There are several reasons for the cloud of secrecy surrounding the discovery of anti-gravity. One of them is the preservation of the status quo of science. The fact that gravity effects are produced by electromagnetic radiations within a certain frequency range is enough to shatter the superstructure of modern theoretical physics. Concepts such a black holes, the general theory of relativity, popular ideas of cosmology and other misconceptions go down the drain. As every physicist is fully aware, no electromagnetic radiation will effect in any manner the propagation or the direction of propagation of any other electromagnetic radiation which, of course, includes visible light. Radiations of the same frequency can produce the normal interference effects observed under special conditions which give the illusion that light is a wave phenomenon. Such experiments do not involve the different aspects of propagation which the concepts of black holes and general relativity are dependent. According to general relativity, a gravitational field is supposed to affect light the same way it affects any body or mass. The concept of black holes is an outgrowth of relativity. A black hole is conceived as being a body of such enormous mass and commensurate gravitational field that no light can escape from it. Long before the discovery of the true nature of gravity, scientists should have been aware there was something seriously wrong with the concept that gravity does not discriminate. A rational and unbiased look at some natural phenomena reveals that gravity is very discriminating in its ability to attract different kinds of bodies. For example, clouds seem oblivious to the earth's gravity and show absolutely no tendency to fall to the ground. Yet they are comprised of water droplets many times denser than the surrounding atmosphere and, therefore, defy the law of floating bodies. If Einstein's and other physicist's ideas about relativity and black holes were valid then clouds could not exist for long. They would settle to the ground in a very short time. It might be argued that the viscosity of the air and air resistance prevents them from falling. This could only slow their rate of fall. Clouds of meteoric dust over 50 miles above the earth also show no tendency to fall and the air at that altitude is less than 1/100,000th as dense as it is at sea level. One "scientist" the author knows intimately, tried to explain the phenomenon away with the argument "Brownian movements" were responsible. Brownian movements are the random motions of tiny suspended particles in a fluid. It has been determined that unequal molecular bombardments at any instant on opposite sides of each particle produces the constant motion. What this illustrious gentleman failed to comprehend was that this phenomena in itself creates the same enigma as the inability of clouds to fall. Over a period of time the bombardments working against gravity will actually be weaker than the bombardments working with it. This is because the velocity of bombardment will be slowed by gravity. Therefore, there will be a net force tending to force the particles out of suspension equal to the gravitational force on the particles plus the difference between the average bombarding force working with gravity and the average force working against gravity. Fine dust can also be introduced in a perfect vacuum and it will not fall. (It has always been claimed that in a vacuum all things will drop at the same rate). The reason for this behavior will be presented later. If gravity has little or no effect on clouds or fine dust, how can it be expected to attract anything as tenuous as light?

Other facts equally damaging to orthodox concepts have been revealed by the space program. Views of the earth from satellites show unmistakable evidence of a large egress from the hollow interior of the earth in the north polar region. Early satellite pictures showed this entrance to be located just south of the north pole in northern Canada. It is hundreds of miles across. After comments were made about the apparent opening in these early photos, subsequent pictures releasd to the public failed to show it. The experience and practice of NASA had in doctoring such photos no doubt "came in handy" so to speak when they had to cope with pictures taken on the moon. One might explain away those earlier satellite pictures as merely showing unusual cloud formation. However, another satellite picture which appeared in November 10, 1967, issue of *Life* magazine is more difficult to dismiss. If such an opening does exist in northern Canada, then a satellite picture taken in the right position or where the line of sight is parallel to the plane of the opening will show a flat in the outline of the earth. This is precisely what the *Life* magazine photo showed. It is about 1,600 miles across. It looks like a sizeable portion of the earth has been sliced off and thrown away. It is significant that this flat is located in the same area as the opening in previous pictures of northern Canada. It was taken during the hurricane season or when the north polar region was still in view of the sun. Once again NASA was caught napping. This same flat appeared in at least one picture taken from the moon. (There is another large egress located in the vicinity of the south magnetic pole). The plane of the moon's orbit about the earth intersects the plane of the earth's equator at an angle of about 28 degrees. This means the moon will be in a position from which this flat can be seen for a brief period twice every lunar month. Fortunately, at least one of the earth pictures taken from the moon occurred at the time the moon was in such a favorable position. The flat showed up again in televised pictures, and in the same region of the earth.

Since these lapses, it is evident NASA has tightened its "security" system. The public no longer sees gaping holes or truncated spheres at least as far as the earth is concerned.

The concept of a hollow earth is not compatible with the orthodox theories of gravity and other established concepts of conventional physics. Consequently, one can expect all-out attempts to suppress any facts or evidence indicating the validity of the hollow earth concept. Later on in this treatise, it will be shown that the dogma of a solid earth is a product of irrational and shallow thinking. It will also be established beyond question that our planet, like all other planets, is hollow.

Another important finding of the space program which understandably has received little publicity is missile weight loss in space. It was found that missiles returned to earth after a sojourn in the Van Allen radiation belt lost considerable weight. For example, one missile with an original weight of 300 pounds only weighed 125 pounds at the time of recovery. The satellite even continued to lose weight afterwards. It was also found that the jar in which fragments of the recovered satellite were placed also lost weight. Such findings are among the most damaging of all to current theories of orthodox physics. This will be thoroughly analyzed and explained in Part III.

THE SIGNIFICANT WORK OF CHARLES FORT

Few have ever dared to openly question the validity of the major concepts and supposed findings of conventional science. Fewer still have gone so far as to cast doubts upon the integrity of the scientific community. By far the most successful of them all, thus far, has been Charles Fort. He was born in 1874 and died in 1932. He devoted the last 21 years of his life to uncovering and recording strange phenomena, which scientists are still wishing had remained covered up. He compiled thousands of referenced notes during the process. From these notes he wrote four books entitled *Book of the Damned*, *Lo*, *New Lands*, and *Wild Talents*. They created a sensation when they were published and openminded readers and book reviewers were lavish in their praise. Reviews such as the following have been given:

> The most provocative, challenging, startling collection of occult and psychic phenomena recorded in the 20th Century — by the brilliant and internationally controversial man who dared to speak out against blind ignorance. Fort's books not only liberate the mind from those sublimated hard — dogmas of science. They also liberate the mind from all sorts of other prepossessions and idolatries of the marketplace.

Those who read Fort with an unbiased attitude will find such evaluations are justified. It is expected that Fort did not show the scientific community in a favorable light. Therefore, it is no mystery that few, if any, scientists jumped on the bandwagon.

His books cite hundreds of instances of unusual falls from the sky, including various forms of marine life, rocks and boulders of all kinds, rocks with inscriptions, flesh, dead and mangled birds by the hundreds, bundles of hay, black rains, red rains, and even rains of blood, etc. In the realm of cosmology, his information was equally startling. References are given to dark shadows cast on the moon covering a significant portion of it. Similar shadows have been cast on the earth, blotting out the sun and creating darkness over wide areas. The cause was never revealed. Fort also discussed UFOs thirty years before many people became aware of them.

He made brilliant observations puncturing some of the dogmas of science. For example, the constellations have remained fixed since they were observed by astronomers 2000 years ago. According to Fort, this seems to contradict the idea that stars are rapidly moving away from each other. If this were true, then some of the constellations should have lost some of their original shapes. This relative motion should have at least put a dent in the Big Dipper after 2,000 years; yet some stars have changed position to a considerable extent in just a few years, while all the others remained essentially fixed. Some stars disappeared and others appeared for the first time.

Many incredible blunders of astronomers are documented by Fort, as well as misleading claims that will not stand up under close scrutiny. For example, everyone has been led to believe the planet Neptune was discovered as a result of brilliant mathematical deduction and application of celestial mechanics, based on Newtonion concepts. Its exact position was determined by this method, and all the astronomers had to do was point their telescopes in that direction. Careful research shows such was not the case. When Neptune was finally discovered, it was not in a position anywhere close to the calculated one. Fort noted that when pointing in a given direction, an astronomer, instead of using one finger, must use all his fingers in a widely separated position.

Fort also uncovered a strange coincidence where astronomers were concerned. It was found that the uncanny precision and accuracy of astronomical determinations always occur in areas that cannot be checked on by the public or even amateur astronomers. As an example; the accuracy of the calculated time and position of eclipses of the sun is always far greater in the remote and unpopulated regions of the earth. When they occur in civilized and heavily populated areas such as New York City, the errors do not conform with the accuracy generally attributed to modern astronomy.

Fort probably foresaw the likelihood he might be labeled a biased cynic because of the unfavorable picture of the world of science he was painting. It seems he did make an effort to avoid such an image by showing the positive aspect of professional astronomers. His task was a formidable one, since it was difficult to find anything about them to laud. The more he uncovered, the darker the picture became. He did note that most, if not nearly all, of the significant discoveries were being made by amateur astronomers. He gave the professionals the benefit of a doubt and assumed it was because they, the professional astronomers, went to bed early every night. He praised them for their high moral character! Such a fine gesture was never reciprocated by the astronomers or any member of the scientific community. Instead he was vilified.

Fortean phenomena also include the discovery of implements used by ancient people. The implements seemed to be made for people of all sizes, from giants to "pickle-sized" people. Among these was a stone axe weighing 300 pounds and other implements which have to be viewed with magnifying glasses. Evidence of strange and terrifying monsters that would be good subjects for horror movies was also recorded. All of this and much more is included in books of Charles Fort.

It is apparent many scientists in Fort's time behaved as illogically as they do today. They used inane arguments to explain away the Fortean phenomena. In the face of the unknown, they weren't able to act like true researchers and maintain an open logical thinking pattern. In turn, this eliminated all hope of using the valuable data to advance the frontiers of knowledge and gain a better understanding of the universe.

The image of the typical scientist the scientific community has tried to foster on the world deviates somewhat from reality. The search for, and the upholding of, Truth are supposed to be his primary aim. In addition, he is thoroughly logical and objective in his approach to any problem, as well as being openminded. If this is the beautiful image some readers have naively harbored of scientists in general, the material presented thus far must be a shock to them. If so, there are still great surprises in store for them as this treatise unfolds.

George Orwell, in his famous novel "1984," describes a mode of thinking termed "doublethink." In the novel, this was supposed to be the ideal state of mind and a goal worth striving for. It is the strange ability to accept two mutually contradictory ideas simultaneously. No doubt, many thought such a thing only a fantasy that could never happen in real life. They were wrong. Orwell had a remarkable insight into human nature. He was actually describing a type of thinking utilized by scientists for ages, as will be proven in the chapters to follow. Many physicists of the present day have become adept in this art. No doubt it has its rewards. It seems to have enabled them to live comfortably with concepts steeped in contradictions.

EVIDENCE OF UFO INTERFERENCE AND PARTICIPATION IN THE SPACE PROGRAM

The mere existence of the UFO, with its extraordinary performance, poses a major threat to cherished beliefs of present day physicists. Their right angle turns at extreme velocities, sudden disappearances, and other antics tend to undermine the basic laws of Newton, the Einstein Theory, and other universally accepted ideas. It is small wonder the bulk of the scientific community still refuses to accept the idea they are more than just natural phenomena that can be explained away by established concepts or the old standby of weather balloons or hoaxes. It is difficult to understand the mental processes that enable a group to reject the reality of a phenomenon, in the face of such overwhelming evidence accumulating for decades, establishing its actuality beyond question. The members of such a group are indeed worthy candidates for mastership in the art of doublethink.

It is to be expected the UFO involvement in the Apollo program would not be publicized. A number of Canadian radios picked up the astronaut's broadcasts directly from the moon. At least one Canadian newspaper published an account of the more significant parts of the conversation which transpired between the astronauts and their mentors in Houston. The Houston-monitored broadcasts deleted all of the UFO-related conversations.

It seemed on one occasion the Astronauts Armstrong and Aldrin were frightened out of their wits. A fleet of UFOs lined up close to the lunar module just after it landed. There is probably more than one reason astronauts go through a decontamination process after their return from such trips.

Peculiar activities occurring on the moon have been seen by both professional and amateur astronomers over a period of many decades. This includes such phenomena as lights going on and off and changes in some of the moon's craters. Numerous photographs taken by NASA show colossal, "man-made" structures and engineering feats which could make any on the earth seem insignificant.

From the evidence presented in this chapter, it can be safely concluded there has been a coordinated effort by officialdom to suppress all of the facts discovered during the space program that are a threat to dogmas promulgated by institutions of "higher learning" in regard to the laws of physics and cosmology. Despite these precautions incredible breaches in security did occur which opened the door for such revelations as have been described above. In fact, the discrepancies in some instances were so horrendous they were even noticed by many observers who have been victims of academic brainwashing. People like Bill Kaysing were convinced that the Apollo missions were faked and staged in some remote area on the earth. He no doubt believed that the moon was airless and had one-sixth earth gravity. If this belief were valid then the conclusion that the entire program was faked is inescapable. Consequently, he wrote a book in 1976 entitled, *We Never Went to The Moon*. His assertions have not been denied by NASA or the astronauts. They no doubt find it best to ignore them rather than assume the impossible task of explaining away all of the contradictions. The government and NASA would much sooner have the public believe Kaysing's book than to believe the astronauts reached the moon and found earthlike conditions there.

It is reasonable to conclude that space exploration since the Apollo missions has not been restricted to small probes such as the Pioneer and Voyager. In keeping with NASA policies regarding the moon landings, it can also be concluded that except for security lapses as with the Apollo missions, none of their reported findings concerning other planets will deviate significantly from old textbook versions. For example, Mars will continue to have atmospheric and climatic conditions much too severe to support life as we know it and Venus will always have sulphuric acid clouds and a surface temperature of about 800° F. It can be expected that any deviations from old beliefs will not be of a nature that will conflict with major academic theories. Falsification of data in this realm is habitual. However, facts cannot be mixed with fallacies to any extent without contradictions showing up somewhere along the line. This has become glaringly evident with information released concerning Venus and Mars, which indicates conditions on the planets are somewhat different than is claimed. The source of this will be discussed in Chapter 15.

CHAPTER 2

INCONTROVERTIBLE FLAWS IN THE THEORY OF RELATIVITY AND THE ROLE IT HAS PLAYED IN CURRENT TRENDS OF COSMOLOGICAL THOUGHT

THE ORIGIN OF THE SPECIAL THEORY

Although the facts revealed in the previous chapter have shattered the theory of relativity, they are still not likely to convince the more ardent Einstein worshipers and zealots. This fallacy has become so deeply rooted in the consciousness of scientists and the rest of the world in general that it will not be easily disposed of, despite the fact it can be readily refuted from many different aspects. This concept has gained such a foothold, and become so much a part of modern physical theory, a mere demolition job on it will be inadequate. It must be completely pulverized from every conceivable angle. This will be accomplished in the following pages. Any reader who digests this chapter and remains an Einstein admirer should put this book aside and not read any further.

Before the advent of Einstein and the theory of relativity, the transverse wave theory of light was universally accepted. Waves cannot exist without a medium to transmit them, or in other words, a medium which vibrates in some manner. Therefore, physicists postulated the existence of a subtle medium which permeates all space. They called it the ether. It follows that if light is a result of transverse waves transmitted through an ether, then, since the earth travels through this ether in its path about the sun, an ether drift should be detected. It's a situation analogous to sound waves being transmitted through a stationary atmosphere, and an observer moving through or relative to this atmosphere. His motion relative to the atmosphere would result in a wind, or atmosphere drift, according to his observations. Similarly, the earth's motion through the ether should produce an ether wind. Experiments were devised to detect this ether wind, or drift, and its velocity. They are known as the Michelson-Morely experiments. A light ray was split into two parts, each traveled different but identical length paths, and then they recombined. The apparatus was mounted on a platform that could be rotated in any direction. It was correctly reasoned that if light were transmitted in the assumed manner, then at the point the rays were recombined interference fringes should be observed. Negative results were always obtained, to the consternation and amazement of the physicists.

Some explained away such results by assuming the earth carried some of the ether along with it. If such were the case, it could certainly account for the negative results of the experiments. It was accepted by some of the famous physicists of the day but was rejected by the majority, although no sound arguments against it were proposed. Evidently, they all failed to realize the idea was contradictory. They were all aware of the fact that a body can travel through free space at a constant velocity and encounter no resistance. This means matter has no measurable attraction or affinity for this hypothetical ether. Light couldn't be transmitted through this medium in the manner assumed, without interactions taking place within the ether. It follows that no part of the ether can be displaced from the rest of it without encountering resistance. Therefore, the earth could not carry ether along with it, and not experience the same kind of resistance. This would deaccelerate the earth, and bring it to a stop. Likewise, no material body could travel through free space without requiring a steady application of force to counteract this resistance. Consequently, the orbiting of planets and other bodies would be an impossibility. Evidently, none of the scientists involved recognized this serious flaw in the above idea. One might have expected more from such a collection of distinguished intellects. It is not surprising in view of subsequent mental lapses concerning the interpretation of the experiment.

The Michelson-Morely experiments actually proved that the assumption that light is propagated as transverse waves through an all prevading medium is not valid. He would, therefore, have concluded the transverse wave concept is not necessary to account for the diffraction and interference effects of light. The physicists were unable to reject the transverse wave concept. Therefore, the only way out of the dilemma created by the results of the Michelson-Morely experiments was the absurd conclusion that the observed velocity of light was independent of the velocity of the source or that of the observer. In other words, the velocity of light is a universal constant. This idea, of course, violates the principle of relative velocities encountered in all of our experiences. This is clearly a case of doublethink.

With this as a starting point, the physicist H. A. Lorentz derived a set of equations bearing his name. As expected, they predicted an assortment of ridiculous phenomena such as:

(1) Time slows down on a moving system. In other words, if two systems are moving relative to each other, an observer on each one will note that the clock on the other system is ticking off the seconds more slowly than his clock.

(2) A body will shorten in the direction of motion and the dimension will approach zero, as its velocity approaches that of light.

(3) The mass of a body increases with its velocity and approaches infinity as the velocity approaches that of light.

In 1903, a physicist derived the famous equation $E^5 = mc^2$ from the Lorentz equations. This was two years before Einstein was heard of. Most of the physicists considered the conclusion derived from the Lorentz equations little more than mathematical oddities, since they were somewhat unpalatable and difficult to believe.

This was the state of the art when Einstein got into the act in 1905. He proceeded to compound the original error. He devised new interpretations for the Lorentz equations by transforming them into something that was supposed to have physical reality. Physicists were still in a daze over the results of the Michelson-Morely experiments, and apparently their mental state made them vulnerable to any idea, regardless of how illogical it might be. Consequently, Einstein's ideas were readily accepted, and he was hailed as the man who saved physics. He was also given credit for the equation $E^5 = mc^2$. It will be proven in Part II this equation is meaningless and represents only a minute part of the physical energy contained in any given mass. This monstrosity that Einstein put the finishing touches on became known as the special theory of relativity.

If the mathematics used to develop a theory are valid but the basic premise is wrong, the final conclusion will also be wrong. It is simply a cause and effect relationship. The conclusions will reflect the characteristics of the original assumption. The algebra of the special theory is valid, therefore, the conclusions are necessarily as vacuous as the original assumption. A review of the conclusions just mentioned is in order.

A body is supposed to shorten in the direction of motion, and this dimension will approach zero as its velocity nears that of light. With this conclusion, two mutually contradictory statements emerge. Since one of the dimensions of a body tends to vanish, the body itself will tend to disappear, yet according to a conclusion mentioned earlier, its mass becomes infinite!

The conclusion that time slows down on a moving system presents another impossible situation. Consider the case of the observers on two systems moving relative to each other. The observer on each system is noting the behavior of the clock on the system moving relative to him. Each one notes that the other clock is losing time relative to his own. The systems finally return to each other and stop. According to the Lorentz equations, each observer should notice the other clock has lost time relative to his own. Einstein had originally stated that the time equation for each system is equally valid. In other words, it doesn't matter which is taken as the moving system. Earlier writings on relativity by the authorities continually reiterated this.

The reality of this troublesome enigma must have eventually filtered down to the consciousness of the more "brilliant" physicist, since now the consensus is that only one of the observers would have this experience; and it did matter what was considered the moving system. By seeming to avoid this dilemma, our resourceful relativists are faced with another equally distasteful one. Some of their other beliefs are dependent on the assumption that each moving system deserves equal consideration, which is a factor they have now rejected.

According to them, the one to be considered as the moving system is the one that has been subjected to an acceleration to acquire its velocity. Which is to be considered the moving system, if both have been subjected to the same accelerating force, but in opposite directions? In any event, the ability to doublethink has come to the rescue of many physicists in the face of such a potentially disastrous situation, and they have done the only thing possible. They have ignored the dilemma.

At this stage, it is interesting to note how a well-known science fiction writer has handled this clock paradox of relativity. This particular individual, a typical orthodox scientist, has been essentially a mouthpiece for the scientific community over a long period of time. He has written over 200 books covering a wide variety of subjects. His fame initially came through his science fiction writings. He is now looked upon as an authority on all things of a scientific nature. It will become increasingly apparent as the reader continues that this "authority" should have confined his activities to science fiction only. This is essentially about all that he wrote anyway. Much of his writings have merely been improperly labeled. An article of his on the time paradox appeared recently in a science magazine of considerable popularity.

He began the discussion with the false and highly misleading statement that the theory of relativity has met all tests without exception, and so triumphantly that no physicist now doubts its validity. These "tests" and their alleged confirmation will be discussed shortly. This writer tackled the paradox by avoiding the real issues. He admitted that the Special Theory of Relativity is inadequate to deal with the situation, since it is supposed to apply only to objects traveling at a constant velocity. According to him, this means the two systems, having flashed by each other, must continue to separate forever if the Special Theory is to be involved. They can never come together again to match clocks. Therefore, there is no paradox!

To the less gifted readers of this article, this specious evasion may have appeared to take the special theory off the hook, but did it? The theory is supposed to apply to any velocity below that of light. Therefore, the velocity can change, and during the change the theory should still hold for any velocity assumed at any instant during that change, and afterwards. The paradox thus remains, despite the ostrich type of thinking that tried to sweep it under the rug.

Attention was then focused from the Special Theory to the General Theory which Einstein proposed in 1916. Armed with this aspect of relativity including accelerated objects, our resourceful and daring writer tackled this time paradox again. He argued that the General Theory of Relativity shows it is the ship that undergoes acceleration that experiences a real change in the rate of time. The ship that undergoes acceleration will end with its clock behind when the two systems approach and compare. The system called A that doesn't accelerate will notice that only B, the accelerating system, will appear to accelerate while B is the only one accelerating relative to the universe and A likewise. By this argument, the slowing of time is supposed to be real. This means the occupants of a space ship that accelerates up to near the speed of light and maintains this velocity will show little or no tendency to age. During the process, their clock will seem to them to be ticking the seconds off as rapidly as before.

It might appear this much-loved and respected writer resolved the time paradox. During his vacuous arguments, he carefully avoided the case of the two spaceships undergoing identical accelerations in opposite directions, before coming together once more and stopping. This brings the paradox back to life again with as much vigor as it ever had. Other scientists with less daring and perhaps more wisdom have remained silent on the issue. No doubt with the hope that if they closed their eyes, it would go away. The identity of this distinguished writer is already apparent to most readers. He is, of course, Isaac Asimov, a perfect example of the typical academic scientist whose peculiar mental characteristics and vacuity will be thoroughly analyzed and demonstrated during the unfolding of this treatise.

The time paradox, of course, is only one aspect of the contradictions and basic fallacies of the special theory. For example, one of the conclusions is that the mass of a body increases with its velocity and approaches infinity as the velocity nears that of light. This contention is easily disproven. At times, hypothetical experiments are extremely useful to illustrate a principle, or demonstrate the fallacies of a concept, even though Einstein tried it on occasion, but never with effect. This method will be employed to demonstrate the absurdities in the above idea.

Consider a closed system or one in which no energy in any form can enter or leave. Inside this system are two bodies heavily charged with the same electricity. Being of like charge, they have a tendency to repel each other. They are prevented from flying apart by a string holding them together. Assume that a little demon with a knife cuts this string. The two charged bodies then fly apart at a high velocity. According to Einstein, these bodies have gained in mass. This means an increase in the total mass energy of the system and also the total energy available in same. This violates the energy conservation law, and something has been created out of nothingness.

Although this adequately demonstrates the fallacy of the relativistic increase of mass with velocity, the author was surprised to learn it did not satisfy all members of the scientific community. For example, one distinguished scientist argued that during the bringing of the two charges together, the energy of the system increased! This, of course, violates the original premise. Also, this gentleman apparently overlooked the fact that basically energy exists in two forms, potential or static energy and kinetic energy. One transforms into the other and vice versa. Two other proofs of this fallacy will now be given which are even more convincing than the one just presented.

Consider a planet of near infinite size with no atmosphere. A certain mass is raised to a given height above the surface and allowed to drop. By the time it reaches the surface it will have acquired a kinetic energy equal to the energy or work required to raise it to the altitude from which it was dropped. This is in accordance with the energy conservation law. Now the kinetic energy equals one half the mass times the square of the velocity. This means that the mass must remain constant in order for the conservation law to hold. According to Einstein and other relativists, gravity doesn't discriminate. This assumption is an integral part of the theory.

Therefore, the acceleration of the mass as it falls will remain constant, regardless of any increase in mass! Therefore, the kinetic energy of the falling body will exceed the energy required to raise the mass to the required elevation. This also demonstrates an inherent contradiction in the relativity theory. It is apparent that the velocity will increase without limit depending on the height from which it is dropped. As the mass approaches infinity, the gravitational pull will keep pace and exert a force approaching infinity. It will be shown later that the velocity under these conditions will reach a limit, but it will be many times that of light.

The behavior of light shows conclusively that mass does not increase with velocity. Photons of light, of course, travel at the velocity of light but display a finite mass and momentum. Relativists get around this paradox by assuming a rest mass of zero. However, if this is so, then they will also have a zero mass at any velocity less than the velocity of light in free space. Photons moving through the atmosphere travel at a lower velocity than this, yet they show the same mass and momentum!

Physicists will argue that particle accelerators demonstrate this relativistic increase in mass. Such experiments, instead of confirming Einstein, actually demonstrate a very important principle providing a better understanding of many physical phenomena.

It is an established fact that a magnetic field develops around a charged body when it is given a velocity. Where did the magnetic field come from? Consider again the experiment just described. As the bodies moved, magnetic fields developed around them. Since the total energy of the system remains constant, there can be only one conclusion. The magnetic field developed at the expense of the electrostatic field. This is a transformation of one form of energy into another, or potential energy into kinetic energy. What really takes place in the particle accelerators can now be understood. As the charges in the accelerators increase their velocity, the magnetic field around them increases, while the electrostatic charges decrease. This means during the acceleration of the particles, their mutual magnetic attraction increases, while the electrostatic repulsion decreases. By now, it isn't difficult to see what creates the illusion of an increase of mass with an increase in velocity, and the apparent vindication of Einstein. At speeds approaching that of light, ever larger clusters of particles become more tightly bound together by powerful magnetic fields. By this time, the electrostatic charge on the particles is practically non-existent, and the accelerating force, which is dependent upon charge of the particles, approaches the vanishing point. This seemed to support relativity, because the particles can't exceed a certain limiting velocity. When all the electrostatic charge has been transformed into magnetic fields, the accelerating force dependent upon the charge becomes zero, and the particle cannot be accelerated any further. This limiting velocity will be shown in Part III to equal the velocity of light relative to its source.

The extremely heavy concentrations of magnetic fields, brought about by the particles being clustered together inside accelerators, requires the application of far more intense magnetic fields to hold the clusters in their circular paths inside the accelerators. It is a simple case of mathematics. It requires a certain magnetic flux to hold a single particle traveling at light velocity in the circular orbit. If the particles are evenly distributed in the accelerator, the flux or intensity required to hold all of them in orbit will be considerably less than if the particles become bunched up in groups. Requiring a more intense magnetic field gave the illusion of an increase in inertial mass of the individual particles.

It is indeed ironic that, according to relativity, a material body cannot exceed the speed of light, as the particles in the accelerator seemed to indicate. This is false, as has already been indicated. It will be shown also in Part III that in spaceship propulsion an entirely different set of conditions exists, and it is possible for a material body to travel many times the speed of light.

Prior to the development of particle accelerators, the deflections of fast-moving particles in powerful magnetic and electrostatic fields showed the decrease of charge with increase of velocity. It was found that the ratio, e/m, where e is the charge on the particle, and m is the mass, decreased with velocity and approached zero as the velocity neared that of light. Of course, relativists interpreted this as an indication of an increase of mass with velocity. Since mass does not increase with velocity, such experiments proved the charge on a particle is a variable, and decreases as the velocity increases.

The next fallacy of the special theory is the idea that the observed velocity of light is independent of the velocity of the source or that of the observer. There is no telling how often it has been disproved in laboratory experiments. At least one incident was given brief publicity about three decades ago. A naval research team photographed a spot of light moving across a cathode ray tube at a velocity of 202,000 miles/sec. The basis of this phenonemon was the interaction of particles moving about 16,000 miles/second. This is about the average velocity of the flow of electrons in the tube. This velocity, added to the velocity of light about "186,000 miles per second", produced the 202,000 miles per second. The esults of this experiment were quickly hushed up and forgotten because it was an affront to something sacred.

An ingenious experiment providing direct proof that this basic ssumption of special relativity is false was given no publicity. It is called the Saganac Experiment, and was performed in 1913. Two simultaneously emitted light signals were sent in opposite directions around a closed path, and a photographic plate was arranged to record the interference fringes at the place where the signals met. The apparatus from which the light source originated was supported on a turntable, which was free to rotate. The two light signals traveled identical distances, not along the turntable but the same distance along the surface of the earth.

The turntable was given a spin with a rotational velocity of v relative to the earth. The signal moving in the same direction in which the apparatus was turning had an initial velocity of (v plus c) relative to the surface of the earth, where c is the velocity of light relative to its source. The signal moving in opposite direction of rotation had a velocity (c minus v). If the basic premise of relativity were valid, both signals would have traveled these equal distances along the surface of the earth in identical times. They did not. The signal which initially traveled in the same direction of rotation reached the point where the camera was set up before the other signal. This produced the expected interference fringes. When the turntable was stationary, no interference fringes were produced.

It was evident, by the time this experiment was performed, the special theory was too deeply entrenched in the consciousness of the scientific community for such an eventuality to be tolerated. This is not surprising. It will be proven many times throughout this treatise that the scientific community is far more concerned about maintaining the status quo of science than in facing the truth.

Actually, there has been considerable indirect proof of the fallacy of the basic foundation of relativity before and after the Saganac Experiment. The photo-electric effect of light shows that light is transmitted as particles, and not transverse waves.

This automatically accounts for the results of the Michelson-Morely experiments. The particles of light which encounter no resistance in traveling through the ethers will have a velocity relative to the earth, independent of the direction they travel. In other words, the observed velocity of the particles will be the same, regardless of the direction in which they may be moving away from their source. Additional evidence that light is propagated as particles and not waves is the fact that a beam of particles such as electrons, protons, and even molecules produce the same interference and diffraction effects as light.

To an individual versed in the elements of physics and the origin of the relativity theory, such facts alone would be sufficient reason for him to reject the theory. But it has become painfully evident that orthodox physicists are not rational people. How did they react to such findings? They demonstrated once again their proficiency in doublethinking. They accepted both aspects, diametrically opposed to each other, and called it the dual nature of light. This dual nature supposedly causes light to behave both as waves and particles. This has also been called the "wave particle paradox", because of the impossibility that a stream of particles would behave as transverse waves, of which light is supposed to consist. It will be clearly shown in Part III how a stream of particles can produce diffraction and interference effects. It will also become evident that such a demonstration is in accordance with other important principles, to be introduced in Parts II and III.

There is another incredible contradiction, which was mentioned earlier, inherent in the special theory that automatically invalidates it. Mass and energy are supposed to be equivalent and, therefore, energy has inertia, according to Einstein. Photons of light are described as packets of energy traveling at light velocity. This is the same as a mass traveling at the velocity of light, which is supposed to be impossible. Relativists get around the dilemma by claiming photons have a rest mass of zero and can only travel at light velocity. When light passes through a medium, it slows down and consequently the photons travel at less than light velocity during this period. The assumption that anything which has momentum or kinetic energy has a rest mass of zero is a crass violation of the energy conservation law.

Besides the behavior of particles in accelerators, Einstein's disciples have cited other experimental props for the Special Theory. For example, a jet plane carrying a highly sophisticated atomic clock and traveling at 30,000 feet for 24 hours supposedly demonstrated the contention that time slows on a moving system. After 24 hours, the clock lost 55 billionths of a second.

The result of this experiment involved a principle diametrically opposed to relativity. When one body is given a velocity relative to another, a magnetic field develops around the former, as a result of its kinetic energy. This applies to a so-called uncharged body, as well as to a charged one. The reasons for this will appear in Part III. This magnetic field distinguishes it from the other body, and so it does matter which is considered the moving system. (As indicated earlier, physicists have partially come around to this way of thinking. The author suspects this is due to ideas he has been expounding for over two decades, which include this concept. Prior to this, the consensus was it did not matter which was considered the moving system. As mentioned earlier, the Lorentz equations make no distinction). The magnetic field which resulted from the kinetic energy of the plane and everything moving with it, including the clock, although extremely minute, interfered with the moving parts of the clock and slowed down their action slightly.

Another experiment which allegedly confirmed the time dilation of moving bodies was the fact that high speed mesons last longer than those traveling at a lower velocity. So-called mesons are highly unstable particles and, after being created by artificial means, quickly disintegrate. The actual reason for this phenomenon should have been apparent to even the most obtuse physicist. The faster a particle travels, the stronger the magnetic field that develops around it. The pinch effect of the magnetic field tends to hold the particle together. It follows that the faster the meson travels, the greater the tendency of the magnetic field to keep it from disintegrating.

One of the most incredible aspects of the odd thinking of relativists is that the Special Theory is actually based on the concept of an ether. Yet, Einstein and his colleagues rejected this concept. This is like sawing off a limb on which one is sitting.

By now, it should be thoroughly apparent to the reader, assuming he or she is not a doublethinking member of the scientific community, that the Special Theory of Relativity is completely devoid of substance. It has been established, as well as any truth can be, that the Special Theory is a ridiculous fantasy based on very bad logic, without a shred of experimental evidence to support it.

THE GENERAL THEORY

The intelligent reader, whose sensibilities have been shocked by what has been revealed thus far, should brace himself before being exposed to the following analysis of the General Theory of Relativity. This theory is supposed to provide an insight into the nature of gravity and cosmology. One of the main foundations of the theory is the famous equivalence principle. It states that gravitational and inertial mass are equivalent. This idea is based in part upon the fact that the weight of a body is directly proportional to its inertial properties, and that the proportion is always a constant.

As expected, Einstein combined a fact with a fallacy, and ended up with a concept far removed from reality. For example, according to the equivalence principle, there is no way the occupants of a closed room could tell whether they were on a constantly accelerating spaceship or on the surface of a planet. The force holding them to the floor is supposed to be the same, regardless of whether it is the result of a gravitational pull or of being accelerated. According to Einstein, there is no experiment that could be performed which could show the difference.

Once again Einstein demonstrated a mental prowess that was less than acute. There are several experiments that could be performed to show the difference. If the room were on the surface of a planet, a sensitive gravity meter would show a difference in weight, if it were moved a short distance above the floor. On an accelerating spaceship or elevator, there would obviously be no difference. This is the least significant test. A ball held up in the air and dropped would fall to the floor in identically the same manner, regardless of whether it was on the planet or the accelerating spaceship. However, there would be one essential difference. If this occurred on the surface of a planet, a steadily increasing magnetic field would develop around the ball, as it appeared to fall. If the ball were dropped on the spaceship, the ball would not be subjected to an acceleration as the floor moved up to contact the ball. Therefore, no additional magnetic field would develop around the ball while it was in the air. To render the argument even more convincing, it could be assumed the ball was heavily charged with electricity. In addition, a charged ball resting on the floor would develop a steadily increasing magnetic field if it were on the elevator or accelerating spaceship, since it would experience a steady increase in absolute velocity. Obviously, this wouldn't occur on the surface of a planet, since the accelerating force is directed toward the floor, preventing an increase in velocity. The specious arguments Einstein employed to establish the equivalence principle have been hailed as some of the greatest achievements in the history of human thought! Yet, it has just been proven that the equivalence principle is a fallacy based on inferior logic.

Einstein used the equivalence principle to derive another weird concept. It is the idea that a gravitating mass produces warps or curvature in the space around it. This is probably the origin of the idea of "space warps" used in science fiction and various illogical speculations. It does seem strange that something formless and without substance, and obviously independent of time, should possess some of the properties of matter and also time, as indicated by his term "space-time continuum."

According to this theory, when one body is attracted to another or vice-versa, it follows certain warped lines in space.

It follows, according to this odd concept, that nothing can travel in a straight line. Straight lines do not exist and anything that moves, including light, goes along some space-warp line. Therefore, the universe is closed and shaped something like a cylinder.

By combining this idea of space warps with the Special Theory, Einstein was able to make certain cosmological determinations deviating only slightly from those of the Newtonian method. These "deviations" supposedly accounted for certain precise astronomical measurements which did not conform with those derived from Newton's approach. Since it has already been shown that Newton missed the mark by a wide margin, it is not difficult to see what this fact alone does to Einstein.

According to Einstein, light from stars near the sun's disc would be bent by the gravitational space warps produced by the sun. (It has already been shown that gravity can in no way affect light or bend it, since gravity has been proven to be caused by electromagnetic radiations within a certain frequency range.) He calculated the amount of light would be bent by the sun's field. This has been tested many times by eminent scientists during eclipses of the sun, and they reported that Einstein's Theory has been confirmed almost exactly. This alleged vindication of Einstein has been the main factor in making his name a household word.

A closer examination of the facts reveals these reports were entirely misleading. Integrity has continually been proven not to be one of the scientific community's most redeeming qualities. These particular cases have done nothing to alter this viewpoint. Charles Fort provided evidence that the observation of eclipses did not confirm Einstein. The truth about this was inadvertently revealed in the May, 1959, issue of *Scientific American*, on pages 152 and 153. A diagram showing the stars' positions observed during the total eclipse of 1952 indicate the predicted positions of the stars, compared to the actual positions. It was admitted that changes in star positions agree only roughly with those predicted by the General Theory of Relativity. This was a gross understatement. At least one-third of them were displaced in a direction opposite to the one they were supposed to be! There were considerable variations in the extent of agreement for those that were displaced in the right direction. It is extremely significant that the stars closest to the sun show the best agreement between observed shifts and predicted shifts.

There are three factors the scientists did not take into consideration during these tests. They are the atmospheres of the sun, the moon, and the earth. Any one of these is sufficient to render the alleged confirmation invalid. Consider first the earth's atmosphere. The refraction effect of our own atmosphere is variable and indeterminate. This makes precise astronomical measurements impossible. This has been thoroughly demonstrated by the errors made in the time and position of eclipses of the sun, as mentioned earlier.

Charles Fort continually mentioned the difficulty astronomers have in making accurate determinations with only our own atmosphere to contend with. In the case of detecting the amount the stars are displaced during an eclipse, they also have the dense atmospheres of the moon and sun to consider. With all of this taken into consideration, a close to random displacement of stars further from the sun's disc may be expected. This means that some of them will be displaced in the direction opposite to that in which they were supposed to be, as the diagram showed. For stars closer to the periphery of the sun, where the atmospheres become progressively more dense, there should be a closer agreement with the calulated values. This is because light passing close to the sun and moon will have a greater tendency to be bent toward them by refraction. This pattern was confirmed by the diagram appearing in *Scientific American*, which actually disproved Einstein, instead of vindicating him.

Other alleged confirmations of General Relativity are even more ludicrous. Consider the case of the advance of the perihelion of Mercury's orbit. According to astronomers, the application of the Newtonian Concept of gravity to the calculated amount of the advance of the perihelion was off by 43 seconds of arc in one century from the true and observed amount. The General Theory allegedly accounted for this 43-second discrepancy! The degree of precision required to establish such a minute error is mind boggling. Remember, 43 seconds is only slightly more than one percent of one degree, and it requires over 400 orbits of Mercury, for even this amount of error to show up. There is a far greater margin for error in making such a determination, than in establishing time and position of eclipses. Their relatively big errors in this department have already been discussed.

Once again, the integrity of the scientific community is called to question. It seems they will go to any length to create the image of infallibility. The advance of the perihelion, if it exists, is completely unknown, if there is such a thing and another prop for relativity has been dissolved.

Efforts to prove Einstein correct have been greatly accelerated in recent years with the development of more sophisticated devices. Instruments employing the Mossbauer Effect have allegedly confirmed the gravitational red shift predicted by Einstein. Light moving against a gravitational field will drop down in frequency, while light moving in the opposite direction will experience an increase in frequency. This seemed to be verified by directing gamma rays up a 75-foot tube and then down the tube. Gamma rays moving up the tube did seem to shift toward the red end of the spectrum, and when directed down the tube the shift was in the opposite direction.

Once again, physicists with their ignorance concerning the laws of nature have put the wrong interpretation on the results of their experiments. This experiment confirmed another kind of phenomenon far removed from relativity. The earth is being bombarded continuously by soft particles of all kinds from outer space, and these particles affect the passage of light. When the beam of gamma rays moved away from the earth, it was moving against the stream. This tended to slow them down with an apparent drop in frequency. When they moved toward the earth, this moved with the stream, and consequently, traveled at a higher velocity with the opposite effects. This will be explained in more detail after the nature of light and the properties of these soft particles have been thoroughly analyzed.

The slowing down of clocks on moving bodies, as predicted by Einstein, has been tested recently with Cesium clocks placed on commercial airliners traveling around the globe. It was believed a plane traveling east, or with the earth's rotation, would lose time relative to a stationary Cesium clock. A clock traveling west would gain time relative to the same fixed clock. After traveling around the world in an easterly direction, the clock had lost 50-billionths of a second, while the one that had gone around the world traveling west had gained 160-billionths of a second. This was allegedly in close agreement with the prediction of relativity.

It was assumed the real velocity of the plane traveling east was equal to its ground speed plus the velocity of rotation of the earth. The fixed clock had a velocity equal to the rotational velocity of the earth, while the one traveling west had an actual velocity equal to the rotational velocity, minus the ground speed in the westerly direction. By now, the intelligent reader knows the cause of these differences could not have involved the relativity theory, and that one must look elsewhere for the causes. One does not have to look far. There are two factors that affect these clocks. One of them is the magnetic field developed by the kinetic energy imparted to the clock. The other, and the greater factor in this particular case, is the concentration of the subtle energies, or soft particles impregnating the mechanism of the clocks. These energies permeate all known space. The higher the concentration, the greater the tendency they have to affect the working parts of the mechanism. It is analogous to the friction of the atmosphere slowing down a moving projectile. A clock moving in the direction of rotation of the earth will tend to capture or concentrate more of these particles throughout the moving parts of the clock than a stationary one. A clock moving in a direction opposite to that of the earth's rotation will have a lower concentration than the other two clocks. Therefore, it will run faster than the others.

According to General Relativity, a gravitational field will tend to slow the passage of time. The stronger the field, the greater this tendency. It was found that Cesium clocks run faster at high elevations than those on the ground. This has been taken as another proof of the validity of Einstein's ideas. The concentration of soft particles is higher near the surface of the ground than at high elevations. (This will be shown later.) It follows that clocks at high elevations should run faster than those at ground level.

Another alleged confirmation of Einstein that occurred recently demonstrated once again a complete lack of insight and common sense of present-day researchers trying to confirm Einstein. Bureau of Standards researchers, with new, elaborate devices, once more supposedly checked out the hypothesis that the velocity of light is independent of the velocity of the source or that of the observer. They found that light traveled as fast in the direction the earth goes through space as it does in the opposite direction. The final conclusion, according to them, is "The speed of light is constant and Einstein's theory is right." Incredibly, all phases of their experiment took place in the same reference system. All they showed was that the velocity of light relative to its source was independent of its direction of propagation, regardless of the velocity of the source. This is as it should be, and is what the Michelson-Morely experiments actually indicated! Why didn't they revive the old Saganac Experiment of 1913 which provides direct proof that the observed velocity of light is dependent on the velocity of its source, and thus destroys relativity?

A question that may come to the mind of the more discerning reader at this time is: since the bombardment of soft particles to the earth produced the red shift, why isn't the velocity of light affected by a change in the direction in which light is propagated on this earth? A light ray traveling in the direction of rotation of the earth or its direction of revolution about the sun should encounter more soft particles, than when it travels in the opposite direction. The red shift noted was extremely minute and the degree of precision employed in such an experiment utilizing the Mossbauer effect was greater than in any experiment trying to confirm the constant light velocity hypothesis. Also, the velocity of the earth in its orbit was small compared to the average velocity of bombardment of soft particles to the earth. It was the high velocity of bombardment of these particles that made possible the detection of the red shift.

The reader has now been exposed to all of the essential facets, of what has been hailed as the highest achievement of the human mind, and the greatest advance toward our understanding of the universe, in the history of science. All of the universal accolades and reverence heaped upon Einstein have made the fact that his achievement was a fallacy based on superficial reasoning and very bad logic all the more incredible.

Einstein has had his detractors even in the scientific community. Amazingly, none either inside or outside this distinguished body has ever put his finger on the real flaws of this celebrated concept. Yet, as the reader has been shown, the contradictions and infantile logic have been apparent for many decades. Why hasn't it been accomplished before? Perhaps one of the reasons is that it was too obvious. People in general, and especially students of science, have been brainwashed into thinking that common sense rules don't apply in the higher realms of physics. Consequently, scientists get away with all kinds of irrational behavior. If an average citizen were to consistently display such fatuity in everyday affairs, he would be in danger of being picked up by men in white uniforms.

The concept of time has been so badly abused by Einstein and his disciples that a simple and obvious look at its true nature is in order. This will render the fallacies of the relativity concepts even more apparent. Time is simply another aspect of activity, motion, or dynamics in the guise of a symbol. It actually denotes the amount of activity in terms of a definite unit using space as a background. This makes possible the correlating of events and the bringing of order in the universe. This is all that it is. This means that, being an integral part of activity or motion of all forms, it is inseparable from them. Consequently, it cannot take on any of the weird properties attributed to it by a host of fuzzy thinkers, including Einstein, in their futile attempts to account for unusual phenomena beyond their comprehension. It is one of the great mysteries that such an obvious and simple concept has been overlooked. Yet, it is adequate to count for all of the supposed anomalies associated with time. This will be done in later chapters, when many of the strange occurrences which led to the delusions about time will be cleared up.

Scientists like Einstein have not been the only offenders in spreading misconceptions regarding the nature of time. Philosophers and metaphysicians are equally guilty. Readers in esoteric subjects are continually bombarded with prattle such as there is no time beyond time, and space; etc. The definition just given readers renders the absurdities in such caprices more than obvious.

It is thus apparent that time would cease to exist if, and only if, all thought and all motion throughout the universe came to a halt. The slowing of the passge of time on a moving system is now seen to be self-contradictory. This concept treats time as an entity, separate from activity or dynamics. With the General Theory of Relativity, Einstein carried this absurdity to unbelievable lengths when he talked about a gravitation field warping time and space. This inanity no doubt spawned such mental crutches as "time warps" and "space warps" to account for anomalies beyond the understanding of present day theorists and speculators. Such terms have also become a popular tool of science-fiction writers. When one discusses "time warps" he is actually prating about energy or motion warps. Whatever that is supposed to mean has never been made clear.

Some readers may feel that too much space has been devoted to shooting down the relativity theories, when any one of the topics presented would have done the job. In other words, it has been a case of overkill. As indicated earlier, the Einstein myth and the Special and General Theories will not die easily. These ideas have had, perhaps, a more stultifying influence on scientific thinking than any other theory. Such misconceptions have been clearly pointed out to leading scientists for many years. Instead of reacting as scientists are supposed to, according to the definition of the term "scientist," the scientific community has defended the old dogmas more vigorously than ever before. It seems they do not allow truth to stand in the way of such endeavors. Another indication that integrity is not one of their more noble attributes is given in an article entitled "Fraud Grows in Laboratories." It appeared in the June, 1977, issue of *Science Digest*. The article indicated that a high percentage of scientific data is falsified in order to make it conform with the results hoped for.

One can only speculate on how much of this was practiced during recent efforts to prove Einstein correct. There is another factor to consider concerning such tests, which require an amazing degree of precision. It has been shown repeatedly that the mind and thought forms can affect the behavior of various kinds of reactions. The phenomenon of telekenesis is not some science fiction writer's fantasy, as the scientific community would like to have the world believe. In any event, the experiments involving the relativity concept were not conducted with scientific detachment. There was always the great hope that Einstein would be vindicated. It is no stretch of the imagination to assume such strong desires did tip the delicate balance seemingly in favor of Einstein. Reports consistently stated the results agreed with the calculated values almost exactly.

The case against relativity rests. It has been made clear that the Special Theory is based on the faulty interpretation of the Michelson-Morely experiments, which were set up to detect the drift. It was shown that the fact that light propagates as particles, not as transverse waves through an all pervading medium, violates the basic tenets of the theory. It was also proven that the brand of logic employed to establish the theory violated all the basic rules of rational thining. The absurdities and impossible conditions derived from the foundation of the theory were rendered self evident. The popular conception that the theory has a wealth of experimental evidence to support it has been thoroughly debunked.

The General Theory of Relativity has been as thoroughly confuted as the Special Theory. The famous Equivalence Principle, on which the theory is largely based, has been proven to be false. The idea that gravity is produced by space warps has been shown to be a ridiculous fantasy. As with the Special Theory, it was established that there is not a shred of experimental evidence to support it and all of the alleged confirmations are explained in an infinitely more effective manner than with the General Theory. It is interesting to note the already experimentally proven fact that gravity is produced by a highly penetrating radiation in the electromagnetic spectrum completely demolishes the General Theory. Interestingly enough, well documented phenomena observed over the centuries also confutes the theory such as levitation. If gravity were produced by space warps, there is no way levitation could take place. Even the levitating beams employed by UFOs and observed on many occasions could not possibly work. The phenonemon of levitation will, of course, be explained later.

EINSTEIN'S INFLUENCE ON MODERN TRENDS OF COSMOLOGICAL THOUGHT

UFO sightings suggest there is a possibility that extraterrestrials are among us. Evidently, this likelihood has finally come to the attention of some prominent physicists, after more than thirty years. According to their way of thinking, if UFOs are visiting us, they would have to come from other solar systems. This strongly suggests faster-than-light space-ships. Unfortunately, the theory of relativity stands in the way of this concept. Since academic theorists would renounce their own flesh and blood before they would relativity, devious steps had to be taken to surmount the difficulty. One of the most distinguished among these physicists, John A. Wheeler, a devout Einstein disciple, came to the rescue with a theory which could permit faster-than-light spaceships without desecrating relativity.

Wheeler was given high acclaim for this theory, an account of which appeared in *Saga* magazine in March, 1972. He gets around the difficulty with an extension of the General Theory of Relativity. Briefly, the Wheeler Theory contends that space is not only curved, but is shaped like a doughnut. It is supposed to be infested with "wormholes" which lead to a hyperspace, where time and space do not exist! UFOs allegedly come to us through some of the wormholes. Perhaps the reader may already be speculating as to where these wormholes, if any, really do exist. Such an idea is stretching even irrationality beyond its elastic limits and enters the realm of hyperirrationality. How an object that occupies space can enter a region of no space and still exist has not been made clear. It seems that Wheeler has outdone his collegues who are only skilled in the realm of doublethink.

This is an interesting study in the avenues a brainwashed individual of the academic world will take in order to retain a cherished concept that has been threatened. What is equally incredible is that such an idea has been taken seriously by many outside the scientific community. They look upon Wheeler as the man who will point the way to interstellar space travel.

Another outgrowth of Einstein's ideas that has gained considerable popularity and wide publicity is the concept of "black holes." Practically all of the leading scientists have jumped on the bandwagon and have added some of their own flavor to theories involving black holes. The concept of black holes has already been discussed briefly and completely debunked. The confuting of the General Theory of Relativity and the fact that gravity has no effect whatsoever on the propagation of light, automatically wipe out the black hole concept. If black holes are a reality, there is only one place they could exist.

Another widely accepted concept is the big bang theory. It is based on the idea that the universe originated from a giant explosion a few billion years ago. Everything has been flying outward and away from the center of this explosion. This supposedly accounts for the expanding universe, which has seemingly been confirmed by the famous red shift. The red shift is defined as an apparent doppler effect indicating that the more distant stars are receding from us at higher velocities. According to astronomical observations, more of the light from distant stars is shifted toward the red end of the spectrum. This and other phenomena, improperly interpreted by astrophysicists, will be cleared up for the first time later in this treatise. During the process, it will become evident that the big bang theory is as devoid of sound thinking as the ideas already discussed. Such a thing is to be expected. The chief representatives of the scientific community have repeatedly shown that they are inept thinkers with an inability to look at more than one side of a problem.

One of the major stumbling blocks in academic thinking is the idea that natural phenomena are the result of chance and probability, and not the effect of intelligent design. Causality is sinking into the background. Absolute materialism is the general theme. Judging by the quality of thinkers in the academic world this also is not surprising.

A broad and logical examination of the facts shows conclusively that there is intelligent design behind the operation of the universe. As the title suggests, it is what this treatise is all about. The vast majority accept this truth on faith alone. Since this fact does become obvious from any intelligent look at the world around us, it can be stated categorically that materialists, who constitute the bulk of the scientific community, as well as atheists and even agnostics, are all of very limited mental capacity. This will also become increasingly apparent in the pages to follow. Of course, this does not imply that nonmaterialists are necessarily brighter in many respects than the materialists. All it does is brand the materialists.

It may seem that Part I has been slanted too much in one direction by showing only the negative side of the world of science. This is the wrong impression. As mentioned previously, in order to pave the way for the introduction of vastly more fruitful ideas, it is mandatory to concentrate on this predominant side of conventional science and those who promulgate it and show a true perspective of it. For ages a greatly exaggerated and distorted version of the bright side has held the stage. The author admits that scarcely anything is all white or all black. There are nearly always the intermediate shades of gray.

In the interest of fair play, the author will attempt a brief and impartial look at the other side of the picture. The dedicated plodders of the scientific world do make discoveries that benefit the planet. This isn't necessarily accomplished by brilliant deductions, but by following tried and true procedures, or methods of research. Although the academic world has given us many discoveries that make life more enjoyable in some respects, they are also largely responsible for the suppression of better things than those they have contributed. Outside of the contributions they have made to society, the author has found, as Charles Fort did, a few aspects that could be considered praiseworthy. Perhaps the most admirable of these is their loyalty and steadfastness to an idea or an image. Although misdirected, it is real and is better established than was Fort's conclusion concerning the moral character of astronomers. Their unquenchable loyalty to Einstein and his ideas in the face of all odds is touching. If this degree of fidelity were to be applied in other kinds of relationships, the world would be a utopia.

After considering the pros and cons, the composite picture of the scientific world emerging is not all black, although it appears to be in the darker and dirtier shades of gray. It differs somewhat from the beautiful portrait the world is accustomed to viewing.

Although the author has in some measure attempted to smooth over ruffled feelings that may have been created by previous comments on the merits of academic scientists, the gnawing suspicion he has done a miserable job of it persists.

Part I has been devoted to proving the highly touted theories of academic science and their vaunted claim of accuracy in the field of cosmology are false. It was shown that suppressed findings of the space program invalidate some of the most highly acclaimed ideas of conventional science. The Theory of Relativity was the main target discussed and it was proven, beyond any question, that it is a preposterous speculation based upon an atrocious brand of logic. It was also shown the alleged confirmations of the theory are a result of faulty interpretations of experimental data and superficial thinking. A dark cloud was also cast around the integrity of the scientific community.

The information and new ideas presented have paved the way for revealing some revolutionary insights in Part II. Additional evidence will be given that the earth is hollow, as well as other surprising facts about the earth and the universe. For the first time, an adequate explanation for tides, earthquakes, continental drift and other earthly phenomena will be introduced.

More of the bastions of academic science will be invaded and torn down in the process. Also, for the first time, a unifying principle will be introduced, opening the door to a clear understanding of many phenomena long considered beyond human understanding.

NEW INSIGHTS INTO EARTH AND STELLAR PHENOMENA

INTRODUCTION TO PART II

Startling facts in regard to our planet, introduced in Part I, need further analysis and clarification. They will be explained in greater detail in this section, in addition to other related enigmas and paradoxes of long standing never before resolved.

The process of throwing new light on these topics makes mandatory the intrduction of two entirely new concepts. One of these is an insight into the nature of the ethers, the origin of all phenomena. The other is the concept of the soft electron. Heretofore, science has recognized the existence of only one type of such particles, hard electrons and protons. These two ideas will be employed throughout this book to unravel the mysteries of the universe.

CHAPTER 3

THE CAUSE OF TIDES AND THE NATURE OF GRAVITY

In order to understand the behavior of tides, an entirely new concept of the nature of gravity is needed. Gravity has always been the most baffling of all the common physical phenomena. So far, nothing even remotely resembling a satisfactory explanation for how it actually works has ever been advanced. A complete explanation will be forthcoming in Part III; but for the present, a broader look at gravity and directly related subjects will suffice.

The evidence is overwhelming that gravity is responsible for tides. However, the explanation in vogue since Newton's time is so inadequate that some cults believe gravity has nothing to do with tides. An analysis of the incredible flaws in the conventional explanation for tides will first be given before introducing the valid explanation.

One of the most extraordinary examples of irrationalism in the history of orthodox physics is the standard explanation of tides. In this case, the discrepancy between reality and orthodox speculation is so colossal it is one of the great enigmas in the history of human thought, that it has not been challenged since the time of Newton. The origin of the difficulty is an obvious flaw in the Newtonion concept of gravitation. It is the idea that gravity effects have unlimited penetration. In other words, there is no attenuation of gravity effects other than that due to the inverse square law as it passes through matter. This is an outrageous violation of the law of conservation of energy.

It is indeed amazing this obvious fallacy has been the basis of nearly all astronomical calculations for about 300 years. This, of course, has led to many false conclusions in the field of cosmology, as will be shown later. Although this affront to common sense has been a gargantuan liability when applied to cosmology, it has created a travesty of impossible proportions where the explanation of tides is concerned. As every student of elementary mechanics is aware, a body cannot be given an acceleration relative to another, if the same acceleration is applied to each body. Therefore, it can be concluded that, since large bodies of water are accelerated relative to the earth to produce tides, such bodies are given different accelerations than the earth as a whole. Otherwise, there would be no movement of water across the surface of the earth. It follows that the concept of unlimited penetration presents orthodox theorists with insurmountable difficulty in any attempt to understand tides.

Since the distances of the moon and sun are great compared to the diameter of the earth, all parts of the earth will experience very nearly the same gravitational attraction from these external bodies, if the above premise were valid. Any differences would be of an infinitesimal magnitude. High tides tend to occur when the moon is approximately at its zenith and simultaneously on the opposite side of the earth. This gave rise to the idea of tidal bulges, since the high water seemed to be almost directly below the moon. The high water on the opposite side of the earth presented the theorists with major technical difficulties. They surmounted the problem with nebulous discussions of centrifugal forces, horizontal components of the differential gravitational forces and other vagaries. The gibberish does not merit a reproduction. With such an impossible task facing them, the Newtonian advocates could do nothing else without abandoning Newton's concept, and that would be unthinkable. The shortcomings of the explanation are compounded by the fact that it contains an incredible contradiction.

It is stated that high water is not caused by any lifting of the water against the force of the earth's gravity, but rather by horizontal tractive forces unopposed by gravity. The horizontal component of already infinitesimal forces reduces them almost to the vanishing point. At the same time, the raising of water above the general level by an almost non-existent horizontal force is in opposition to earth gravity, which will tend to pull the "high" water back to the original level.

The Newtonian approach did seem to account for the annoying fact that the moon is a far greater factor in producing tides then the sun, but it created far worse problems than the one it seemed to solve. The plane of the moon's orbit intersects the plane of the earth's equator at about 28 degrees. This means that the moon never wanders above 28 degrees north or south latitude. According to the standard theory, the greatest tides should all occur within this zone. Instead, the highest tides are experienced in much higher latitudes, both north and south.

To give the reader an idea the minuteness of the tide producing force as based on the Newtonian concept, the following calculations are presented. According to conventional astrophysics, the moon's average distance is about 235,000 miles from the earth. Its surface gravity is supposed to be one-sixth that of the earth or an ability to produce an acceleration of 5.36 ft./sec^2. The moon's diameter, according to their findings is 2,160 miles. Since the force of gravity varies according to the inverse square law, the gravitational force the moon would exert at the earth's surface would be

$$5.36 \frac{(1{,}080)^2}{(235{,}000)^2} = .000113 \text{ ft./sec.}^2$$

Without considering horizontal components, the maximum total force could not exceed the difference between the force the moon would exert at the earth's surface and that exerted at the center of the earth. This value turns out to be

$$.00013 - 5.36 \frac{(1{,}080)^2}{(239{,}000)^2} \text{ ft./sec.}^2 = .00002 \text{ ft./sec.}^2$$

This force is so minute that it would require 13.8 hours for it to accelerate any object to a velocity of one foot per second! It must be remembered, however, that the actual tide-producing force would only be a very small fraction of this amount. It should not be difficult for even the most obtuse mind to realize such a force could never even overcome the natural viscosity of the water. Yet it is supposed to produce tidal bulges and distort a solid earth with an iron core 4,000 miles in diameter! Orthodox physicists are stuck with this monstrosity, since abandoning it would mean the collapse by the domino effect of everything they hold dear in the realm of theoretical physics. Their great skill in the realm of doublethink has enabled them to live with the contradictions inherent in this concept for the past 300 years. This case of mental ineptitude is only one of many others of similar proportions scattered throughout the realm of orthodox physics.

It is stretching credibility too far to assume that at least some of the brighter members of the scientific fraternity have not checked on tidal theory from a quantitative standpoint after all this time. If so, they would have noted the horrendous discrepancy. Since no mention has been made of it, the conclusion seems inescapable the experience was something akin to the opening of a pandora box. Suppose one has observed an attractive but sealed box and wishes to learn what is inside it. As he loosens the lid the odors issuing from the box become so overpowering he is forced to clamp the lid back on as quickly as possible before his olfactory nerves are seriously damaged.

It is now apparent the idea of unlimited gravity penetration is not valid. This means the surface gravity effects of the moon penetrate the earth for only very limited distances. Therefore, the total acceleration the surface gravity of the moon imparts on the earth, as a whole, is very small compared to the acceleration force exerted on an object at the earth's surface, such as a body of water facing the moon. This means the water not being fixed to the earth is free to move across the surface by means of the moon's gravitational influence. The difference in gravitational accelerations is so great the acceleration given a body at the surface follows very closely the inverse square law, since the acceleration given the earth as a whole can be disregarded.

For any given portion of a body of water, the horizontal component of the moon or sun's gravitational pull will be greatest when such bodies are seen at the horizon. This is when the tide producing force is at its maximum. When either body is at the zenith or directly overhead, the tide-producing force drops to zero. As it passes the zenith position, it tends to accelerate the water in the opposite direction. This force reaches a maximum at the time the moon or sun begins to drop below the horizon. The cause of two high and low tides during an approximate 24-hour cycle now becomes apparent.

Consider a western shore line. As the moon, for example, rises above the horizon, a large mass of water is accelerated toward the shore. This volume of water attains a significant momentum by the time the moon reaches its zenith. The momentum is great enough to cause large quantities of water to back up on the land above the general level of the sea. As the moon passes the zenith, it tends to accelerate the water in the opposite direction. The water soon loses its momentum in an easterly direction, and moves back away from the shore and acquires a similar momentum in a westerly direction by the time the moon drops below the horizon. Both the moon's accelerative force and the earth's gravity moving the high water back to a lower level produce the movement toward the west. An oscillatory or wave motion of the water is produced. This causes another high and low tide before the moon rises again.

The center of the mound of high water produced during a high tide will tend to lag behind the moon as it moves across the sky. This is to be expected. Frictional forces and the fact that no acceleration is produced on water directly below the moon cause a time lag. The mounds of high water in approximate positions below the moon created the illusion of tidal bulges, especially since another mound of high water is produced on the opposite side of the earth at the same time for reasons just given.

The relative positions of the moon and sun, depth of the water and the shape of the land masses affect the timing and magnitude of tides. The reason for the greater tides occuring in the higher latitudes becomes apparent from the anlaysis just given. Since the moon doesn't stray more than 28 degrees above the equator, it is closer to the horizon most of the time in the high latitudes and thus exerts a higher average horizontal force on water masses.

As expected, the greatest tides will occur during a new moon or when the gravitational influences of the sun and moon are both in the same direction, or during a full moon. During the moon's advance to the quarter position, the sun works in opposition to the moon for increasingly longer periods of time. This tendency reaches a maximum at the quarter moon. At this position the sun opposes the moon for nearly 12 hours out of 24, and so called neap or low tides will result. As the moon advances past the quarter position, the sun opposes the moon for even shorter periods and assists the moon during the rest of the time. This tendency for the sun to oppose the moon reaches a minimum when a full moon is attained. At this stage, the sun is assisting the moon approximately as much as it does during a new moon. High tides will again occur during this period. A similar cycle follows as the moon moves to the last quarter and finally to a new moon again.

It is now clear that this new approach to understanding tides easily accounts for all the basic facts concerning tides from a qualitative standpoint. It also explains tides from a quantitative aspect. In the analysis to follow, the effect of only the moon will be considered and that the moon is orbiting in the plane of the equator.

There is powerful evidence the surface gravity of the moon is very nearly as great as earth gravity. This possibility will be thoroughly explored and proven in Part III. However, to be ultra conservative, it will be assumed that moon gravity is only 75 percent earth gravity. It is also assumed that the moon is orbiting at its closest approach which is supposed to be 220,000 miles.

Therefore, the moon's gravitational attraction, F, at the earth's surface equals

$$Gm \frac{(1,080)^2}{(220,000)^2} \text{ ft./sec.}^2 = .75 \quad (32.2) \frac{(1,080)^2}{(220,000)^2} \text{ ft./sec.}^2 \text{ or}$$

$.000582$ ft./sec.^{2}

With this force, volumes of water will be given momentum toward a shore with the moon behind it. This momentum reaches a maximum when the moon reaches a maximum oblique angle with the water, at which time it will tend to accelerate the water in the opposite direction. Now assume that the moon is orbiting in the equatorial plane of the earth, and when it is at the zenith it no longer accelerates the water. A calculation of the velocity the water attains may now be given. The acceleration at any time is, a = A cos Ø, where A is the acceleration, at the time the moon is at the horizon which has been shown to be about (.000582) ft/sec^2. At this stage Ø = 0.

The velocity is most easily determined by finding the average acceleration over a six hour span, or from the time Ø increases from 0 to $\pi/2$. This avoids troublesome integrations and manipulations. All that is necessary is to find the area under the curve a = A cos. Now, oA' = A cos Øo Øwhere A is the area under the curve from

$$\emptyset = 0 \text{ to } \emptyset = \pi/2.$$

$$A' = A \int_{\emptyset=0}^{\emptyset=\pi/2} \cos \emptyset \text{ o } \emptyset = -A[\sin \emptyset]^{\circ} = A$$

If a had remained constant from Ø = 0 to Ø = $\pi/2$, this area would have been ($\pi/2$)A. Therefore, the average acceleration = $A/(\pi/2)$ =

Figure 1
THE FORCES WHICH PRODUCE TIDES

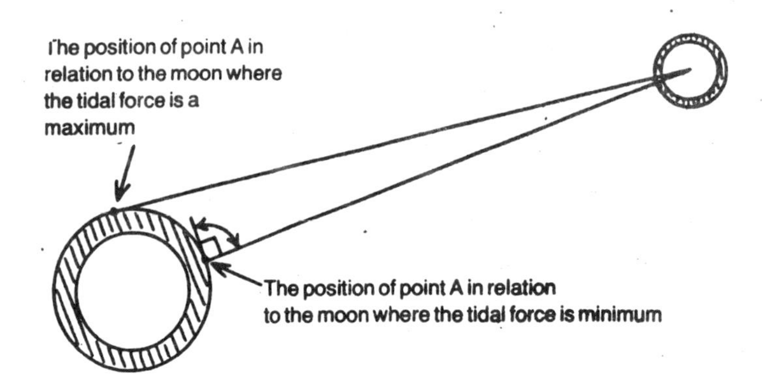

It is the horizontal component of the moon's gravitational pull on the earth which produces tides. The same effect is also produced by the sun. This results from the direct gravity radiations of both bodies which penetrate the earth for a very limited distance. The accelerating force imparted to the surface facing the source of the gravity-inducing radiations is far greater than the acceleration given to the earth as a whole.

Orthodox science assumes that gravitational force has an unlimited penetrating ability. Scientists are then forced to conclude that tides are the result of tidal bulges produced by the gravitational influence of the moon and sun. However, the conventional theory cannot account for a force substantial enough to produce tidal bulges.

.63A which equals .63 (.000582) ft/sec.^{2}. At the end of 6 hours the mass of water attains a velocity of about .63 x 3,600x6(.000582) ft/sec.

$$= .000366 \times 3600 \times 6 \text{ ft/sec}$$

or 7.9 ft/sec. which is more than five miles per hour. This is due only to the moon effects at the equator where tidal effects are less. The value just obtained is of the same order of magnitude as the observed velocity of many tidal currents. It is apparent this approach deals effectively with tides, both from a quantitative and a qualitative standpoint. In the higher latitudes the additional effects due to the sun can create tidal currents with velocities much greater than five miles per hour.

There are many factors which produce variations in tidal effects, such as the difference between a solar day and a lunar day, the shape of land masses, water depths, and latitude. This results in a very complicated tidal picture.

Tidal forces are largely responsible for ocean currents which, to be expected, are stronger in the higher latitudes. Tidal effects are not apparent in small bodies of water since a large enough volume of water cannot be set into motion to offset frictional forces and there is not enough time for much of the water to attain a significant velocity.

The analysis of tides presented above forms the basis for proving the surface gravity on the moon is greater than that on the sun. Since the sun and the moon have the same apparent diameters, viewed from the earth, tidal effects produced by them are directly proportional to their surface gravities. This will become evident from the following analysis: gravitational effects vary inversely as the square of the distance away. Their apparent diameters are inversely proportional to the distance; therefore, their apparent surface areas also vary inversely as the square of the distance. The gravitational effect of an external body on another is directly proportional to its surface area, therefore,

$$F_s \sim \frac{G_s A_s}{r_m^2}$$

and

$$F_m \sim \frac{G_m A_m}{r_m^2}$$

Where Fs and Fm are the tidal forces produced by the sun and moon, Gs and Gm are the surface gravities of the sun and moon; Rs and Rm and As and Am are their respective areas. Dividing,

$$\frac{F_s}{F_m} \sim \frac{A_s r_m^2 G_s}{A_m r_s^2 G_m}$$

Given that their apparent diameters are the same.

$$\frac{A_s}{r_s^2} = \frac{A_m}{r_m^2}$$

or

$$A_s r_m^2 = A_m r_s^2$$

and substituting in the above equation yields

$$\frac{F_s}{F_m} < \frac{G_s}{G_m}$$

Since the moon is a greater factor in producing tides, the conclusion that the moon has a greater surface gravity than the sun is inescapable!. To the orthodox mind this produces insurmountable paradoxes. The time has come for these to be resolved. This can only be accomplished by probing deeper into basic causes.

Much of what follows will be completely lost on some segments of the scientific community. Incredible as it may seem some honored members of the scientific world seem to be totally incapable of rational thought. Recently the author was astounded when one of these individuals, after reading this chapter, suggested that the author read the explanation of tides given in the *Encyclopedia Britannica*! Here is a classic example of the fact that many conventional scientists have and will continue to reject any reality that is damaging to that they hold sacred, regardless of how obvious and incontrovertably true it may be. It will become increasingly evident that few in the academic world are of sufficient stature to escape the intellectual straight jacket imposed on them by academic authority.

CHAPTER 4

MORE ON THE NATURE OF GRAVITY AND DIRECTLY RELATED TOPICS WHICH INCLUDES THE NATURE OF LIGHT, SOFT PARTICLES, THE ETHERS AND HOW THE SUN HOLDS THE PLANETS IN ORBIT

As mentioned previously, gravity effects are produced by a highly penetrating portion of the electromagnetic spectrum, which falls between the lowest fringes of the infrared and the higher frequencies of the radar band. It is on the order of about a trillion cycles per second. Most of the energy radiated by the sun is in the ultraviolet range and above. Only an infinitesimal part of it is in the lower frequencies which contain the gravity radiations. Therefore, the sun has a very low surface gravity as evident by the tidal effects it produces.

The law of redistribution of energy, not stated in any textbooks, plays a vital role in the benefits any planet receives from a sun. Briefly, it states that when radiant electromagnetic energy interacts with matter, the resulting radiation as a whole is of a lower frequency than the original light. The Raman effect, named after the physicist who discovered it, C. V. Raman, partly confirms this principle. Some of the aspects of the Raman effect seemed to violate this law when part of the resultant light was of a higher frequency than the original. This light was produced by triggering the release of higher energies in the atoms during Raman's experiments and was not a part of the original light.

The redistribution law is still only a special case of a more general law which states that energy, regardless of form, can only flow downhill or from a higher potential to a lower one. The famous second law of thermodynamics is a special case of this law.

The law of redistribution of energy accounts for temperatures at lower elevations being generally greater than at the higher altitudes. As the radiant energy from the sun passes through the atmosphere, increasing portions of the light are transformed into lower frequencies such as infrared, which activates the thermal motion of atoms and molecules, and produces heat. This process continues downward, even after the energy from the sun reaches the surface. Before continuing with this phase of the discussion, another concept of paramount importance must be introduced.

For thousands of years, occult masters of the Far East have stated that all matter is comprised of light. They must have known what they were talking about, since the by-product of the transformation of matter into energy is light. Brilliant investigators such as Brunler and Reichenbach, whose work will be discussed in more detail later, have shown that light has a dual nature always overlooked by academic science. This duality consists of a visible portion, if in the visible range, and an invisible portion which is extremely penetrating. Reichenbach proved that it is this invisible part responsible for the effects of color therapy, since if light only bounced off the surface of an organism, it would have only miniscule effects on it. This penetrating and invisible part of light produces visible light when it disintegrates. It is safe to conclude from these considerations alone that when light is produced, particles comprised of this light are also created which accompany the light.

Since matter can produce light without the loss of matter, light must be a manifestation of something other than matter as defined. This manifestation is the much talked about but little understood ethers, permeating all space. This is the stuff from which all matter is created and all things manifest. Many properties of the ethers can be deduced by application of the cause and effect relationship, and the hermetic axiom to be discussed later.

The ethers cannot be the rigid, inert medium pictured by many theorists. How can something inert manifest as life and intelligence? The ethers manifest life through a near infinite variety of particles, of which the most sluggish are far more active than the most active particles of physical matter. It will be shown in later pages that each particle of the ethers must consist of a universe within itself. Such particles may then be subdivided into other components. This process can continue to an infinite regression. It seems impossible to conceive of an ultimate beginning. One can only think of beginnings in terms of cycles. The term infinity has been used quite often by speculative thinkers, but its relationship to reality can only be applied by looking at the microcosm. When viewing the macrocosm, only the finite is seen.

The following principle must be kept in mind when examining the properties of the ethers: any dynamic unit is less active as a whole than the individual parts comprising it. Consider the fundamental particles of the atoms as an example. This principle is another outgrowth of the law mentioned earlier that energy can only flow from a high potential to a lower one. Growth of progression follows this same pattern, from the simple or more active to the complex or less active. The ethers must be thought of in the same manner. Therefore, there are what will be henceforth termed the higher and lower ethers. The higher ethers consist of the smaller and more active particles, while the lower ethers are comprised of the large, more complex and consequently less active particles. Both the higher and lower ethers occupy the same three dimensional space. Incidentally, this is the only space there is, in contradiction to the intellectual meanderings of many of the present day theorists. The ethers have a tendency to interpenetrate in a manner similar to the various frequencies of light. Space is permeated wth electromagnetic radiations of all kinds which have little or no tendency to interfere with each other.

The ethers will be discussed in more depth and detail in Part III. This in depth analysis is necessary in order to explain the seemingly inexplicable Fortean-like phenomena, and the science of psionics now considered beyond understanding. The picture just introduced will suffice for the remainder of this chapter.

When light of a given frequency range is produced, only the ethers associated with this light are directly activated. Light photons are comprised of combinations of ether particles. Photons combine to form the penetrating particles which accompany this light. Academic science has only recognized the existence of particles which comprise the atom and the artificial particles created in cloud chamber experiments. These artificial particles have nothing to do with the functioning of the atom, contrary to the beliefs of physicists. Their infinitesimal life spans should have told the physicists something. How could such unstable particles, with such fleeting life spans, play any role in the manifestation of stable matter. These physicists would deride anyone who suggested that the sound produced by water lashing against a rock was originally a constituent part of the water. Yet they apply identically the same kind of reasoning regarding these artificial and phantom particles to which they assign a weird assortment of names. During the high energy bombardments, the higher ethers are disturbed and corresponding photons are created. Some of these partially combine to form the very unstable particles.

The recognized electrons and protons are made of photons of light in the ultrahigh frequency range of the gamma rays. It follows from this concept that electrons, comprised of light in all frequency ranges below the gamma rays, must also exist in the physical realm. This means that there is a near infinite variety of stable particles with a near infinitude of properties.

Due to its more complex structure, soft protons are not as likely to be created during energy interactions as the much simpler soft electron.

Particles comprised of light in the lower frequency ranges will henceforth be referred to as soft particles, while those associated with gamma rays and above will be known as hard particles. Hard particles always accompany gamma rays, because they are comprised of gamma ray photons. For light in the lower frequency ranges, it is the soft particles which accompany it and constitute the invisible and penetrating portion of light. The reason soft particles are more penetrating than the photons of which they are comprised will now be given. Photons have relatively great surface areas in proportion to their masses. When a myriad of them combine, the resultant particle has a relatively great mass in proportion to its surface area. To compare the relative penetrating ability of such a particle with a photon is like the comparison between a cannonball and a bird shot, when they are both traveling at the same velocity. If the velocity is high enough, the cannonball will pass through great thicknesses of matter, while the bird shot will only bounce off.

Soft particles, and particularly soft electrons, play a vital role in all of the life processes and other chemical reactions. The discovery of the concept of the soft electron was a major breakthrough. It makes possible simple explanations for a wide range of phenomena, including the occult, which would otherwise remain hopelessly unresolved. The effectiveness of this concept will be demonstrated as better explanations of how this planet functions are given.

The energy or field intensity of and around the higher ether particles is greater than that of the lower ethers. This is the reason the higher ethers are more active. Consequently, the field intensities around particles comprised of higher frequency photons are greater than those around softer particles. In fact, the field intensity around a given particle is directly proportional to the light frequency of which it is comprised. The diameter of a particle is inversely proportional to the average frequency of its constituent light. This can be deduced from the photoelectric effect to be discussed in Part III. The structural difference between positive and negative charges will also be shown in Part III, as well as the reasons like charges repel and unlike charges attract.

THE REASONS THE SUN HOLDS THE PLANETS IN ORBIT DESPITE ITS LOW SURFACE GRAVITY

The visible photon radiation from the sun is scattered and quickly dispersed or recombines to form soft particles, after it reaches the surface of the earth. The soft particls continue on and penetrate below the surface. During this process, soft particles are continually breaking up with the formation of new particles, generally of a softer nature. Some of the photons released recombine with others to form new particles. At the same time, lower ethers are disturbed to form lower frequency photons from which softer particles result. This is in accordance with the law of redistribution of energy. Much of the disintegration of soft particles results from their encounters with other soft particls radiated in all directions from the atoms and molecules of matter. All matter radiates such particles continuously. This will be explained in more detail in Part III.

The energies radiated from the sun are continuously transformed into ever lower frequencies, as they penetrate deeper into the earth. In this manner, nearly all the original ultraviolet is transformed into lower frequency radiation by the time it penetrates the shell of the earth. A direct confirmation of this transformation principle is evident from the relative brightness of the sun at different elevations. For example, at the Dead Sea, the lowest depression on the surface of the earth, the sun is generally brighter than any other place on the earth. In this locality, the sun's radiations must pass through more atmosphere and therefore more ultraviolet is transformed into visible light. This is accentuated because the depression covers a considerable area. There is little difference in the brightness of the sun when it is near the horizon and when it is at zenith, because of the wide scattering effects. A depression of large area concentrates more of the transformed radiations.

It is the transformation of some of the radiation from the sun into gravity-inducing radiations which holds the earth in its orbit. Only a very small portion of the radiations from the sun are transformed into gravity radiations during their passage through the earth, because of the high average frequency of the radiation. The amount is enough, however, to keep the earth and the other planets in orbit about the sun and create the illusion that the sun has about thirty times earth gravity. It should be mentioned that soft particles penetrate solid matter more readily than hard particles, because they are associated with ethers which differ considerably from that of matter. Hard particles are, of course, an integral part of matter. This discrimination is analogous to waves of widely differing frequencies which have little effect on each other. It will be shown later that some of these soft particles radiated from the sun are the "cosmic rays" academic scientists have been speculating about for the past several decades. Sufficient groundwork has now been laid for understanding the source of the high gravity of the earth and moon.

AN EXPLANATION FOR THE MAGNITUDES OF EARTH AND MOON GRAVITY

All matter continuously radiates soft particles of many different kinds due to the interactions of the fundamental particles. These radiated particles undergo a transformation effect, according to the redistribution law, when passing through large concentrations of matter. When this occurs, some of the radiation is transformed into gravity-inducing radiations. This is the source of some of the earth and moon surface gravity. The greatest contributing factor to earth and moon gravity is the transformation of radiation resulting from the thermal agitation of atoms and molecules. The particles resulting from this activity are comprised of lower frequency photons. Such radiation is more readily transformed into gravity-inducing radiations, because it is closer to this frequency band to begin with. A significant portion of such radiation, originating miles below the surface, is transfered into gravity-producing energies by the time it reaches the surface. Most of the earth and moon gravity radiations are created in the first fifty miles of their crusts. Below that level, much of the energy from the sun has been transformed into softer particles, and the material of the earth and moon is permeated with them.

These soft particles will screen out gravity radiations more effectively than solid matter, because the ethers they are associated with, are closer in frequency to those of the gravity radiations. The reason moon gravity is nearly equal to earth gravity now becomes apparent. At the same time, it is clear why the famed Cavendish experiment for determining the so-called gravitational constant was misleading. There wasn't enough material in the bodies used in the experiment to produce any transformation of radiations. The gravitational effects produced by the bodies were due entirely to the thermal agitation of the molecules without transformations. The thermal agitation of molecules produces infrared frequencies and only an infinitesimal portion of this radiated energy is in the gravity-producing frequency range. The force the gravitating body used in the Cavendish experiment exerted on the other body was the result of iese same gravity radiations emanating from the body. The well-known gravitational constant was derived from the known mass of the gravitating body, and the force as exerted on the other body of known mass. his constant, and the idea of unlimited gravity penetration, required the arth to have tremendous mass in order to account for the gravitational force it produces. Scientists assumed the earth must have an iron core 000 miles in diameter to account for such a mass.

It is significant that some of the Cavendish experiments indicated gravity effects varied with the termperature. When the large gravitating sphere used in the experiments was heated, the attracted smaller sphere had a greater tendency to move toward the large sphere. When the larger sphere was cooled, the smaller sphere receded. This was explained away by convection currents, although they failed to explain how convection currents could produce such an effect. A detailed account of this can be found in the 11th edition of Encyclopedia Britannica within the subject "Gravity."

As mentioned before, matter produces infrared radiations which are partially transformed into gravity radiations. In the case of mountain ranges, there is not enough matter to transform significant portions of such radiations into the gravity radiations. Much of the radiation will escape from the tops and slopes of the mountains before they can be transformed since their average heights are generally small compared to their horizontal extension. The gravity radiations produced deep in the interior of the mountains are partially dispersed by the overlying mass. This is the cause of the plumb bob enigma, a source of annoyance to conventional physicists. The plumb bobs are not pulled out of line by the mountains to the extent the Newtonian law demands.

Another paradox emerges from the above presentation. The earth radiates only an infinitesimal amount of radiation per unit of surface area in comparison to the sun, but it is still able to hold the moon in its present orbit about the earth. This means the earth is more dependent on the gravity radiations emanating directly from its surface to keep the moon in its orbit. However, this isn't enough to account for the earth's ability to keep the moon in orbit. The earth is radiating infrared in addition to the gravity radiations. This infrared is more easily transformed into gravity-producing radiations and is an important contributing factor. In spite of this, the moon would still be much too massive to be held in its orbit if it had a shell as thick as the earth's. The conclusion is that the hollow condition of the moon is far more pronounced than the earth's. This is supported by evidence supplied by the space program not given wide publicity. Seismic experiments produced strange reactions indicating an extremely hollow condition and even a metal shell! Some scientists speculated that the moon was a giant, camouflaged spaceship. A very thin shell probably not over 100 miles in thickness could account for the possibility that moon gravity may be slightly less than earth gravity.

A critically thin shell accounts for the abnormal gravitational anomalies on the moon noted since artificial satellites from the earth first orbited it. In some areas, the increase in gravity was enough to drop the orbit as much as a kilometer during a single revolution. The following passage relating to this subject is taken from an article in the *Saturday Review*, June 7, 1969 on page 48:

> Periwiggles continued to betray orbit irregularities 1000 times the size of those expected from lunar gravity theory.(71)

The kind of explanation from physicists for such discrepancies is completely predictable. Large chunks of nickel and iron must be buried in the moon's crust. They have been called mascons and some of them must be as much as 100 kilometers in diameter to account for the gravitational anomalies. They supposedly bombarded the moon in the distant past and are imbedded a relatively short distance below the surface.

This deduction must give way to one which is in conformity with the principles already outlined. Apparently, the moon's shell is relatively thin; hence variations of just a few miles in the thickness over extended areas would result in very noticeable differences in its surface gravity, enough in fact, to produce the observed differences. Such large variations do not exist on the earth because of the overall thickness of the earth's shell which must be about eight times as great as that of the moon. The slight variations which do exist over and above those caused by the centrifugal force of the earth's rotation, are probably due largely to the effects of underground caverns. It may be shocking to some readers to realize that a solid ball less than 150 miles in diameter would have a surface gravity approximately that of the earth, and that many of the asteroids have earth gravity.

Recent findings by astronomers and astro-physicists indicate that this is indeed the case. The scientists were shocked during 1978 and later when they discovered that some of the asteroids have moons that revolve about them at a respectable velocity. According to Newtonian concepts, this should be impossible since the gravity effects of the asteroid would be much too feeble. It is understandable why this monumental finding has not been given much publicity. Nevertheless, the truth has the habit of rearing its ugly head when least wanted and expected. An account of this interesting discovery was revealed over radio Station KCRL, Reno, Nevada on the evening of January 20, 1981.

At this stage it may be advantageous to show how the gravity effects around a body changes with the size and mass starting with a small body of laboratory dimensions. It will also promote a better understanding of the plumb bob enigma. Within certain limits the gravity effects will be directly proportional to the mass as the size and mass increases with only very slight deviations. As the mass and size continues to increase, the outer gravity effects will for a certain increase, become less per unit mass than that of a smaller mass because the screening effect of the outer layers will more than compensate for the amount of infrared radiations generated within the body being transformed into gravity inducing radiations. This tendency will continue until the body reaches a diameter of several miles. This is the main reason for the plumb bob enigma. Beyond this stage the body becomes large enough for a significant proportion of infrared produced within the body to be transformed into gravity radiations. From this point onward the gravity effects will increase rapidly with increase in size since far more infrared is transformed than is screened out by the outer layers of mass.

This tendency will continue until the body becomes about 150 miles in diameter. Beyond this size there would be scarcely any increase in surface gravity as the size increases. The outer layers become thick enough such that the screening effect keeps pace with the rate of increase of the transformation of infrared into gravity radiations. This means that all planets have practically the same surface gravity.

CHAPTER 5

THE CAUSE OF EARTH UPHEAVALS, CONTINENTAL DRIFT, EARTHQUAKES AND VOLCANOES

Geologists and geophysicists are a bit vague when they discuss the forces producing earth upheavals and the folding of strata to produce mountain ranges. Their explanations for the forces causing continental drift are equally tenuous, if they exist at all. This is understandable since they are dealing with phenomena completely beyond the scope of present day theoretical physicists. It is apparent that tremendous tensional and lateral forces are involved. There are high concentrations of primarily soft, negative particles in adjacent strata and fault lines. It will be shown in Part III that soft particles are impregnated with harder particles whose presence is not apparent, due to the camouflaging and mitigating effects of the softer particles. When soft particles penetrate matter, they carry hard particles with them. When soft particles disintegrate, the hard particles are released. Therefore, most of the great forces inside the earth's crust are the result of released hard particles.

The concentration of negative charges, resulting from the penetration of soft particles from the sun, and the radiation of the matter inside the earth combine to produce tensional forces. Such forces at work in the earth's crust cause fractures and the sliding and folding of strata over each other. The gravitational forces holding the earth in its orbit also produce stresses in the crust, adding to these lateral forces.

If the earth were a completely solid ball and the Newtonian version of gravity were correct, the earth would be completely rigid and no earth changes could ever occur with the exception of minor erosion. There would certainly be no mountains left by now. The frictional forces along plates and strata would be so colossal that no sliding could ever occur. A major factor responsible for sliding is the tremendous repulsive electrostatic forces. They result from the concentrations of soft particles and their disintegration along plates and faults acting like condensers for soft particles. The sliding tendency is expedited because the gravity effects are considerably weakened at those depths. If the particles were all comprised of the same frequency photons, the concentrations would not be nearly as great. When there is a great range of frequencies involved, far greater concentrations can result. Particles differing greatly in the photons of which they are comprised tend to interpenetrate. The repulsive forces are therefore correspondingly higher.

The evidence for continental drift is overwhelming. This idea does not seem to be in conflict with conventional beliefs; hence, it is universally accepted by the scientific world. The electrostatic forces and stresses produced by the sun's influence, just discussed, make continental drift possible; and are a greater factor than gravitational pull in producing earth changes. Continental drift indicates the earth is slowly expanding.

Since a hollow sphere cannot expand in this manner without creating major breaks or openings in the shell at approximate antipodes, the origin of the large egresses into its interior is explained. In addition, the sliding of plates over each other no doubt produced the large caverns which honeycomb the earth's shell.

A major objection to the existence of giant caverns deep inside the earth covering millions of square miles, is the roofs should collapse, even in low gravity. The high concentrations of combinations of soft particles inside these caverns screen out gravity radiations far more effectively than solid matter. Therefore, the roofs of these caverns have little or no gravity affecting them.

The expansion of the earth and continental drift are helped along by the gravitational pull of the sun. The gravitational force due to the sun varies throughout the earth's shell. This creates tremendous stresses increasing the tendency for plates to slide over each other. The origin of earthquakes is now apparent. There are times when the concentration of charges reaches a critical state. A condenserlike discharge of particles then occurs. The sudden discharge of hard electrons when this happens produces an explosion. Since the hard particles are partially confined, tremendous forces are released causing the earth to shake. A similar phenomenon produces lightning. Many of the discharged particles find their way back to the surface. Some of them break up their constituent photons and thereby produce color effects sometimes preceeding a quake. Animals and sensitive people can sense these energies. These discharges could be a means for predicting earthquakes.

Prior to a quake the discharge of soft particles will cause an increase in temperature of strata far below the surface. As the particles move to the surface, many of them disintegrate and release large quantities of hard electrons. This process will be relatively slow at first; but as the temperature increases, larger quantities will disintegrate with also a consequent increase in the rate of discharge. Consequently, the rise in temperature of lower strata prior to a quake will be slow at first, followed by a rapid increase in temperature.

THE ORIGIN OF VOLCANOES

The academic explanation for volcanic activity is somewhat vague. Since the temperature of molten lava disgorged by volcanoes is so great, the orthodox viewpoint is the molten lava would have to originate at levels hundreds of miles below the surface. It has not been made clear how lava could find its way to the surface from such depths, since the earth is supposedly a solid ball.

Mine shafts and oil drilling operations have indicated significant increases of temperature with depth. This phenomenon is a result of two factors, the law of redistribution of energy and the disintegration of soft particles. It has already been shown the redistribution law is responsible for the higher temperatures at lower elevations. This process continues as the radiation from the sun penetrates the earth's crust. The lower frequencies are readily transformed into infrared radiations which produce increases in temperature. The temperature gradient in the first few miles below the surface is reasonably steep. This temperature increase practically ceases after several miles of penetration. The more unstable particles radiated by the sun have disintegrated by the time they reach this level. The temperature decreases slightly from this point downward. The disintegration of soft particles, with the consequent release of energy, and hard electrons, is an important factor in the temperature increase. Most of the soft particles that disintegrate during this interval are comprised of photons below the visible range of the electromagnetic spectrum.

The more stable, higher frequency particles remain after several miles of penetration. Consequently, disintegrations become less frequent and lower intensities of infrared are produced and also fewer hard electrons are released. As a result, the temperatures in the caverns are maintained at a comfortable and constant level. The desirable temperatures experienced deep inside the earth have been mentioned in various accounts, including the Etidorhpa book.

Since volcanic activity is not a result of uniformly high temperatures deep inside the earth, one must look elswhere for the cause. According to Etidorhpa, (a book to be discussed in the next chapter) most volcanic activity is due to vast deposits of sodium in certain regions of the earth's crust. Large quantities of water periodically reach some of these deposits at great depths. The shifting of plates and fault lines opens fissures allowing water to reach them. The contact of water with sodium results in great temperatures and pressures, and melted rock is then forced through these fissures to the surface.

Etidorhpa implied that some volcanic activity is produced by other means. The buildup of ultrahigh concentrations of radiated particles from the sun in certain portions of the earth's crust, could cause the temperature increases necessary to produce molten rock. Faults and areas between plates in the crust act like great condensers for accumulating large quantities of hard electrons. The presence of these electrons greatly increases the temperatures of the surrounding rock. This results in the disintegration of increasing numbers of soft particles and the subsequent release of more hard electrons. The released hard electrons have little chance of readily escaping from the region, and the temperature of the rock steadily increases until it is well beyond the melting point. There is usually water present during the process. The superheated steam, mixed with the molten rock, enables it to be expelled to the surface with explosive violence.

It is interesting to note that if the cooled down lava is reheated to temperatures far above that of the original molten lava, it will not melt. This has never been explained. The high concentrations of soft particles permeating the rocks, in conjunction with the superheated steam which adds to this concentration, lowers the melting point to a considerable extent. All of the excess particles have escaped or disintegrated by the time the lava cools, and the melting point is consequently higher.

It is extremely significant that most of the large earthquakes occur in the regions of present or past volcanic activity. This is another indication that high concentrations and disintegrations of soft particles play an important role in volcanic phenomena. It has already been shown that fault lines promote high concentrations of soft particles.

There is strong evidence that volcanic activity has been decreasing down through the ages. This adds support to the causes of such phenomena presented in this chapter. If deposits of sodium and radioactive materials are the basic cause, then, as these deposits are depleted, volcanic activity will decrease.

CHAPTER 6

THE HOLLOW CONDITION OF THE EARTH

As mentioned in Part I, some of the pictures of the earth taken from satellites and the moon have indicated a large egress into the hollow interior of the earth. It is located just south of the North Pole in northern Canada. This, of course, is only a small part of the evidence of a large entrance into the earth.

Arctic regions well above the Artic Circle periodically experience a fall of red pollen which discolors the snow. Some species of birds in the higher latitudes migrate north instead of south during the fall. Warm north winds often occur in these areas. Also, large quantities of driftwood are found along shores in the far north that couldn't have come from the forests and trees to the south. The ocean currents are in the wrong direction. There are indications that some of the driftwood came from large trees. Trees of comparable size only exist in the temperate regions of the outer earth. Icebergs in the North Atlantic are comprised of fresh water. This means they were not formed from ocean water. If so, they would contain large quantities of salt. The driftwood and the icebergs suggest that a great river flows out of the opening, carrying driftwood with it and freezing, as it enters the outer earth to form the icebergs.

Such a large opening clears up the discrepancies in Admiral Peary's alleged trek to the North Pole. Leading explorers of the day seriously doubted the validity of Peary's claims. Even the U.S. Navy had serious doubts. To prevent a scandal which would cast a cloud over the service, he was officially given credit for reaching the pole. Interestingly enough, the route taken by Peary intersected the lip of the opening shown by the satellite pictures. The later stages of Peary's trek showed daily increases in latitude that indicated mileages impossible to cover by dog-sled over the kind of terrain that exists in the area. In fact, even under ideal conditions, such mileages would have set new records for travel by dog-sled during a 24-hour period. As Peary entered the region of the opening, the curvature of the earth would rapidly increase and his instruments would have greatly exaggerated the degree of latitude attained. Finally, there would have been an indication of 90 degrees latitude while he was still far from the actual pole.

The earth and other planets are hollow from logical and theoretical considerations. Since electromagnetic radiations, including those in the gravity-inducing range, have limited penetration, it follows that they, the planets, could not remain in their present orbits at their present orbital speeds if they were the solid balls academic science claims. Even a hollow earth would be too massive if its shell were solid and not honeycombed with the vast caverns it possesses. The satellite pictures of the earth, including the view described in Part I showing the flat in its outline provide a clue for estimating the thickness of the shell. The flat is about 1600 miles across and the actual hole seems to be about 800 miles in diameter. If the curvature around the lip is uniform, then the shell must be about 800 miles thick. The book, Etidorhpa, to be reviewed briefly in this chapter, also states that the thickness of the shell is 800 miles.

The planets are hollow from a still more logical standpoint. They were created by intelligent planning to support life and for the progression of various life forms. It follows they would be designed or engineered for the most efficient operation. A hollow planet with caverns throughout its shell could support many times the amount of life, since it would have many times the surface area available than would a solid planet. More important yet, such a planet could be maneuvered into various positions (as they are at times) far more readily than if they were solid. The Logos, who created the planets are, of course, far more intelligent than any human. Therefore, they would not be so stupid as to produce solid balls, for planets, as an academic scientist would if he possessed the power to create a planet. They utilize every scrap of material. The changing of the position of planets by space ships with giant levitating beams will be discussed in Part III. This accounts for great changes in the earth through the ages, including the great flood and other cataclysms.

A description of a hypothetical trip into the interior of the earth by means of a tunnel will now be given in order that the reader may better understand what the earth's interior is like. Descending below the five-mile depth, the traveler will begin to notice a rapid decrease in his weight.

This is because of the limited, penetrating ability of the gravity radiations and the gravity effects of the earth above counteracting the gravity effects of the earth below. These counteracting effects are enhanced by the mass of earth above, tending to transform some of the infrared radiations emanated by this matter into the gravity-producing radiations, according to the redistribution law.

One will begin to notice the darkness tending to diminish after about ten miles. This is due to some of the soft particles radiated from the sun which begin to disintegrate into their constituent light, after passing through several miles of solid matter. The deeper one goes, the lighter it becomes, since ever larger quantities of these highly penetrating particles from the sun are disintegrating into light. The less stable particles disintegrated during passage through the atmosphere. After a considerable distance, the traveler will notice a significant improvement in his physical strength and vigor. This is due to the higher concentration of beneficial particles found at these depths.

There are no shadows in the lighted portion of the earth's interior, because the light comes from all directions, instead of from a central source. Plant and animal life flourish in the deeper caverns and are larger than on the surface, because of the higher concentrations of soft particles, and the almost complete absence of soft particles, comprised of light, in the higher ranges of the ultraviolet, as well as the lower gravity experienced at these depths. The traveler will enter the zone of zero gravity relatively close to the surface of the inner shell. This is where the gravity effects toward the surface of the earth exactly counteract the gravity effects from the opposite direction. This inner shell of the earth is finally reached after approximately 100 additional miles of travel.

In the inner earth, the traveler will see a glowing ball of light called the central sun, located at the earth's geometric center. It consists of a high concentration of soft electrons. The reader no doubt wonders why it is there. A high gravity exists at the surface of the inner shell, because the countergravity effects from the upper half of the shell are screened out by the high concentration of soft particles in the space between. Negative charges tend to be repelled by a gravitational field, in direct contradiction to concepts of academic science. Positive charges are attracted by the field. This will be explained in Part III. It will also be shown that ordinary, supposedly uncharged, matter behaves like a positive charge. In view of this, the reason for the concentration of soft electrons at the center forming this glowing ball becomes apparent. The particles have their greatest concentration at the center because they are repelled by the gravitational field on all sides. The light is produced by the continuous disintegration of particles, due to their interactions. They represent the excess of negative charges from the sun reaching the inner shell of the earth.

Recent findings of satellites confirm the existence of this central sun and especially the existence of a large opening into the earth's interior in the north polar region. Photographs released show the earth topped by a glowing halo, hovering about 60 miles above the icecap. According to to the reports, satellite pictures in the past have shown a partial halo, but recent photos show the ring in its entirety "making the earth look as if someone placed a white wreath around the north pole."

From an orthodox standpoint there is no way this ring effect can logically be explained and all attempts have been devoid of sound thinking. From what has just been presented, the explanation is obvious. The central "sun" would naturally radiate high concentrations of soft electrons in all directions. Those whose paths take them close to the edge of the opening will encounter much of the earth's atmosphere. Many of these will tend to disintegrate as they pass through the atmosphere. Most of these disintegrations will occur some distance above the earth's surface as they leave the opening. Those whose paths are further from the edge, including the center, will encounter little or no atmosphere, and thus travel to outer space without disintegrating. A ring effect is the result. Although this ring is close to the North Pole, it could not be centered there, but must be offset a few hundred miles, since previous satellite pictures show this opening to be in the vicinity of the magnetic pole in northern Canada.

The diameter of this ring fluctuates and will always be much larger in diameter than that of the opening. The particles which hit the atmosphere when ejected from the openings will travel some distance beyond the opening before many of them disintegrate. They are forced outward in all directions by a continuous flow of particles from the interior. Resistance produced by the atmosphere and the particles it already contains tends to slow them down. This causes a heavy back up of particles a considerable distance beyond the lip of the opening. The increased interactions results in more disintegrations.

The diameter of the ring becomes greater during auroral displays. This is the result of greater discharges from the sun which penetrate the earth's shell in greater numbers. A higher rate of particle accumulation at the earth's center will result, with a consequent higher radiation through the openings. The particles reaching the atmosphere around the lip of the opening have a higher velocity than before. The cause of the auroras becomes self evident. The increased concentration of soft electrons radiated from the openings as a result of increased sunspot activity produces a higher percentage of soft particle disintegration in the upper atmosphere.

The author predicts that a halo effect will also be found in the antarctic region. This will be in the south magnetic polar region south of Australia.

If it were not for the large entrances into the earth's interior, all life in the inner earth, including the great caverns, would be obliterated. The excess particles radiated by the so-called "central sun" would accumulate in increasing numbers through the earth's crust. There would be an ever increasing number of soft electrons disintegrating and releasing ever greater quantities of hard electrons, causing a steady increase in temperature through the inner earth. It would be something akin to the greenhouse effect. A smaller body with a much thinner shell, like the moon, does not require large egresses. Most of the excess particles can escape back through the relatively thin shell without disintegrating. Also, the moon has about six percent of the earth's surface area. The particle accumulation in the interior will thereby be much less. It is highly significant that a picture of the planet Venus' surface taken recently by Pioneer Orbiter shows unmistakable evidence of a great egress into the planet's interior. It has a diameter about one-fourth that of the planet itself! This picture is shown in color in the September, 1982 issue of *Science Digest*.

Later pictures which appeared in the November-December, 1982 issue of *Planetary Report* showing a series of pictures covering the entire surface and taken by the Venus orbiter, display the other opening, which is just about the exact antipode of the former. This one is much larger and has a diameter about 40% that of the diameter of Venus. This is to be expected. Venus receives far more intense radiation than the earth and requires much larger openings in order to prevent excessive heat build up.

A further analysis of gravity conditions to be expected along this hypothetical tunnel, leading from the earth's surface to the concave inner shell, is in order. The gravitational force produced by a large body such as the earth or moon is the result of the transformation of radiations from matter of a higher frequency than the gravity-inducing radiations. Some of it comes from the radiation produced by the interactions of the fundamental particles. However, most of this radiation has such a high frequency that only a very minute percentage is transformed into gravity radiations. Therefore, most of the gravity produced is due to the transformation of lower frequencies resulting from the thermal agitation of atoms and molecules. These radiations are mostly in the infrared range, not far removed from the gravity range. This means that such radiation, or the soft electrons associated with it, does not have to travel great distances through matter, without significant portions of it being transformed into gravity-producing radiations.

The concentration of soft particles radiated from the sun begins to increase significantly after a few miles below the surface. This is due to a steady retardation of their passage through the earth and the resulting back up of particles. The increased concentration diminishes after a time, and the concentration gradient becomes smaller from about the halfway point to the inner shell. The pattern of the gravitational attenuation gradient can be easily deduced from this picture. After only a very few miles below the earth, gravity begins to diminish rapidly. This is because the mass of earth above is beginning to transform significant portions of the infrared radiations emanating from the matter into gravity radiations. This decrease starts to taper off at about 25 miles below the surface, because the gravity radiations produced by the matter below this level encounter higher concentrations of soft particles, which screen out gravity radiations more effectively. Gravity decreases more slowly from this point on and doesn't reach the zero point until most of the shell is penetrated. This is due to the energies which permeate the crust, and because gravity radiations are being continuously dissipated and new radiations created. Since the concentration of soft particles in the last 100 miles is higher than in the first 100 miles below the surface, the gravity on the inner shell will be less than the gravity on the surface. Figure 2 depicts the gravity attenuation curve for the earth shell. Gravity effects on the inner shell at any point are not offset by the gravity effects of the earth on the opposite side, because the concentrations of soft particles in the inner earth screen out these gravity effects.

It is apparent from the foregoing discussion that if all the matter of any gravitating body were cooled to absolute zero, its gravity effects would all but vanish. Heating a body such as the one used in the Cavendish experiment causes a slight increase in the gravitational force. Further heating would produce only very slight increases because the average frequency of the thermal radiations increases; and therefore, the gap between the gravity frequencies and the average thermal frequency widens.

It is important at this stage to mention a book concerning the hollow earth, the finest that has yet been written. It not only contains more important factual material about the hollow earth than any other book, but also goes far beyond them in other respects. This great book probably

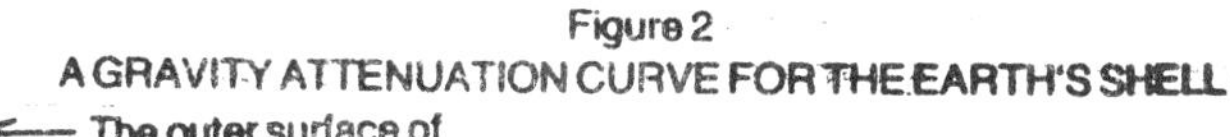

Figure 2
A GRAVITY ATTENUATION CURVE FOR THE EARTH'S SHELL

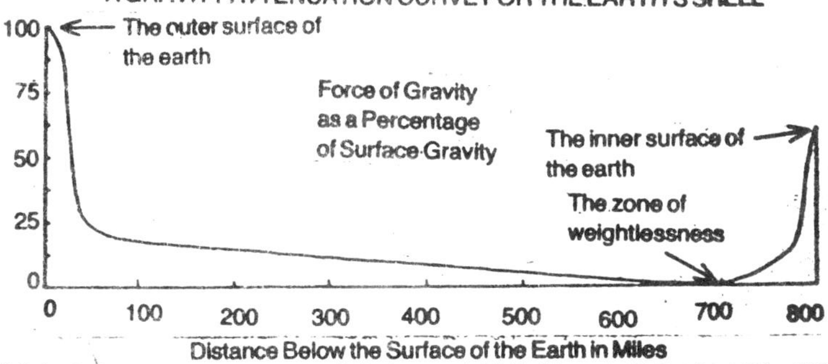

Gravity drops off rapidly in the first 25 miles below the earth's surface due to the limited penetrating ability of gravity-inducing radiations. From that point downward the rate of decrease becomes progressively less until it drops to zero 700 miles below the outer surface. The force of gravity begins rising again proceeding toward the inner surface which is at the 800 mile depth. At the inner surface, the force of gravity reaches a value which is somewhat less than that on the outer surface of the earth.

Figure 3
CROSS SECTION OF EARTH TAKEN THROUGH NORTH AND SOUTH OPENINGS

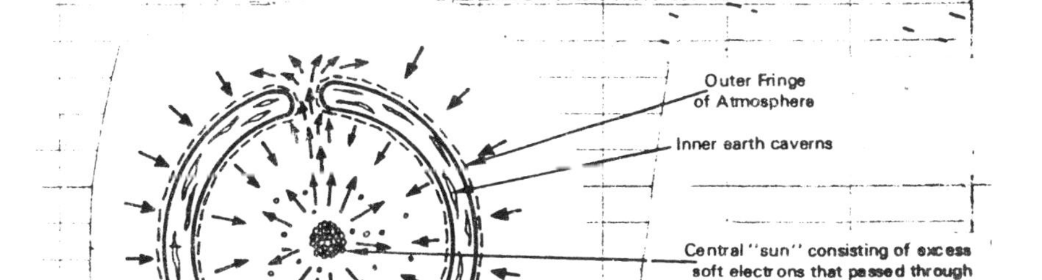

Large openings prevent excessive accumulation of soft electrons inside the earth. They function as an exhaust system for the excess particles to escape into outer space. Were it not for this there would be a steady build up of heat throughout the inner earth and the crust with disastrous results. Radar pictures taken of Venus show enormous openings at almost the exact antipode of each other and they are round. Being closer to the sun, Venus would require much larger openings. The surface is protected from the extreme radiation from the sun by a very extensive mantle of water vapor. This belies the claims of conventional science which state Venus has a surface temperature of about 1000 °F with sulphuric acid clouds. This is consistent with other false pictures they paint of the universe.

contains more profound metaphysical and scientific truths than any other book written up to the present. The book is entitled *Etidorhpa* and was first published in 1895.(78) Some books are written in the form of a novel in order to present certain ideas or truths without inviting undue attack from various quarters. *Etidorhpa* is considered by most to be a science fiction book. Any intelligent and discerning reader realizes that it isn't.

The book concerns a story within a story. In Cincinnati, Ohio, during the 1860's, a young student of science had an unusual visitation from a mysterious stranger of striking appearance. This strange man, whose name was never revealed, extracted a promise from this student to publish a manuscript which the stranger was to read to him. The time of the publication was to be 30 years later. The manuscript was then read aloud over a period of time requiring many sessions. After the last reading the manuscript was presented to him along with sealed instructions to be opened at the prescribed time.

According to the subject matter of the manuscript, the stranger was taken into the hollow of the earth through a cave in Kentucky during the early part of the nineteenth century. His guide was a cavern dweller who was a member of a secret organization whose objective was the preservation of vital knowledge for the future enlightenment of mankind. The objective of this trip was the inner shell of the earth, where the nameless one was to receive advanced schooling in the mysteries of the universe. The book *Etidorhpa* described this amazing trip through the caverns of the inner earth in detail. It also presented some of the philosophy and scientific truths the guide imparted to this man.

The author was astounded when he read the book, since it confirmed many of the new ideas he had already formulated. In fact, some of the factual material presented in the book enabled him to extend the new concepts to a more comprehensive view of the universe. It was then possible to explain many things not properly resolved in the book.

According to *Etidorhpa*, the shell of the hollow earth is 800 miles thick, which an analysis of the satellite pictures confirms. Gravity at the 25-mile depth was one-third normal earth gravity. From that level, gravity decreased gradually until it disappeared at the 700-mile depth. At that point, the narrative ended. The reasons for these conditions were not given, but they are to be expected from the principles already outlined.

The protagonist was also taken on a boat ride for several thousand miles on a lake 150 miles below the surface. Evidently, this boat utilized gravity-inducing radiations for its motive power, since the occupants experience no accelerating stresses, even though the boat accelerated from a standing start to 1200 miles per hour in a flash. They felt no rush of air, since the air surrounding the boat was carried along with them. The nature of this propulsive force was not divulged, although the guide said that some day the outer world would utilize this principle. Another significant scientific truth revealed was that magnetic fields are the result of ether currents. This concept forms one of the principles to be introduced in Part III.

An outline of this nature cannot do justice to a book such as *Etidorhpa*. Limited space does not permit a more extensive summary. It is not surprising that *Etidorhpa* presented academic science in an unfavorable light. In this vein, a quotation from page 355 of *Etidorhpa* is congruous with the trend of this treatise:

> Science has confined its labors to superficial descriptions, not the elucidation of the fundamental causes of phenomena.

This was actually a very charitable statement in view of what has been presented so far.

Seismologists believe their findings verify the conventional belief that the earth is a solid ball consisting of an iron core 4000 miles in diameter tapped by an inner mantle of molten material and an outer mantle that is more solid. Over all of this is a relatively thin crust. They allegedly do this by tracking speeds of earthquake waves by a network of seismometers scattered around the globe which furnish a record of digital data which is fed into computers. When a quake occurs seismic waves spread through the planet from the center of the rupture. There are several points where travel times of seismic waves change considerably. Such zones are called discontinuities, and supposedly occur at the so-called crust mantle boundary or "Moho" and at depths of 400 to 670 kilometers.

As is the case with other members of the scientific community, the seismologists lack the mentality to properly analyze their data and to realize that more than one interpretation can be placed on them. They display the peculiar mental process that is common in the world of academic science. It is known as reasoning in a circle. They start out with an assumption which they consider an incontrovertible fact which is treated as such in their subsequent analysis. By following this trend of thought they arrive at a final conclusion which is the same assumption with which they started!

One important factor seismologists fail to realize is that they have no reliable means of determining the exact path a given wave has followed when it reaches a certain point. The great network of caverns and huge underground bodies of water throughout the shell of the hollow earth would conform perfectly with the seismic data. Great masses of water could be interpreted as molten rock. Discontinuities would be nothing else but boundary lines between solid portions of the shell and bodies of water along with caverns and also the inner parts of the shell. It is extremely significant that different groups in different places on the globe come up with different conclusions as to structural detail in regard to the inner earth. On the basis of conventional beliefs concerning the structure of the earth, this would be extremely difficult if not impossible to explain away by any rational approach. However, such results are to be expected from the information revealed thus far in this treatise. The caverns which make up the network in the earth's shell vary considerably in their extent and distance below the earth's surface. This would obviously create complex and variable seismic data over different parts of the globe.

Seismic data which directly refute the claims of a solid earth have been conveniently ignored by seismologists. Earthquakes of inordinate magnitude, such as the Alaska earthquake of 1962, have caused the earth to ring like a bell for several hours following the quake. This could not have occurred if the earth were the solid ball that our obtuse scientists keep saying that it is. It is significant that seismic experiments on the moon caused it to behave in a similar manner. Being of far less mass than the earth, relatively small shocks would produce such an effect. Also the reverberation time would be less. However, the moon did ring for nearly an hour following the experiments. This caused some scientists to speculate on the possibility of the moon being a hollow space ship.

SUMMARY OF PART II

Many of the facts and principles introduced in this part have not appeared in print before. It was shown that science has failed to explain any of the common everyday phenomena, such as tides, which are taken for granted. Further evidence was supplied showing that our planet is indeed hollow, with far better living conditions in the interior than exist on the outside. Additional steps were taken toward resolving the mystery of gravity. It was shown that popular theories in the field of cosmology are as devoid of sound thinking as many other debunked academic theories. Also, a new insight into the nature of the ethers was introduced for the first time, laying the groundwork for a deeper understanding of a wide range of phenomena to be given in Part III and IV.

Greater surprises are in store for the reader in Part III. Some of the ideas introduced in Parts I and II will be developed still further and new concepts given, embracing the entire field of physics. This will also include the explanation for geomagnetism not discussed in Part II, since more groundwork in the nature of magnetism needs to be presented for a proper treatment of this subject.

PART III

DEVELOPING A NEW PHYSICS OF THE UNIVERSE FROM THE UNIFYING PRINCIPLE

INTRODUCTION TO PART III

It has been suggested that the laws of the universe are basically simple. The operating functions, or laws of life and existence, can be defined by building upon the unifying principle to be introduced in Part III. The more attentive reader probably realizes that a powerful wedge has already been driven into the crack of the door leading to this evolution. This door will be torn assunder in the following pages. A number of surprises await the reader during this process.

This treatise has been written to appeal to the widest range of individuals. There is a considerable amount of highly technical material in this section on the new physics, and some readers may find it difficult. Part III also has something to offer those who do not comprehend much of the technical material.

Concepts presented in the first two parts will be expanded upon, and others will be introduced for the first time. The reader will be given a bird's-eye view of the fundamental particles of matter, and how they function within the atom. The nature and relationship between electrostatic and magnetic fields will be clearly shown. The properties of light and methods of propagation are part of this program. A complete analysis of the nature of gravity is given, followed by new interpretations of some of the revolutionary discoveries of Wilhelm Reich.

The last subject in Part III concerns "free energy" devices. Free energy is a misnomer since the conservation of energy must hold true. It is the heretofore misunderstood and unknown nature of the universe which leads researchers to speculate on what is called "free energy."

Many of the devices described herein obey the conservation law, even though the term "free energy" is associated with them. Also included is the description of a simple and practical self-sustaining electrical generator. It will be shown that the so-called "energy crisis" is a gigantic fraud thrust upon the world by mental degenerates in high places, and that many practical free energy devices have been suppressed for many decades by such miscreants.

Perhaps the most significant aspect of the section on free energy is an analysis of the nature and growth of crystals, and a demonstration that they are the greatest potential source of energy. More of the shallow and faulty reasoning fostered by academic science is brought to a sharp focus as this section unfolds.

CHAPTER 7

FUNDAMENTAL WEAKNESSES IN CONVENTIONAL MATHEMATICS INCLUDING FLAWS IN A WELL ACCEPTED CONCEPT ON NUMBER THEORY AND A DISQUALIFICATION OF THE FOUR COLOR THEOREM

Modern theorists have nearly always assumed that the phenomena of the universe cannot be explained in terms of mechanical models. Consequently, they rely on mathematical descriptions as a proper treatment of the subject. This trend has been carried to such ridiculous extremes they have come to believe such procedures constitute satisfactory explanations! Quantum mechanics is a classic example. An article on the subject, by the well known physicist Freeman J. Dyson, entitled "Innovations in Physics," appeared in the September, 1958 issue of *Scientific American*. This article was revealing in a manner the author obviously never intended. It was stated on pages 77 and 78 that during the difficult learning period, the student finally discovers that there is really nothing to understand about quantum mechanics. He learns the subject when he becomes able to manipulate the mathematics so as to get the right answers. The training period to which Dyson alluded was a perfect description of a brainwashing process. Also, it is similar to that described in Orwell's novel, *1984*, which enables one to become an artful doublethinker.

This excessive dependence upon mathematics as a tool probably had its origin in the works of James Clerk Maxwell, generally considered the greatest theoretical physicist of the nineteenth century, and rightly so. Maxwell had an extraordinary ability to use mechanical models to explain physical phenomena. In fact, he made his greatest discoveries in this manner. He coupled this with an unequaled ability to translate physical imagery into mathematics. Unfortunately, he then published his findings in terms of mathematics with the models left out. His predictions later proved to be so accurate in certain respects that subsequent theorists assumed that mathematics was the only approach to understanding the mysteries of the universe. These physicists were not Maxwells, and, as such, lacked the imagination to use such models as well as Maxwell did. The many bizarre and nebulous ideas being expounded upon by today's theorists demonstrate that too much dependence upon mathematics can lead one into a dream world with little bearing upon reality.

There is always the hope that some unique solution to certain equations will bring about a new revelation concerning the mysteries of the universe, and thereby duplicate Maxwell's achievements. A simple fact many physicists do not seem to understand is that the validity and significance of a conclusion, derived from mathematics, is dependent upon the quality of the assumptions and thoughts upon which it is based, regardless of the mathematics employed.

There is no reason to believe mathematics has attracted any better minds than has conventional physics. It is reasonable to conclude that the quality of thinking among mathematicians is generally no better than that demonstrated by physicists. It then follows that mathematics should be steeped in blunders as egregious as those already uncovered in physics. Just a little digging below the surface reveals this conclusion to be thoroughly justified.

By following this process, two outstanding blunders crop up rivaling the theory of relativity and the theory of tides in vacuity.

The first mathematical flaw to be considered concerns the work on transfinite numbers by the nineteenth century mathematician George Cantor. His theory is considered a milestone in the history of mathematics, and is still a part of college curriculums in higher mathematics. He allegedly proved, by the most specious type of reasoning, that the real numbers having a finite number of places are not countable. This laid the groundwork for his theory of transfinite numbers. Briefly, his proof, called the "diagonal proof", consisted in the hypothetical arrangements of all the numbers in horizontal rows. He claimed that a diagonal path can be drawn through this list which contains a number not in the list. This, of course, is a crass violation of a basic principle involving permutations and combinations which are taught in high school math. The ten digits used in our numbering system can only be arranged in a finite number of ways, if the number of digits in any number is less than infinity. The formula for this maximum number is 10^n-1, where n is the maximum number of places or digits in the number. This assumes that zero by itself is not a number. When n is 2, there are 10^2-1 or 99, if n equals 3 it is 10^3-1, and so on.

A mathematician, A.L. Kitselman published a pamphlet about two decades ago entitled, "Hello Stupid". He ridicules Cantor for some of the outrageous conclusions derived from his theory of transfinite numbers. This same booklet describes a phenomenon known as the Biefeld-Brown effect which physicists continue to ignore, since it is damaging to current theories and they are at a loss to explain it. This effect will be analyzed and explained in this part.

The second mathematical blooper centers around the famous four-color theorem which has been stumping mathematicians for the past 140 years. This theorem states that four colors are sufficient to color any map on a plane surface, so that no two adjacent regions are the same color. The consensus among mathematicians is that this conjecture is valid, since no one has ever been able to disprove it by devising a map that requires more than four colors.

It has been disturbing to the mathematical world that no one has come forward with acceptable proof of that theory until recently. Before starting this book, the author decided the most logical approach to the quandary was that the mathematicians were wrong. He decided that a simple proof showing the fallacy of the four-color theorem existed. With this in mind, the author tackled the problem with the decision not to devote an inordinate amount of time to the pursuit. The results soon justified the above assumption. A simple proof did emerge: let a map be drawn so that, by necessity, four different colors lie along a common border, and the problem is easily solved. It is then only necessary to surround this border with another region which obviously requires the fifth color. This is the approach that was employed. Any complex map with a myriad of regions requires four colors, and in fact, each of the four colors will appear many times. Now consider a map with an infinitude of regions of all sizes and shapes, and that this map is colored in the most efficient manner possible. Also assume that by some miracle, only four colors were used. This means that each of the four different colors will appear a near infinite number of times. A line is now drawn through this map separating it into two parts. It can be drawn in any number of ways and can even be a closed curve. This line will necessarily cut through regions of four different colors. Now there are two different maps, each of which has been colored in the most efficient manner, with four different colors along a common border. Either one of these maps can be surrounded with another region requiring the fifth color.

One might argue that the map can be recolored by first coloring the regions along the border, using only three colors in this process. The regions along the border can indeed be three colored, but this immediately creates a new problem. This has so restricted the coloring of the inner regions that a fifth color soon becomes mandatory and possibly even a sixth color. By the recoloring process, the map as a whole cannot be colored in a more economical manner than it was before.

Two mathematicians at the University of Illinois were striving to prove this theorem prior to the author's venture into the four-color quandary. Their work was considered to be of sufficient importance and so they were granted unlimited use of one of the most sophisticated computers in the country. After years of hard work and 1600 hours of computer use, they finally announced a successful conclusion to the project. The October 1977 issue of *Scientific American* featured an article about this milestone in the history of mathematics.(7) This article included a complex map of hundreds of regions successfully four-colored to illustrate the validity of the theorem. Each of four different colors appeared along the outline of the map a minimum of 12 times, thereby making it a five-color map with the addition of the surrounding region.

The author immediately sent the mathematicians air-tight proof showing the four-color theorem was not valid, and that the map which accompanied the article in *Scientific American* was actually a five-color map. He expressed his regrets that all of their work had been fruitless, and that one of the nation's biggest computers had been tied up for so long a period in such an endeavor. The author, needless to say, has not, as yet, received any thanks for this bit of enlightenment. It is not likely that any will be forthcoming or that mathematicians will recognize this proof.

The reader may be shocked to learn that a map can be drawn that requires at least seven, not five colors. Once again, consider a map with an infinitude of regions of all sizes and shapes. Instead of being surrounded with a bordering area of just one region as before, this area is broken up into three parts each of which borders on the other two. The coloring process begins near the center and extends outwards. Again, the coloring is done in the most economical manner possible. There is no way the process can be completed without each of at least four different colors bordering each of the three outer segments many times. Each of the three segments must be colored differently from the other two and, in turn, each must have a different color from the four or more on the outer portion of the inner map. This means at least seven different colors are required.

A four-color advocate might argue that the outer regions of the central map can be colored so that each outer segment borders on just three different colors. The combination of three colors is different for each segment. For example, let A, B, and C represent the outer segments, and 1, 2, 3 and 4 represent four different colors. A could border on colors 1, 2 and 3; B on 2, 3 and 4 and C on 1, 2 and 4.

In this manner, only four colors are used. Once again, this creates unsurmountable problems in subsequent coloring. The inner coloring process would be restricted in three different ways instead of the one way described earlier when the outer portion of the map was three-colored. Each one of the restrictions affects the entire coloring process. Therefore, as the coloring proceeds, five colors are soon needed. As more of the map is colored, a sixth color becomes mandatory and long before it is finished, a seventh color would be necessary. Very likely an eights and even a ninth would be used by the time the job is finished, since such a procedure is not necessarily the most economical way to color a map. It doesn't matter, of course, where one starts. If the process is carried out in the most efficient manner, the same number will eventually be used. The process of starting near the center merely demonstrates the requirement of at least seven different colors.

Does seven represent the maximum number of colors needed to color any map, or is there an upper limit? It is apparent that mathematicians and four color enthusiasts have only considered maps wherein the regions are all of nearly the same order of magnitude in area. Under such restrictions, the four color theorem may well be valid. However, when there is a tremendous range in relative sizes, the four color theorem quickly breaks down as has just been shown. Instead of just two categories, the very large and very small, as just discussed, consider an unlimited number of similar categories with each category bordering on all categories below it in magnitude. There are great number of each category bordering on each region comprising all categories of greater magnitude. It is clear that as the number of categories increases the number of colors required will also increase if the above pattern is followed. It can be concluded that there is no limit to the number of different colors required when maps of this type are considered.

The two mathematical blunders, just described, no doubt represent only the tip of the iceberg, so to speak. Careful probing would more than likely uncover many more just as outstanding. This the author will not attempt. There are far more important and fruitful endeavors requiring attention.

Perhaps the most overlooked flaw in mathematics which greatly limits its areas of application, is the loose and indiscriminate use of the term "equal," upon which equations are derived. Certain terms are substituted for others on the basis that they have one thing in common during the derivation of an equation. This is done without considering the possibility that other aspects of these terms may have nothing in common with each other, and, as such, might have a distinct bearing on the problem to which they are applied. Many equations are valid and useful when such a problem does not exist. This has been the case with the mathematics used in this treatise. For example, consider equations involving areas, volumes, and masses. The aspect of shape has not been considered, and has no significance in the final solution of the problems to which they have been generally applied.

The limitation of mathematics is fully demonstrated in a paradox involving the well known kinetic energy equation:

$$E = \frac{1}{2}mv^2$$

This paradox is discussed and resolved in Chapter 13, under the section entitled "Why the Velocity of Light Equals the Ratio Between EMU and ESU Units of Charge".

Mathematicians of the past and present have devoted an unbelievable amount of time to idle speculations and worthless pursuits. There are certain self-evident facts which cannot be proven, at least within the framework of the present system of mathematical logic, and do not require solutions. As an example, consider the following hypotheses: first, "one, and only one, line can be drawn through a point parallel to another line". Second, "two parallel lines will never meet, no matter how far they are extended". Amazingly, many mathematicians have devoted a good portion of their lives trying to prove or disprove these axioms. Many mathematical physicists have come from their ranks. Pure mathematicians have supplied the tools for modern theorists' excursions into impossible dream worlds. For example, the nineteenth century mathematician Reimann invented the type of geometry Einstein employed to develop the General Theory of Relativity.

In this century, the trend has been to solve physical problems using solely abstract mathematics. This approach violates the hermetic axiom, to be introduced shortly, and the law of cause and effect. Intangibles do not produce tangibles. Since we live in a mechanical universe, it follows that the underlying causes may best be shown in terms of mechanics. It seems logical to assume that this is the only way it can be done.

Before continuing to the next chapter, it should be mentioned that scientists have gone from one absurd extreme in regard to dependence on mathematics to an opposite extreme. In the first case mathematics has been overemphasized. Yet in other instances they have failed to take into consideration even the most elementary mathematical principles. A prime example involves the relationship between surface area and volume. Volume increases as the cube of a linear dimension while surface area increases only as its square.

Entomologists have been mystified by the apparent strength displayed by insects in proportion to their size. In reality, this is only a demonstration of this mathematical principle. It does seem unbelievable, but much research is still being made in an effort to discover the secret of their physical prowess. The insect is actually very inept for its size. If an animal or a human were reduced to the size of an insect and still retained its cellular structures, either one would far outperform the insect. Evidently, mental ineptitude in the realm of science is not restricted to the physical sciences. The simple fact that animal tissues are much stronger than those of insects was overlooked.

Assuming that physical or organic structure remains constant, the lifting ability, in proportion to weight, will vary inversely as the cube root of the weight. This is apparent in the lifting records among weightlifters. The smaller men, in general, always lift more in proportion to their weight than the bigger men. In fact, weightlifting records in the various weightlifting divisions from bantamweights to the superheavyweights closely follow this formula. An application of this formula shows that if a top lifter were reduced to the size of an ant, he would be able to backlift thousands of times his own weight. Has an ant or any other type of insect ever remotely approached such a performance?

"It will be shown later that this same mathematical principle is the governing factor in the source of the sun's radiant energy".

CHAPTER 8

NEW INSIGHTS INTO THE NATURE OF MATTER, INERTIA AND THE ETHERS WITH AN INTRODUCTION TO THE MEANING OF PLANCK'S CONSTANT

One of the most fundamental physical laws involves the relationship between the electrostatic and magnetic fields. It was indicated earlier that a magnetic field develops at the expense of an electrostatic field. One transforms into the other and vice versa. They are analogous to different sides of the same coin or another manifestation of the law of duality. Dualities cannot exist by themselves. It requires a third ingredient to give them reality. In order for a coin to have two sides, it must have thickness to give it substance or reality. Things manifest in terms of surfaces in two dimensions. It always requires a third dimension to make them a reality. This third factor is the fulcrum through which and by which dualities must manifest themselves. This is known as the law of the trinity or the triangle. Space, therefore, must only have three dimensions. The idea of fourth or higher dimensions is the product of badly confused minds, unable to comprehend the seemingly perplexing experiences they sometimes encounter.

Inertia, then, becomes the third factor involved in the relationship between the electrostatic and magnetic fields. Energy cannot manifest itself without forces being involved. Without inertia, forces do not exist. Inertia, therefore, is an intimate and inseparable part of all energy phenomena. The cause of inertia or the reason that mass has inertia has remained a mystery to the world's leading thinkers for the 300 years, since Newton first defined it. A clue to understanding it can be found in Faraday's law stating that an induced electromotive force, is produced by a change in the flux. If we substitute "force" for electromotive force in the statement of this law and "velocity" for magnetic flux, which will be shown to concern velocity, then the law can be restated: "the induced force produced by a change in velocity is always in such a direction as to oppose any change in this velocity." This is another definition of inertia.

The factors governing inertia can be derived from the following consideration: the kinetic energy of a moving charge is manifested in its magnetic field. This magnetic field develops at the expense of its electrostatic field in order for the law of conservation of energy to remain intact! The role of inertia and the conditions governing its magnitude are now apparent. The inertia of a body is dependent on its ability to generate a magnetic field when it is given a velocity. The greater its inertia, the greater is this ability.

The magnitude of the inertia of a body is directly proportional to the energy of the magnetic field the body develops for a given increase in velocity. It then follows that inertia is dependent on the total electrostatic charge of a body. This is also true for so-called "uncharged" matter. It will soon be shown that in the supposedly uncharged state, all atoms and molecules have a net positive charge. Therefore, even atoms and molecules develop a magnetic field when they are given a velocity. In order to demonstrate this, the ethers must be considered, as well as the nature of light, photons, and the basic structure of positive and negative charges.

THE NATURE OF THE ETHERS AND THE MEANING OF PLANCK'S CONSTANT

A principle that makes possible the understanding and unification of a wide range of phenomena has been known for thousands of years. It is one of the hermetic axioms that is a part of esoteric teachings. It is usually stated "as above, so below." This boils down to the idea that the same basic principles underlie all phenomena and that all things interrelate in some way. From this come the laws of cause and effect. It follows that much of the nature of causes can be deduced from its effects, or that many of the properties of the unseen can be determined from that which is seen.

This great axiom is the second of seven principles upon which the entire Hermetic Philosophy is based. It has come down to us after thousands of years from its founder, Hermes Trismegistus, who lived in ancient Egypt. All of the basic teachings embedded in the esoteric teachings of every race can be traced back to Hermes. He was regarded by all advanced occultists and those of high learning as the Master of Masters.

His influence was so profound that, despite all the deviations from that which he taught, it has survived the centuries and today there is still a basic resemblance to his teachings which, along with conflicting theories, are still taught by methaphysical teachers of these various countries today. Students of comparative religions can recognize the influence of Hermetic philosophy in every major religion. The original truths expounded by Hermes have been kept intact in their original form by a few wise men in each generation. Consequently, they have been handed down from initiate to initiate and have been preserved for the few who are capable of comprehending them. This second axiom, known as the principle of correspondence, will be applied in this treatise toward the unfolding of mysteries never before resolved. However, this treatise embodies all seven of the Hermetic principles and demonstrates the truth contained within them. In fact, the ancient Hermetic philosophy comprises the skeletal structure of this book.

Since the axiom suggests that the nature of the ethers can be deduced by certain aspects of our surroundings, the most logical one to consider is the property of a perfect gas. Although there must be significant differences between a gas and the ethers, there must be certain properties that they have in common. An object can travel through free space at a steady velocity and encounter no measurable resistance. Yet, it apparently does encounter resistance during an acceleration. A similar pattern occurs during passage through a gas or atmosphere but to a more pronounced degree. When inertia isn't a major factor, a hollow object, for example, will experience great resistance from the gas if there is a great and sudden change in velocity. After it attains a given velocity and this velocity remains constant, the resistance is greatly reduced. Therefore, it is logical to assume that the inertia exhibited by a material object is due to the presence of a subtle medium that possesses some of the properties of a perfect gas. If there were no medium present, it would be somewhat difficult, if not impossible, to account for inertial properties.

The analogy of, and similarity between, the behavior of a near massless hollow ball in a gas and that of a body of great mass in free space is an application of this all-important Hermetic axiom. As will become increasingly evident, further application of this line of thought leads to extremely fruitful results. It has been established that at the same temperature and pressure, all gases have the same number of molecules per unit volume. This means the average distance between molecules from center to center is the same for all gases, regardless of their molecular weight. Since they exert the same pressure, it follows that the average kinetic energy of the molecules is the same for each gas. This means the average velocity of a gas molecule varies inversely as the square root of its molecular weight.

Applying these conclusions to the ethers, it follows that the average distance between ether particles is a constant, as well as is their average kinetic energies, regardless of the ethers considered. Since particles of matter have inertia, ether particles must have inertia as well. The reasons a body traveling through a gas at constant velocity encounter resistance, yet the ethers offer none, will become apparent later. Ether particles, and atoms, or molecules must also have certain properties that are similar. It will be shown later that atoms and molecules have zones of attraction as well as repulsion. It is vital that ether particles also possess such zones with regard to each other. The zonal effects around atoms are the result of the interactions of the fundamental particles, the electrons and protons. Therefore, ether particles also consist of fundamental particles similar in structure to electrons and protons. This is a manifestation of the law of duality. Basically, there are only two kinds of fundamental particles, contrary to the viewpoint of particle physicists.

It follows that the particles of the highest ethers correspond to our hydrogen atom and the basic particles that comprise it are the basic ingredients of all the ethers in all the realms that concern us. The lower ether particles correspond to the largest and most complex molecules.

It will soon be shown here that ether particles combine to form particles known as photons of light. This combining, or sticking together, corresponds to the cohesive forces of atoms and molecules which makes possible the formation of matter. It is the zonal forces around atoms and molecules that are responsible for these cohesive forces. Likewise, zonal forces around ether particles enable photons to evolve. These same forces enable photons to combine to form the fundamental particles of each realm, as will be described in more detail later.

The behavior and function of ether particles is duplicated with other particles in the realms of matter. The more active the particles, the more stable they need to be. The particles of the ethers are far more active than the fundamental particles of matter, and it follows that they are correspondingly more stable. The greater stability is also apparent from the following considerations. When ether particles combine to form photons the areas of contact are minute compared with the surface area outline of the ether particles. When photons combine to form fundamental particles of matter, the combining or sticking forces are the cohesive forces of the ether particles as it was when ether particles combined to form the photons. It is apparent the areas of contact between photons is no greater than between ether particles themselves. Yet, the same net forces are required to hold together far greater masses. It is analogous to using a certain glue to bind together a group of marbles and then using the same amount of the glue to hold a group of huge boulders together.

As will be shown later, cohesive forces or zonal effects are due to electrostatic forces. Electrostatic forces are produced by the bombardment of ether particles against the fundamental particles. In turn, the fundamental units of ether particles generate their version of electrostatic forces as a result of bombardments due to a very special ether from which the fundamental units of ether particles are comprised. Once again the second hermetic principle or axiom is evident. The basic unit of this special ether was the end result of a previous series of major cycles. This ether is the direct manifestation of the great creative intelligence which governs the entire universe. This last statement is a reflection of the first Hermetic principle or The Principle of Mentalism which states "The All is Mind; The Universe is Mental." It is the basic ingredient of all creations in the universe. As such, it is the common denominator of all manifestations and phenomena and is the channel by which all thought is transmitted. The manner by which the creative intelligence controls the particles of this ether is, of course, beyond the scope of this treatise. It is of little concern to us, as far as comprehending subsequent phenomena is concerned, and the material to be presented. It is convenient to think of all the basic ether particles as being interconnected by life lines or lines of communication through which the all pervading intelligence controls them.

Cohesive forces play only a small role during the combination of atoms to form molecules. As will be shown later, there is a partial and mutual interpenetration of atoms. The nuclei of the atoms tend to remain intact but the combination bears no resemblance to any of the atoms involved. This generally results in a stable combination. The same pattern applied, of course, with ether particles. Consequently, they are extremely stable. The larger and more sluggish ether particles of the lower ethers correspond to cells of the physical realm. The number of different kinds of ether particles is at least as great as the number of different kinds of atoms, molecules and cells. The number is astronomical.

Since the electrostatic field around a particle changes with its velocity, velocity becomes very critical to the motion of the fundamental particles of an atom or molecule. For example, if the velocity of an electron in a stable orbit should increase due to the presence of another particle or particles in the vicinity, it would tend to escape from the atom. The electrostatic force holding it in orbit would decrease and it would move away from the nucleus. At the same time, this force which decreases in accordance with the inverse square law will contribute further to the loss of the electron. This means there are two vital factors which govern the stability. It follows that a decrease in velocity in a stable orbit would cause the electron to move closer to the nucleus until a new state of equilibrium is reached.

An orbital electron cannot maintain a steady velocity because of the presence of other orbital electrons whose distances apart are continuously fluctuating. This means that electrons are continually escaping from atoms and being recaptured by adjacent or nearby atoms. (Incidentally, such factors partially account for the number of free protons found in outer space and in the Van Allen Radiation Belt where atoms are widely separated.) As a result, electrostatic field effects around atoms are rapidly changing according to a definite pattern. The greater the number of fundamental particles, the more complex this pattern. At the same time the greater the number, the more restricted the motions. It follows that as there are greater and more frequent changes in velocity, the average velocity of the particles will decrease. This means the negative electrostatic field intensity on the periphery of the atom will increase on the average! What effect does this have on the field zones outside the atoms? The nucleus consisting of positive charges are more closely bunched and the average velocity does not change as much as the number of particles increase. Therefore, the zonal effects around the atoms containing more fundamental particles are not as pronounced as with the smaller atoms and consequently, are more electrically neutral. This accounts for the fact that the cohesive forces binding large atoms together are, generally speaking, no stronger than with smaller atoms, although the areas of contact are greater with the larger atoms.

The same principle can be applied to ether particles. It was shown that the average kinetic energy of the lower ether particles is the same as that of the higher ether particles. This means that collisions or near collisions of like particles tend to occur with the same force regardless of whether they are of the higher or lower ethers. This means that the zonal effects of field intensities around the larger ether particles are less than that around the higher ether particles. This is compensated for by the larger surface areas of the larger particles which results in the same total repulsive forces.

Ether particles of the same kind will interact with each other more readily than with other ether particles because they are moving at the same velocity. A given ether particle will encounter another like particle moving in approximately the same general direction as often as it will encounter one moving in the opposite direction, since the motions are random. This means there will be longer periods where mutual repulsions of great force will occur. As a result there will be more abrupt and greater changes in the direction of motion. Direct collisions never occur because repelling fields cause a sharp change in direction of motion of particles on a collision course. The interaction time of particles of different velocities will be of shorter duration and this time decreases as the difference in velocity increases. As a consequence, there are less abrupt changes in direction of motion. This means that higher ether particles have only slight influence on the motions of lower ether particles and vice versa. Direct collisions never occur between high and low ether particles because of their repelling fields.

This accounts for the ability of the various realms of high frequency matter being able to interpenetrate or occupy the same three-dimensional space with each realm seeming to have no influence on the other. This does not mean, however, that overall attraction forces are completely absent between realms. When huge concentrations of matter are present these minute forces or influences become great enough to bind the various realms together into the same space. This prevents the realms of high frequency matter around a planet from becoming separated.

The picture of the ethers just presented reveals a principle of widespread ramifications. The average distance or mean free path between ether particles of the same kind has been shown to be a constant regardless of the ethers involved. This represents the most basic unit of linear measurement in the entire universe. Also, since the average kinetic energy of all ether particles is a constant, the most fundamental unit of ener gy can be stated. In terms of gram-centimeter units, the average kinetic energy of an ether particle in ergs represents this basic unit. Since all manifestations of energy and energy interactions involve ether particle bombardments, it follows that all energy interactions including light will occur in whole number multiples of this unit! This means that energy exists in discrete amounts or bundles of energy instead of a continuous flow as the world of science believed prior to 1901. It was not apparent in ordinary measurements because of the minuteness of this constant. Finally, in 1901, Max Planck discovered this reality in an attempt to explain the distribution in frequency of the radiant energy in the cavity of a body (black body radiations) as a function of the temperature of that body.

Planck found that he could derive the correct law of distribution only by assuming that energy exists in discrete units of energy, NHV, where N is an integer and V is the frequency of the light involved and H is some universal constant. In order for the energy equations to balance, H is expressed in terms of energy multiplied by time or erg-seconds and is known as Planck's constant. This happens to be the same constant mentioned above except that it is expressed in ergs instead of erg-seconds. The numerical value is the same in both cases. The value of this constant has been determined empirically to be 6.6×10^{-21} erg-secs.

Einstein later used this constant to allegedly explain the photo-electric effect. It was found that the maximum kinetic energy of electrons dislodged from surfaces by light was not dependent on the intensity of the light, but was a function of the frequency. The kinetic energy was directly proportional to the frequency of the light employed. Einstein reasoned that a light photon gave up its energy to an electron, and, therefore, the energy of a light photon was directly proportional to its frequency, according to the relation E equals HV where V is the frequency of the light and H is Planck's constant. Indeed, this relation did fit the experimental facts and Einstein received the Nobel Prize about 20 years later for this speculation. Although Einstein gave the wrong reasons, it is not surprising in view of the above conclusions that his photo-electric equations conformed with the facts. However, the type of reasoning Einstein employed showed that his scientific peccadillos were not confined to the theory of relativity.

In fact, Einstein's conclusions were as usual contrary to the facts. As will be shown later, the kinetic energy of a light photon is inversely proportional to the frequency. The lower frequency light consists of larger and more massive photons traveling at the same velocity as the higher frequency photons. It is incredibly bad logic to assume that only one photon would collide with an electron. Each electron ejected would be bombarded with a barrage of countless photons. The fact that the kinetic energy of the ejected electrons is directly proportional to the frequency of the bombarding light is in perfect harmony with what has been presented in regard to the nature of the ethers and other concepts to be presented later. Light of any given frequency follows identically the same pattern as light of any other frequency. This means that on the average, the number of photons in any given ray and the number of soft electrons accompanying it, will be a constant regardless of the frequency. The average number of photons comprising a soft electron will also be independent of the frequency. This means the diameter or surface area of a soft electron will be inversely proportional to the frequency. As will be shown in the next chapter, soft electrons accompanying light travel at a velocity less than that of light. The soft electrons pick up speed by bombardments of faster moving photons.

From a superficial glance it seems that the average velocity of soft electrons should be independent of the frequency of the light associated with them. Such is not the case. The soft electrons associated with the higher frequency travel at a higher velocity and herein lies the key to the photo-electric effect. Although the lower mass of the higher frequency soft electrons is offset by the lower kinetic energy of the bombarding higher frequency photons, the surface area is greater in proportion to mass. This means that in proportion to mass, the electrons associated with higher frequency light will receive a greater bombardment of photons and thus a greater accelerating force. The ratio between surface area and volume or mass is inversely proportional to the ratio between the diameters of two given spheres. Since the other factors balance out, it follows that the resultant average kinetic energy of soft electrons in proportion to mass is directly proportional to the frequency of the light they are associated with. As soft electrons collide with a surface, the hard electrons they contain are released and bombard the surface. It is these bombarding hard electrons that produce the photo-electric effect. They will be traveling at the same velocity as the soft electrons that originally housed them. It follows that their average kinetic energy will be directly proportional to the frequency of light! Thus hard electrons are ejected from the surface with a kinetic energy or voltage directly proportional to the frequency of the impinging light.

Planck's discovery and Einstein's speculation laid the groundwork for the development of quantum mechanics, considered the most monumental achievement of 20th century physics. In view of the principles presented above, it is not surprising that mathematical juggling with Planck's constant would account for many experimental data in a quantitative sense. Quantum mechanics experts have enjoyed considerable success in this respect, especially in the realm of atomic spectra, without knowing why. In reality, quantum mechanics does not even qualify as a theory or a concept. It is merely an attempt to give mathematical descriptions of certain phenomena with Planck's constant and his valid assumption as a starting point. Modern "theoretical" physicists have absolutely no conception of why their mathematics agree with certain experimental results. Yet, they have led themselves to believe that by giving mathematical descriptions of such phenomena, they have actually explained them. This is as peculiar a mental process as "doublethink." They are like children playing with a sophisticated mechanical toy they do not understand.

Although the properties of a gas were employed to gain some of the insights into the nature of the ethers, it is expected there will be significant differences between the two mediums. In addition to being infinitely smaller than gas molecules, ether particles are also infinitely more active and are more sparcely distributed throughout space, proportionately speaking, than all but the most rarified gases. Despite this relatively thin distribution the total pressure they exert on a single electron is over 14 dynes. This will be shown in a later chapter. It represents a pressure almost incomprehensible, when the minute dimensions of an electron is considered. It will be come increasingly apparent in the pages to follow that the concept of the ethers just given makes possible simple and complete explanation of phenomena that would otherwise remain hopelessly unresolved. Also, the relationship between Planck's constant, the charge on a fundamental particle and other values such as the velocity of light, which has long been the dream of physicists, will become evident. This chapter has demonstrated the power of the Hermetic axiom. It demands that the properties of the ethers be reflected in the external universe or the planes of existence. This great axiom has been known for thousands of years but, unfortunately, it does not seem to have been employed with effect by thinkers of the past.

CHAPTER 9

THE PROPERTIES OF LIGHT

Although Maxwell was highly successful in predicting some of the properties of light, he made an erroneous assumption during the derivation of the famous Maxwell equations which are the foundations of his theory. One of his assumptions was that charges can be neither created nor destroyed, or that the charge on an electron or proton is a constant. It has already been shown that this result in a violation of the law of conservation of energy. This false assumption, in conjunction with the valid assumptions Maxwell made, resulted in a theory consisting of truths mixed with fallacies, some of which will be discussed shortly. The most remarkable aspect of the Maxwell Theory was the conclusion that the velocity of light is equal to the ratio between electromagnetic and electrostatic units of charge. The truth of this highly interesting relationship will be demonstrated later.

The means by which photons are produced will now be made clear. During the creation of a photon, the ethers in the vicinity are suddenly compressed. Some of the ether particles are forced close enough together to adhere to each other. This aggregate is then propelled outward with great force in a manner similar to a compressed spring being released. This process is shown in Figure 3. This photon reaches a maximum velocity, or the velocity of light, after this accelerating force has been expended, which is applied in a distance equal to the so-called wavelength. This process is repeated in the same region, and another photon is produced which follows the first one, just one wavelength behind. A wide range of ethers are periodically affected during the production of ordinary light. This results in a near countless variety of such particles being propagated in all directions with many different wavelengths. Figure 4 shows a typical light ray and beam of light.

Since many photons are projected in all directions, many collisions will result causing a significant portion to adhere to each other in aggregates. These aggregates will move much more slowly in the beginning than the free photons. As a result, some photons created later catch up to them and attach themselves to the combinations. The aggregates then grow larger, and in the process increase their velocity because of the collisons. This is the origin of the particles which always accompany light. It is apparent that the particles formed in this manner will vary greatly in size, stability, and penetrating ability. It has been shown that soft particles will penetrate ordinary matter more readily than the hard particles.

In the interests of better clarification, the concept of zonal effects and the reason particles are comprised of photons instead of the direct combination of great masses of ether particles should be elaborated upon. The attractive zone between two particles such as atoms or ether particles is entered when the attractive forces between unlike charges existing in the particles exceeds the repulsive forces between the like charges comprising the particles. Conversely the repulsive zone exists in the region where the sum of the repulsive forces exceeds the sum of the attractive forces. The attractive zone occupies only a relatively small region of space close to the particles, while the repulsive zone is extensive for considerable distances beyond the particles involved.

The attractive zones around ether particles extend for definite but very limited distances beyond the particles. When a small number combine, the attractive zones become more extensive and intense. In other words, the resultant field is more extensive and has a higher intensity than that which exists around a single particle. However, as the aggregate becomes larger this field extension reaches a maximum and does not become any greater as the number of particles comprising the aggregate increases. The principle is identical to that of combining magnets. For example, consider thin wafer magnets magnetized through the thickness. The magnetic intensity at the surface of two such magnets joined together is greater than that which exists at the surface of a single magnet. As more magnets are added, the magnetic intensity reaches a maximum and remains constant regardless of how many more are added. A large aggregate of such magnets will tend to break up if disturbed or dropped into a series of aggregates, each of which is comprised of the optimum number of individual magnets. This principle is demonstrated in the domain structure of magnetic materials. It has been found that individual atoms or molecules of a magnetic material combine to form separate structures or aggregates which seem to function independently of the others. They behave like separate magnets and the material is magnetized by the alignment or orientation of these separate domains. After the optimum number of particles is reached any increase in number means a less stable structure because similar forces are required to hold together a greater mass.

The domain structure of magnetic materials finds its counterpart in the combination of ether particles to form photons and the combination of photons to form particles. Thus a particle will disintegrate into photons. Once again we see the second hermetic axiom underlying the similarity.

Atoms are comprised of hard particles which are uniform in size and structure, and it is vitally important that they are. If there were no uniformity, matter would be unstable and chaotic conditions would result throughout the universe. This indicates that they were created by intelligent design by the logos. It follows that they were produced by an entirely different process than that by which the particles which accompany light are produced. The fundamental particles of matter were produced directly by great mind power, whereas the particles which accompany light, and those that are created by the interaction of the particles of matter disturbing the ethers, are produced indirectly by same.

Although hard particles of matter must be uniform, it is equally important that the opposite be the case with soft particles accompanying light, which are comprised of the photons of this light. A demonstration of this will be given later in the discussion of the role soft particles play in the life processes of a planet.

Figure 4
THE FORMATION OF A PHOTON

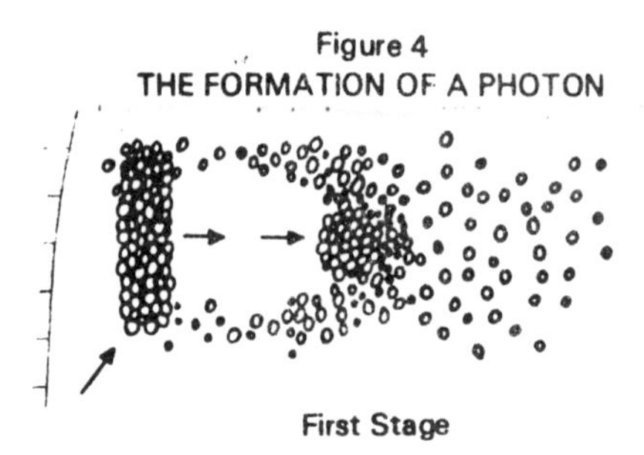

First Stage

Moving edge of a particle that is extensive enough and traveling at such a velocity that a large number of ether particles are crowded so closely they combine to form an aggregate. This leaves a temporary partial void behind it. Although the particle is in most cases comprised of much higher, smaller and more active ether partices, it can disturb and affect far lower ethers because the particles comprising it are crammed close together and their relative motions are greatly restricted.

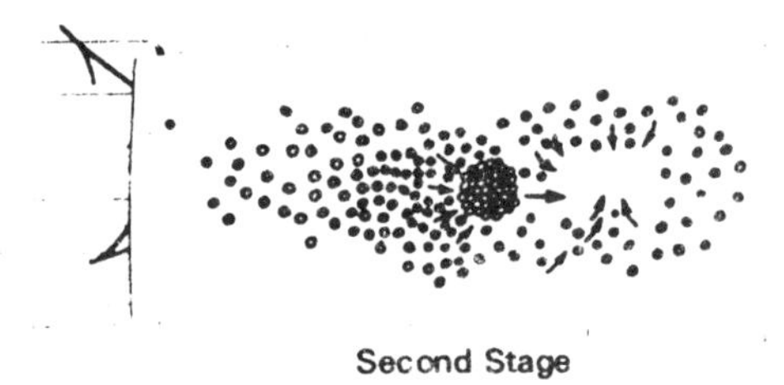

Second Stage

The photon which is an aggregate of ether particles is accelerated by the compressed ether particles returning to their normal distribution. The acceleration is in the opposite direction to that of the compression.

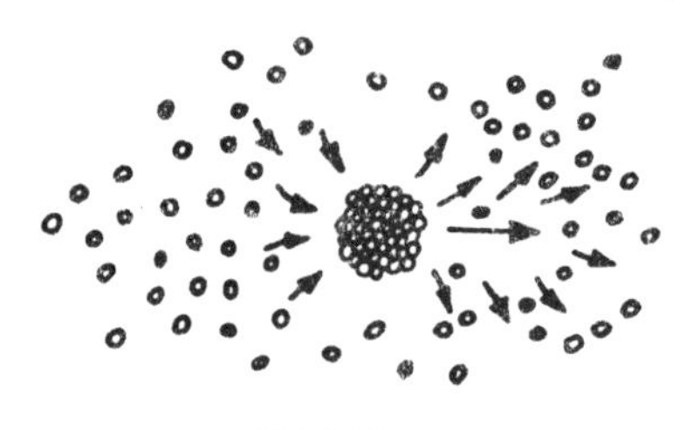

Third Stage

Compressed ethers tend to return to original position after having propelled the photon to light velocity which was accomplished within the distance of one "wavelength". The ethers in front tend to move out of the way of the advancing photon while those to the rear move in to fill the void previously occupied by the photon. The rapid moving in produces a pressure on the rear that compensates for the resistance it experiences at the frontal portion.

Figure 5

LIGHT RAYS, BEAMS, SOFT PARTICLES, AND PHOTONS

A Typical Light Ray

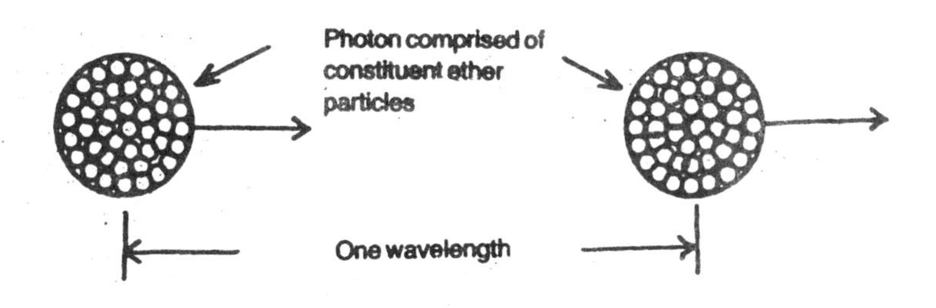

A Typical Beam of Light Made Up of
Photons and Soft Particles

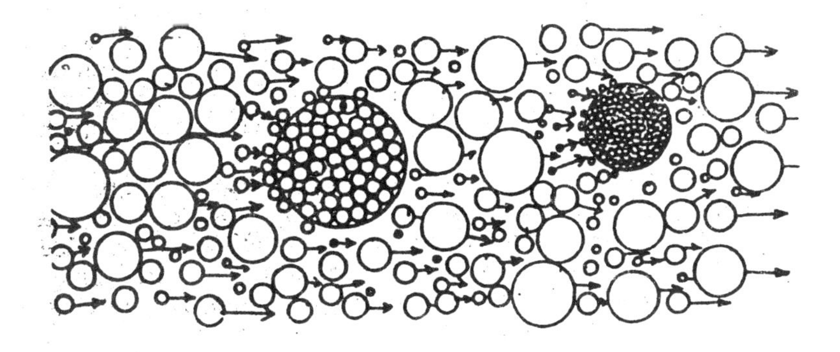

Soft particles are produced by collisions of photons. The soft particles traveling below light speed continue to grow when additional photons catch up and collide with the aggregate.

A typical beam of light consists of a conglomerate of photons of various sizes. It is produced by combinations of individual rays.

A fact extremely adverse to the wave theory of light involves the diffraction and interference effects which should confirm it. It is significant to note that white light produces interference and diffraction patterns when cast on screens. Since many different wavelengths are involved in each bundle, interference effects should compensate, and as such no dark areas should occur on the screen when white light is used.

However, the apparent interference phenomenon is made possible because the light employed is dim, and consists of a limited number of rays or bundles when it transits through small holes or narrow slits. This light also contains a higher percentage of soft particles because the conditions under which they are produced favors their creation. When light enters a diffraction grating or small hole, more photons tend to be crowded together, which forms unstable soft particles. When light rays approach each other near a screen, they tend to be drawn together by mutual magnetic attraction. This is due to the kinetic energy of the particles in the rays. This attraction, which produces a concentration of rays, also leaves a void on either side, because of the limited number of rays. Similar concentrations are produced nearby in the same manner. The interference effects of light are demonstrated in Figure 4.

This concentration effect exists to some extent with normal light propagation, but it is not as noticeable, since in those cases there is a random distribution, and smaller bundles are formed. We see here why it is extremely difficult to separate light into narrow frequency bands. The regular "diffraction" and "interference" patterns result from near equal angles of convergence of the light rays along definite lines. Hence, there is a critical angle beyond which converging rays will not join. This limits the areas in which the light patterns can develop.

Another significant phenomenon that confutes the transverse wave theory but is in perfect harmony with concepts already introduced is the fact that light slows down in passing through a medium and immediately resumes its original velocity after leaving that medium.

When light enters a medium, it encounters a conglomerate of soft particles created by the activities of the fundamental particles of the atoms comprising that medium. (It will be shown later that it is these particles which enable matter to become visible.) This slowing down of the light causes these particles of light to crowd together inside the medium. This results in greater repulsive forces. The light particles tend to be accelerated by such repulsive forces as they leave the medium. This action is analogous to a compressed spring released suddenly. If a light beam enters a medium at an angle, the portion entering first, will travel a

THE INTERFERENCE EFFECTS OF LIGHT

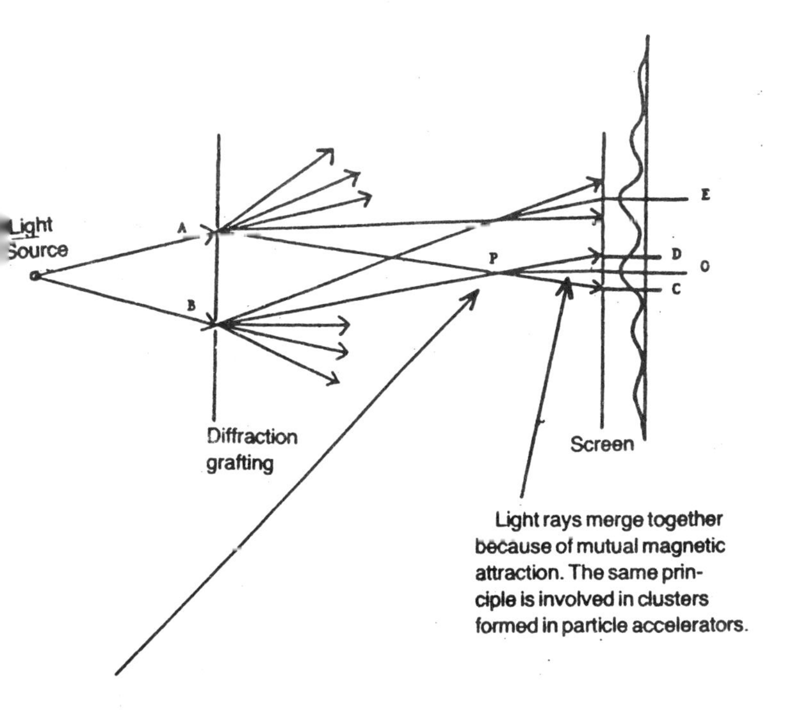

Point P, where the rays of light or soft particles from A and B merge at sufficiently acute angles so as to combine and hit the screen at point O. Points C and D indicate where separate rays would have collided had they not merged. Similarly, point E represents the point where the next bright area occurs due rays from A and B converging at sufficiently acute angles. This principle is involved in all interference and diffraction effects of light and particles.

This effect is observed with light comprised of many different frequencies. If the wave theory were valid, interference effects would only occur with nonchromatic light or light within a very narrow frequency band.

shorter distance than the rest of the beam during the same interval of time. The beam would have almost completely dispersed if it were not for the mutual magnetic attraction of the particles comprising that beam. Hence, the portion of the ray entering the medium later is pulled toward the side which reached the surface first. This causes the ray, or beam, to be bent or to change its direction. This accounts for the refraction of light, which has never before been adequately explained. Higher frequencies of light are refracted more than the lower frequencies. The higher frequency light is more closely associated with the ethers which comprise the soft particles, impregnating that medium, than is the lower frequency light. As a result, the higher frequencies interact more readily with that medium and, consequently, lose more velocity.

As a ray of light passes a given point, it will experience a perirodic rarification and condensation of photons and, to a lesser extent, soft electrons. This is analogous to sound traveling through the atmosphere. It follows that light has the properties of longitudinal waves and not transverse waves.

RESOLVING THE FAMOUS WAVE-PARTICLE PARADOX

Beams of electrons, protons and even atoms produce the same interference and diffraction effects as light. This gives birth to the wave mechanics theory of orthodox physics and the electron microscope. The higher speed electrons give the illusion of shorter wavelengths and are more effective in electron microscopes than slower moving ones. This is because more of their electrostatic potential has been transformed. This reduces the repulsive forces between electrons in a given ray, causing them to be more closely associated. Also, such beams are not as easily diverted from their paths, and since they are much smaller than soft electrons, they will have much a greater resolving power. The wave-particle paradox turns out to be another of the many illusions modern theoretical physicists have been unable to properly interpret. The apparent interference and diffraction effects of various particle beams should have told them immediately that the transverse wave theory of light was in error. This became obvious when cloud chamber experiments showed conclusively that electrons and protons, as well as atoms, were particles and only particles. But, as shown in Part II, the famous Michelson-Morely experiments actually disproved the wave theory.

Despite the evidence of the cloud chamber experiments, physicists still cling to the belief that electrons and other particles can be both waves and particles, and that they have no definite location at any instant. This is in direct contradiction to the evidence staring them in the face. Consequently, an orbital electron is assumed to be only a cloud surrounding a nucleus. Here again, their peculiar ability in the art of doublethink has been clearly demonstrated. And as defined previously, doublethink is the ability to accept two mutually contradictory ideas simultaneously.

THE NATURE OF POLARIZED LIGHT

The phenomena involved with polarized light also conform with the principles already stated. The simplest of these phenomena occurs when light, after passing through certain types of crystals such as nicol, becomes almost obliterated when it encounters a similar crystal. Polarization of light has allegedly been explained by the electromagnetic theory of light. This concludes that light consists of transverse waves vibrating in all planes perpendicular to the direction of propagation. It also concludes that light consists of a magnetic portion and an electrostatic part. These different portions are supposed to exist in planes perpendicular to each other. A conclusion is derived from Maxwell's equations, which is in error, because it is based upon the assumption that charges are neither created nor destroyed, and hence that their charges remain constant. This error of charge conservation becomes more apparent in the electromagnetic wave equations derived from this fallacy, it describes an impossible situation with regard to *so-called* light waves. They refer to the magnetic and the electrostatic portions being isolated from each other.

Polarizing crystals consist of layers of molecules laid down in an orderly fashion. The areas between these layers allow the visible portion of the light to pass through more readily than it does through the rest of the crystal. As with diffraction gratings, photons entering these areas are forced together, forming a much higher percentage of soft electrons than usually accompany light. The resulting sheets of light emerging tend to maintain this planar shape, since they contain a high concentration of soft electrons held together by their magnetic fields. When this light encounters another crystal with layers of molecules perpendicular to the plane of this crystal, most of the light is scattered and dispersed before it can emerge from the crystal. The soft particles formed in the manner described are highly unstable, and therefore will be dispersed more easily when they encounter a crystal oriented in this manner.

CHAPTER 10

THE NATURE OF ELECTRONS, PROTONS AND ELECTROSTATIC FORCES

It must be realized that nature's laws are basically simple. To gain a deeper understanding of the nature of electrons, protons, and electrostatic forces, it is necessary to look for an uncomplicated picture of the fundamental particles and the cause of their behavior patterns. In accordance with the Hermetic axiom, the same rules apply in the realm of the microcosm, as in the macrocosm. Consequently, the collision laws involving the molecules of a gas can be applied to the ethers. Also, it can be deduced that electrostatic forces are the result of an imbalance of ether particles bombarding fundamental particles of matter.

As in a gas, the motion of ether particles in free space is random. In other words, there is no preferred direction of motion for any ether particle. The analogy with the gas ends at this point. The mean free path of the ether particles directly involved with the electrostatic forces is enormous compared to the diameter of the particles. The repulsive forces between ether particles are so great and their velocities so collosal they do not need to be tightly bunched together throughout space.

The random motion of the ethers is disturbed when they encounter a surface such as that of a fundamental particle. Consider, for example, the vertical surface A shown in Figure 6A. The presence of this surface causes an increase in the number of collisions in the vicinity of that surface. The tendency to become random continues as the distance increases away from the surface. The resultant disturbance of this random motion depends on the mean free path, or the average distance a particle will travel in free space before colliding with another particle. The greater the mean free path, the greater the random motion will be for the particles that have been disturbed for any given distance from the surface.

When two surfaces such as A and B are adjacent to each other, as shown in Figure 6B, each surface will receive a greater bombardment than it would if the other surface were not present. It would then seem logical to assume that electrons and protons have a spherical shape, since the sphere is the most stable and efficient geometrical form. It also has the smallest surface area in proportion to volume. However, such an assumption leads to insurmountable difficulties. Electrons and protons have a preferred direction of spin in relation to their direction of motion. The electron follows the left hand rule, while the proton spins according to the right hand rule. With a perfect spherical shape they could not have any preferred direction of spin. But, the preferred directions can be readily accounted for, if these particles are pear or egg-shaped, and are also hollow. This will be discussed in more detail later in this chapter.

When ether particles have a preferred direction of motion away from the electrons due to reflections, a pulsating electric field results. The excessive flow away from the electron tends to reduce the bombardment of incoming ether particles. A temporary low ether pressure around the particle ensues due to the bombardments. Reflections are reduced, and the outside ethers then move in to compensate for this low pressure, and a sudden increase in ether bombardment is a result. The cycle is then repeated. It has been stated previously that all manifestations follow a cyclic pattern. It is to be expected, then, that an electrostatic field is no exception. In this respect the term "electrostatic" is a misnomer.

Two electrons in the vicinity of each other will repel each other with a fluctuating repulsive force. It is not likely that the fluctuations around any two particles would necessarily be in phase. The phase relationship depends on the previous history of the two particles in question, and their interactions with other particles, as well as their origination. The average repulsive force remains virtually the same, regardless of their phase relationship. This has been confirmed by an experiment which determined the charge on a hard electron. The force gives the illusion of being steady due to the ultra-high frequency of the cycles. Figure 6D depicts the fluctuating repulsive force between two electrons.

Since the proton was created by some highly intelligent design, it follows that the proton, as well as the electron, must be a masterpiece of precision. If it has the same basic outline as the electron, yet produces different electrostatic effects, it must have a different surface and internal structure. Economy and efficiency are two of the attributes of good design. A hollow condition for both electrons and protons would indicate such a plan. Less material would be required for their creation, and at the same time, they would be more maneuverable due to lower mass. The other reason for the hollow condition will be discussed shortly.

Figure 6E shows a cross-section of the proton and its effect on the ethers surrounding it. The diameter of the holes in relation to the proton diameter is somewhat exaggerated. The total area of holes is much greater than the reflective surface area on the outside. Also, the particle must have a hollow center. These properties were deduced in order to account for the behavior of the proton. These concepts are also necessary to account for the gravitational forces which will be explained in the next chapter.

It will now be shown that the field surrounding a proton is also cyclic. Consider a surface with a hole, as shown in Figure 6F. The random motion of the ethers is not only disrupted, but many ether particles are temporarily captured, as indicated by the arrows. It follows that most of the ether particles colliding with the proton will not be reflected, but will find their way into the interior. This continues until the concentration of ether particles in the interior reaches a critical stage. Then a sudden discharge of ether particles through the holes results. This is analogous to the function and behavior of a geyser. The field effect around the proton is therefore cyclic. During the buildup of ether pressure inside, there are relatively few reflections of ethers from the surface. The ether pressure around the particle is, therefore, comparatively low during this period.

The repelling force between protons can be resolved from the following considerations: The discharges produce a greater bombardment on other protons in the vicinity for a relatively brief period of time than they would normally receive from the surrounding ethers. The discharged particles between adjacent protons produce a greater pressure on the sides facing each other than occurs on the opposite sides. This is because they are temporarily trapped between the particles. The characteristics of phase relationship and average repelling force are the same as in the case of the electron, depicted in Figure 6D.

Electrons and protons tend to attract each other. Therefore, the average ether pressure is less on the sides facing each other than on opposite sides. As previously stated, the proton can be likened to an entity that breathes in and exhales ether particles. The electron is drawn toward the proton during the inhaling process and tends to be repelled during the exhaling. If it were not for other factors to be considered, this would indicate that the repulsion and attraction forces would cancel out to a net average force of zero. But this is not the case, The period of inhalation is considerably longer than the period of exhalation.

Figure 7
THE STRUCTURE OF THE ELECTRON AND PROTON

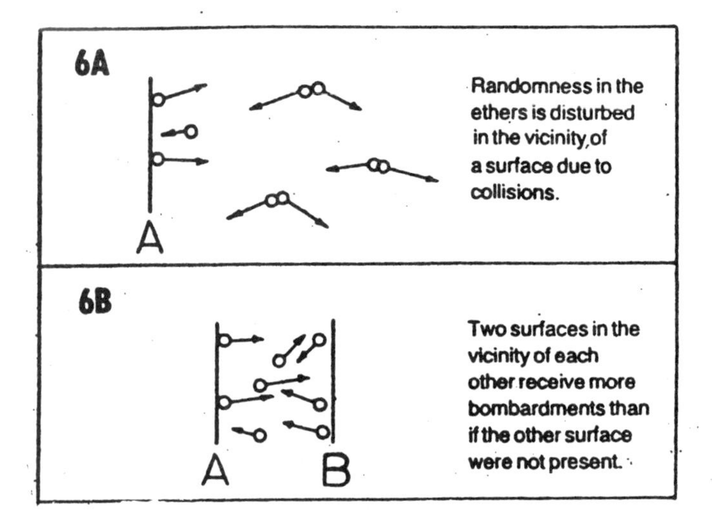

Figure 7 (continued)
THE STRUCTURE OF THE ELECTRON AND PROTON

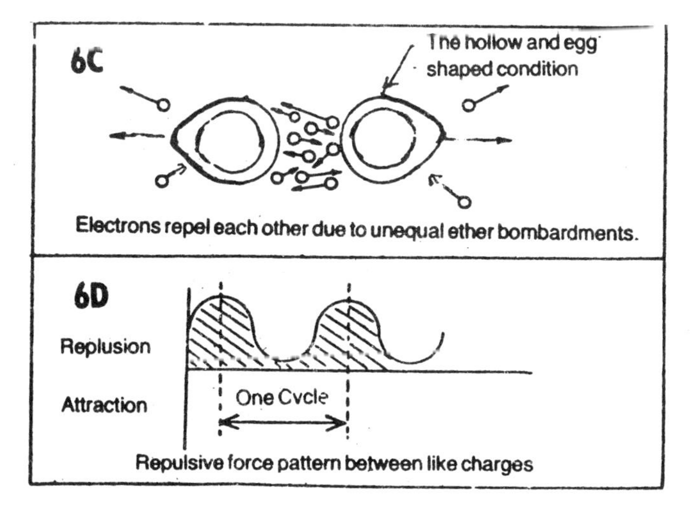

Figure 7 (continued)

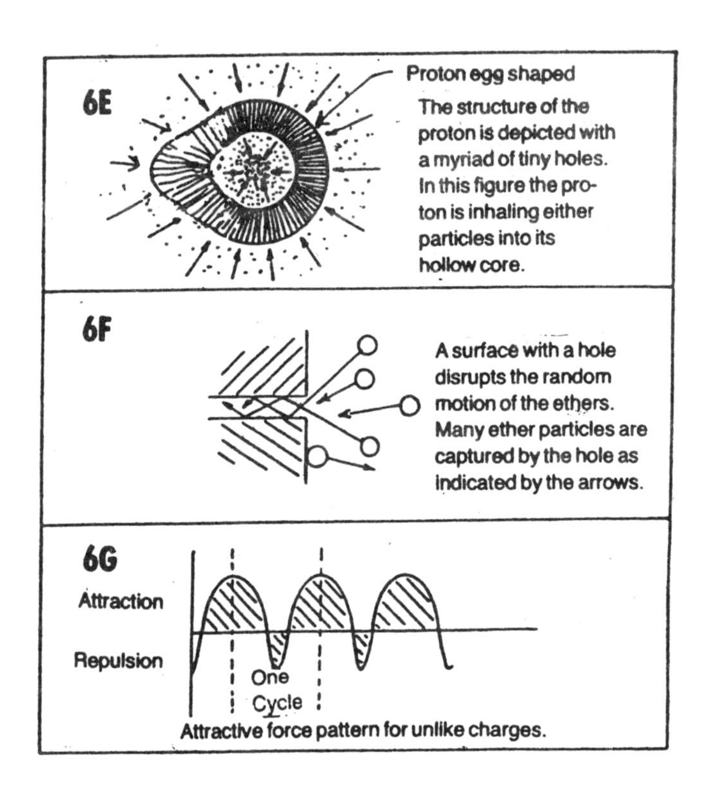

During the inhalation, many of the ether particles that would normally collide with the electron have been captured by the proton. This results in a very strong attraction of the electron toward the proton. A high concentration of ether particles is propelled toward the electron when the proton exhales. However, only a fraction of the ether particles ejected toward the electron actually collide with it. The high concentration causes many particles to collide with each other and scatter in directions away from the electron. This indicates the average repelling force, multiplied by the time during which it occurs. This is considerably less than the product of the average attracting force and its time of action. The total net average force is then that of the attraction, as depicted in Figure 6G.

The existence of the cloud of ejected ether particles between the electron and proton, during part of the cycle explains why the electron never makes contact with the proton to form an electrostatic dipole. Ejected ether particles exert a tremendous repelling force on the electron if it is too close, and the ejected particles are not as readily dispersed. Therefore, the zone of attraction for electrons and protons does not include areas close to the proton. There has been much speculation as to why protons and electrons never combine to form a dipole. It was assumed a mysterious repelling force existed that acted for very short distances. The neutron, or collapsed hydrogen atom, exhibits the closest approach of electrons to a proton.

Due to the structure of the electron and proton, it follows that the electrons have a far greater tendency to be drawn toward the proton, than the proton toward the electrons. This is because the ether pressure on the opposite side of the electrons is always greater than that on the opposite side of the proton.

This tendency means that in a charged parallel plate condenser, the negative charges will have a greater tendency to move toward the positively charged plate than vice versa. Therefore, an unbalanced force exists, causing the condenser to move in a direction from the negative plate, to the positive plate as shown in Figure 7. This phenomenon is known as the Biefeld-Brown effect. T. Townsend Brown was issued patent numbers 2,949,550, 3,022,430, and 3,187,206 for a possible space drive based on this effect(15,16,17). The author found this effect to be quite pronounced when he charged such a condenser to 50,000 volts. What has been the scientific community's reaction to this highly significant phenomenon? The average reader already knows without further elaboration. They ignored it. Is this due to a myopic vision and retarded awareness, or the obvious likelihood that they are more concerned about maintaining the status quo of science than in discovering truth? Perhaps it is a combination of both.

Several questions now arise concerning electrons and protons. Is there a great disparity in their relative sizes? Does the charge on the proton have the same magnitude as of the electron? Does the proton have about 1836 times the mass of the electron as physicists claim?

Figure 8
THE BIEFELD-BROWN EFFECT

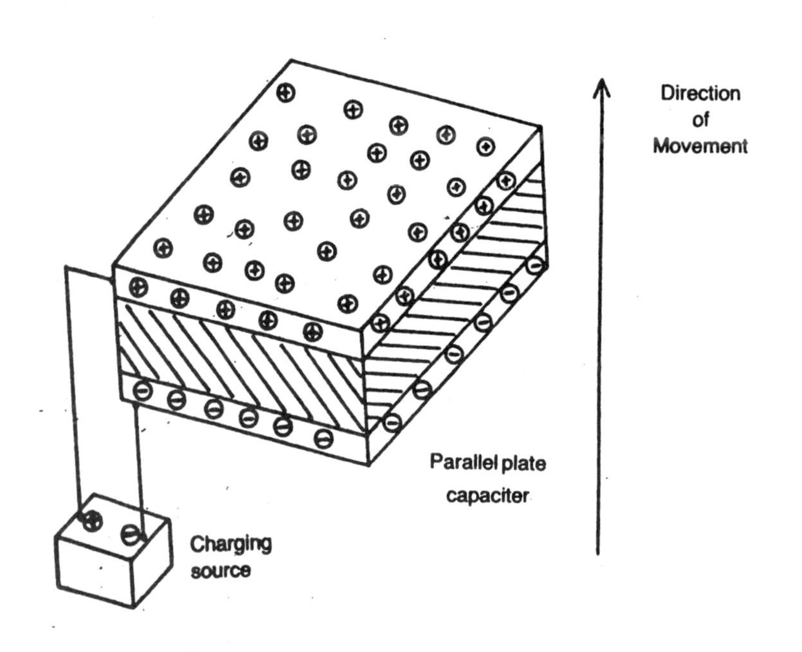

The Biefeld-Brown effect is due to the greater tendency for an electron to move toward a proton than vice-versa. This causes a parallel plate condenser to have the tendency to move in the direction shown.

The behavior of beams of electrons and protons in strong magnetic and electric fields does indicate that protons have about 1836 times the inertial mass of electrons. In this rare case, the conclusions of the physicists are valid, but they lacked the insight to take advantage of this highly significant fact. It has already been shown that inertia is dependent on charge and that inertia is directly proportional to charge. This means that if the proton has 1836 times the inertia of an electron, then its total charge is 1836 times as great as that of the electron! Physicists have always assumed that the charges were equal and opposite. Interestingly enough, the charge on the electron has been measured directly, but this is not the case with the proton. They assumed this equality because of the apparent neutrality of the hydrogen atom. The idea that the hydrogen atom consists of one electron and one proton has never been questioned.

Another interesting conclusion can be derived from the above. The total energy of the magnetic field around a moving proton is 1836 times as great as that around an electron traveling at the same velocity. This means that the volume of space occupied by the magnetic field of the proton is at least 1836 times as great as that of the proton. It is logical to assume that for a given velocity, the proton, due to its perforated condition, must be considerably larger to produce a magnetic field of a given total energy than it would without the holes. It is then safe to conclude that the proton is more than 1836 times as large as the electron.

On the basis of relative charge effects alone, it follows that a hydrogen atom, instead of having only one electron orbiting a proton, there are at least 1836 orbiting electrons. However, since the proton has relatively little movement in comparison to the electron, a far greater percentage of the electrostatic field of the electron has been transformed. This means that in order for the hydrogen atom to have close to a neutral charge, there must be thousands of electrons comprising the hydrogen atom! This seems to create a paradox. The amount of electricity required to liberate a given amount of hydrogen in electrolysis indicates that only one electron is necessary for every atom of hydrogen. It apparently confirms the idea that the hydrogen atom has only one electron.

Scientists have never comprehended the source of the electricity that powers electrical equipment. Later, it will be shown that there are unlimited quantities all around us, and that they permeate all known space. This hard electricity is camouflaged by softer particles also distributed throughout space. The flow of this limitless source of electrons can easily be set into motion! The electricity employed in electrolysis merely triggers the flow of far greater quantities. Also, when a hydrogen atom is ionized, it only needs to lose a very small percentage of its electrons instead of being reduced to only a proton.

Electrolysis, the process of ionization and dissolving of substances in a solvent, the difference between a chemical bond and cohesion, and other aspects of chemistry will be explained in more detail later.

It would be difficult, if not impossible, to account for the phenomenon that hydrogen continuously radiates soft electrons on the basis of steady and uniform electrostatic fields and also the idea that the hydrogen atom has only one electron. If this were the case, hydrogen could not radiate except by thermal agitation. The cyclic electrostatic fields and the myriad of orbital electrons produce oscillations, even if hydrogen is cooled to zero degrees Kelvin. This disturbs the ethers with the creation of soft particles.

Matter is rendered visible by the steady formation of soft particles, generated by the activities of the fundamental particles. It is then apparent that frozen hydrogen would be completely invisible if electrostatic fields were not cyclic and the hydrogen atom had only one electron! Cyclic electrostatic fields are largely responsible for the complex, spectral pattern of all the elements. The atom is not a lifeless entity, but a pulsating, living thing. It is guided by a creative intelligence as all things are.

A more detailed explanation of the manner in which soft particles are produced by the activities of the fundamental particles of atoms is in order. It seems a paradox that hard particles are able to disturb far lower ethers than those with which they are directly associated, since they are oblivious to direct interactions with those lower ethers. This disturbance of the lower ethers is produced indirectly by the hard particles. The normal frequency of interaction of hard particles is much too high to disturb the lower ethers sufficiently to produce soft particles. However, slightly lower ethers are directly disturbed, which in turn disturb ethers slightly below them. This pattern continues until the ethers are disturbed which correspond to the frequency of soft particle interactions. This results in the creation of soft particles associated with these lower ethers.

The cyclic pattern of hard-particle interactions is complex. This complexity increases rapidly as the number of fundamental particles in the atom increases. This means many different lower ethers are indirectly affected with the consequent production of many kinds of soft particles. Interestingly enough, there is a definite ratio between the frequency of the ethers asociated with hard particles, and the ethers associated with the soft particles which render matter invisible.

The picture of the proton just shown indicates that it will be relatively sluggish, and that in any proton-electron relationship, the electron will do most of the moving.

The charge on a particle is defined as the force it exerts on a like charge or known number of charges a unit distance away. In view of the pulsating characteristics of the electrostatic field around a particle, this definition should be modified by substituting "average force," for "force," in the definition. As stated previously, the frequency of the electrostatic cycle is so great that an illusion of a steady force is the result. This is the average force existing for one complete cycle.

CHAPTER 11

ATOMIC STRUCTURE AND THE NATURE OF MAGNETIC FIELDS

Since electrons move at much higher velocities in the atom than pro-
ons and cover much more territory, a higher percentage of their elec-
rostatic charge is transformed into magnetic energy. This means that the
ositive charge in the atom will overbalance the negative charge, and give
he atom an overall, positive charge. This explains why electricity tends
o move toward ground, and the earth must possess a positive charge.
The electrostatic field effects near the atom, in close proximity to the
lectrons, will be negative. Moving outward, this negative effect quickly
liminishes and a zone of positive, field effects exists. The position and
ntensity of these zones, therefore, determine in part the chemical and
hysical properties of the atom. There are regions where the atoms will
ttract each other and also where they will repel. By once again applying
he Hermetic axiom, it is seen that ether particles have a similar struc-
ure, and follow the same pattern.

The velocity of orbiting electrons in atoms is not uniform. There are
eriodic fluctuations resulting from mutual interferences within the atom
self and from adjacent atoms, in addition to the pulsating electrostatic
ields. It must be noted that the properties of the atom are not observed
dividually, but as a collective group. The region of activity for the pro-
ns is relatively small, and a significant number of electrons are trapped
ere. This region is the origin of neutrons, which are actually collapsed,
ydrogen atoms. It is interesting to note that when hydrogen is subjected
ultrahigh pressures, it behaves like a high concentration of neutrons
d passes through the container which is being pressurized, as though it
dn't exist.

A more detailed discussion on the structure of the neutron is in order.
he new concept of thousands of electrons comprising the hydrogen

atom, (to say nothing of the other atoms) provides for the first time, a means of accounting for the properties of the neutron. When a cloud of electrons orbiting the proton is forced into close proximity with the zone of repulsion, as described earlier,their motions become restricted. As a result, there is a lowering of the average velocity with a consequent increase in their negative, electrostatic charge. This provides a stronger bond between the proton and the electrons. The orbital speed cannot be increased because of the zone of repulsion surrounding the proton, and the crowding of the electrons. The higher overall negative charge of the electrons almost completely cancels out the positive charge of the proton. The result is a particle that is electrically neutral, as far as most experiments can determine.

The electron cloud comprising the hydrogen atom is further removed from the proton, and the individual electrons are not restricted in their orbital motions. The average velocity is much higher and consequently, the hydrogen atom has a high positive charge. The atoms of the gaseous elements, such as hydrogen and oxygen, are highly magnetic. Therefore, two atoms combine in much the same way as two bar magnets to form a molecule consisting of two atoms. This is the reason the molecules of nearly all the gaseous elements consist of two atoms. The combination has a still higher overall positive charge than a single atom. As a result, the molecules have a strong mutual repulsion which keeps them widely separated at normal temperatures and presures. Thus, they remain a gas even at extremely low temperatures.

The presence of electrons, in the "nucleus", nullifying repulsive forces and also the magnetic fields resulting from the motions of neutrons, is the major source of the so-called mysterious force, holding the nucleus together. It will be shown later in this chapter that the pinch effect of magnetic fields is the prime force that hold the atom together. Modern, orthodox physicists have complicated the picture by claiming many different forces exist. This includes magnetic, electrostatic, gravitational, nuclear, and others to which they have assigned odd names. In reality, only electrostatic and magnetic forces exist. In addition, there are two, and only two, basic particles: electrons and protons. This conforms to the law of duality.

Since the electrostatic field effects around the electron and proton are cyclic, and the magnetic fields they generate will also exhibit an intensity that is cyclic. This cyclic pattern will be identical in frequency to the electrostatic one. This follows from the dual nature and relationship between electrostatic and magnetic fields.

Despite their stumblings, modern physicists finally managed to make one correct assumption concerning atoms. An atom does consist of electrons orbiting a concentration of positive charges, remaining relatively fixed in relation to the electrons. This, of course, is due to the comparative sluggishness of protons. An understanding of the nature of magnetic fields is mandatory in order to further analyze the structure of the atom.

THE NATURE OF MAGNETIC FIELDS

The electron and proton start to spin in a definite direction when they are given a velocity, but neither one spins when it is at rest. This is contrary to the assertions of modern theorists, who talk about particle spin with reckless abandon. The electron always follows the left-hand rule, while the proton follows the right-hand rule. It is vitally important that these particles are consistent in their behavior, otherwise chaos would reign and matter could not exist.

As stated earlier, the left and right-hand spin characteristics of electrons and protons can be accounted for, if these particles are egg and pear-shaped, in addition to being hollow. When placed in an electrostatic field, they will move in such a manner that the large end is facing in the direction of their motion, regardless of their original orientation. The reason is not difficult to discern. If they are hollow and the shell is of a certain thickness in proportion to diameter, the larger end will have more surface area in proportion to its mass, than will the smaller end. The thickness of the shell at the smaller end will be much greater in proportion to its diameter. This means ether bombardment at the larger end will tend to give it a greater acceleration than that imparted to the smaller end. As a result, the larger end will always be forced ahead of the other portion in the direction of motion.

The picture is still incomplete. In order for the particle to have a preferred direction of spin, the frontal surface must be grooved in the manner of a right or left-hand screw. This design is not expecting too much of the great creative intelligence, which created them. Such a shape is consistent with recent experiments at the Argonne National Laboratory, which studied the scattering of proton beams aimed at target protons. The results indicated that protons were not spherical. A detailed account of such experiments can be found in an article "The Argonne Experiments and The End of Quarkery" by Eric Lerner which appeared in the Oct.-Nov. 1977, issue of *Fusion Magazine*. The article justifiably made a mockery out of a popular theory in particle physics concerning an ever growing family of hypothetical particles called quarks. This is another product of the mental transgressions of certain particle physicists. The article is well written and the author, as the title suggests, displays a sense of humor that is extremely rare among scientists. Unfortunately, he has not broken all of the shackles of orthodoxy, since he still apparently believes in many of the ideas of conventional physics, such as the existence of neutrinos and other non-existent entities. Despite all this, he has displayed a degree of mental acumen well above the great majority of his colleagues. He presented arguments which confuted some of the basic assumptions of quantum mechanics and showed them to be contradictory, such as the ridiculous idea of point particles, as is claimed for electrons. In other words, it is asumed they are infinitely small.

It has been noted that a magnetic field surrounds a moving charge. The magnetic lines are in the form of circles. An electron or proton tends to carry ether particles around with it in a circular motion as it moves through the ethers. This is due to the mutual repulsion between the ether particles and the ether particles comprising the particle. The action is identical in principle to that of a propeller free to rotate on its axis as it moves through the atmosphere. The reactive forces cause a particle to spin, which at the same time produce a vortex motion in the ether.

The greater the velocity of the particles, the faster it spins and the more ether particles are caused to flow around it in the direction of the spin. It is this flow of ether particles around a moving charge, which produces the magnetic field effects observed. A view of this magnetic field, from a three-dimensional standpoint, shows that it resembles a corkscrew spiral or vortex.

Now, consider two like-particles moving adjacent to each other in the same direction. When they were at rest they repelled each other, because of the unbalanced ether bombardments. As the particles move, the magnetic flow of the ethers around the particles disrupts the normal electrostatic bombardment of the ethers. Many of the particles that had contributed to the repulsion, now tend to be diverted into a rotary motion around the particles to produce the magnetic fields. All the ethers that could produce a repulsive force are converted into a rotary motion, or magnetic field, by the time the particles reach the speed of light. This has been unwittingly demonstrated by the behavior of particles in an accelerator, as discussed in Part I. This same principle has also been demonstrated by the behavior of two adjacent wires carrying a heavy current moving in the same direction. The wires tend to be drawn together. Cancellation of magnetic flow between the particles tends to occur, and the particles are encircled by these same magnetic lines.

In addition, consider two unlike charges moving along together in the same direction. When they start to move, the unbalanced ether bombardments producing the attraction tend to be converted into a rotary motion, as in the case of the like charges. The direction of spin of the particles in this case are in opposite directions. The magnetic fields between the particles now tend to meet head on, as they try to encircle their respective particles. This produces a magnetic repulsion. This activity also has a tendency to cancel the magnetic effects of each particle when they are forced to remain in close proximity to each other, as is the case with the atom. It will be shown in the next section that this effect also greatly reduces the inertial properties of the atom.

An electron or proton moving in a magnetic field has two forces acting on it. One of these tends to force it down the magnetic lines of force, because of excessive ether bombardments in one direction of flow of the ether particles. The other is perpendicular to the lines of force, and of course perpendicular to the direction of motion of the particle, if the direction of motion is also perpendicular to the lines of force. If the velocity of the particle is high, the latter force is by far the more significant. It becomes apparent here, by the application of the hermetic axiom, that this force is a result of Bernoulli's principle.

Bernoulli's principle states that the pressure of fluid exerted on a surface decreases when it moves across that surface. The higher the velocity, the lower the pressure it exerts. The molecules of a fluid at rest will bombard a surface in a random manner. The components of these bombardments perpendicular to the surface, represent some resultant pressure. The original perpendicular components start to form acute angles with the surface as the fluid moves. This means that the new perpendicular componenents will result in weaker forces being exerted in this direction. The higher the velocity, the more acute the angle that the originally calculated perpendicular components make with the surface, and with a lower pressure.

Bernoulli's principle will now be applied to explain the behavior of particles in the presence of magnetic fields, as well as the properties of the magnetic field. First, consider the behavior of a spinning baseball thrown by a pitcher. When the direction of spin is in a plane parallel to the direction the ball is moving, the ball will have a tendency to curve or deviate from its original path. The direction of spin on one side of the

Figure 9

THE BEHAVIOR OF ELECTRONS AND PROTONS IN A MAGNETIC FIELD

Spinning Electrons and Protons

The direction of motion of the particles is into the paper. The surrounding ether particles move in the same direction as the spin. This ether movement is the origin of the magnetic field.

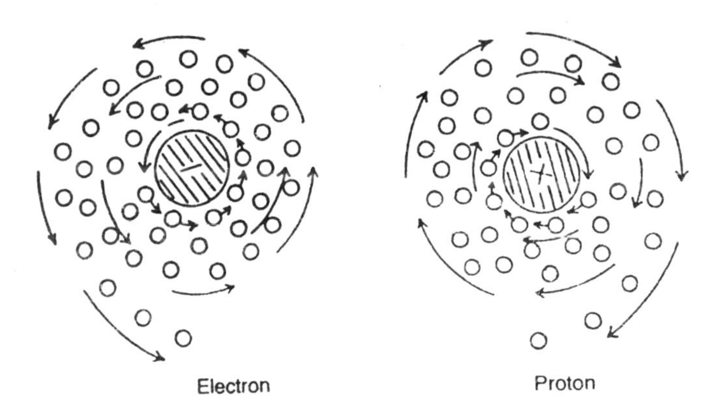

An Electron and Proton Moving Between the Poles of a Magnet

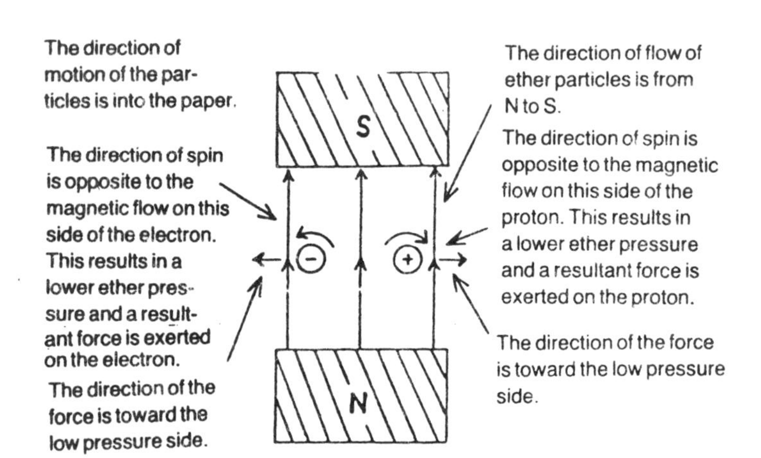

Figure 10
THE PRINCIPLE OF MAGNETS

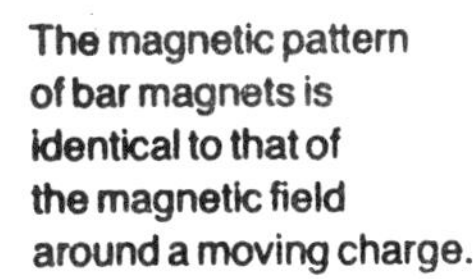

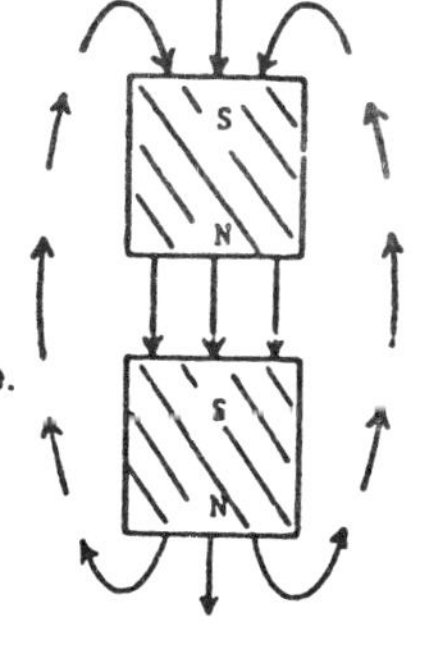

Unlike poles attract because of the pinch effect of magnetic fields.

The magnetic field around a moving particle tends to compress or pinch it as a result of pressures exerted by surrounding ethers. This is the result of Bernoulli's Principle.

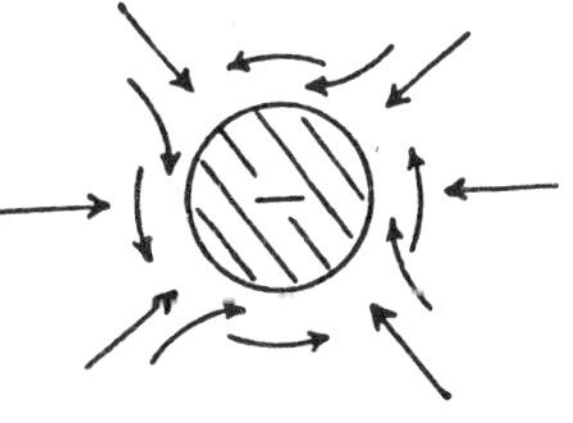

The surrounding ethers tend to move in toward low pressure areas initially created by the spin.

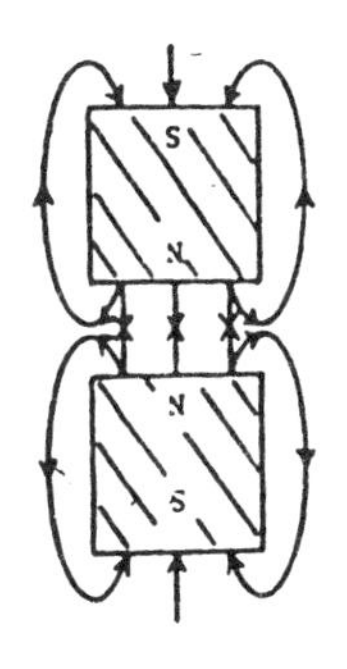

Like poles repel because of excessive ether bombardments against the material of the magnets.

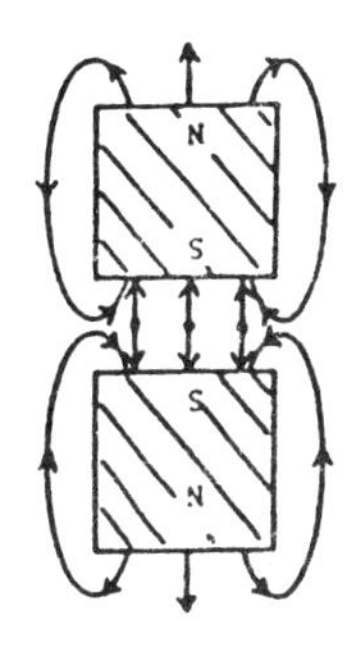

ball is in the same direction that it is moving, while on the opposite side the spin is in the opposite direction. This means that on this latter side, the velocity of air flowing across the surface is less than it is on the other side. The air pressure on the side with the lower, relative air velocity will therefore be greater than that on the adjacent side in accordance with Bernoulli's principle. This imbalance of forces causes the ball to deviate from its intended path.

The same identical principle is involved when an electron or proton moves between the poles of a horseshoe magnet, as shown in Figure 8. The direction of motion is into the paper. The direction of flow of the magnetic lines is indicated by the arrows. The reader can see from the direction of spin and the application of Bernoulli's principle that the electron will be forced to the left, while the proton will be forced to the right. This has been confirmed by laboratory experiments for many decades.

Bernoulli's principle is responsible for the pinch effect produced by magnetic fields. When a particle, such as an electron, is given a velocity, the magnetic field that develops around it tends to compress it, much in the same manner as a rope or string drawn tightly around a ball. The faster the electron moves, the stronger the field becomes around it, hence, the greater this tendency. Bernoulli's principle is the primary cause of this effect. The flow of ether particles around the particle causes a low pressure area outside the flow, and the surrounding ethers on all sides tend to compress the configuration of this flow into a smaller volume. The flow has no place to go except to press tighter against the electron, as shown in Figure 9.

The pressure exerted on the particles from the pinch effect is due to mutual repulsion between ether particles compressing the particle and those of the surrounding ethers. When there has been a complete transformation of electrostatic ether bombardment into a circular magnetic flow of ether particles around the electron or proton there is never an approach close enough for attraction forces to take over.

The pinch effect also explains the behavior of permanent magnets. Consider a bar magnet. Here is an identical situation to the flow of ethers around a moving particle. The ethers flow out of one end of the magnet and into the opposite end or pole. The pinch effect that results tends to compress the opposite poles together. Two bar magnets with opposite poles adjacent to each other create the same pinch effect tending to force the magnets together, as shown in Figure 9. It is like cutting a single bar magnet in two.

When like poles are adjacent, the flow of ether particles is in opposite directions, and these poles receive more than the normal bombardment, tending to force them apart. Identical bombardment occurs regardless of whether it is the north poles or south poles facing each other. See Figure 9.

The resultant force exerted on the ferromagnetic material in these two cases does seem to present a paradox. Why are such forces present yet no resultant forces are exerted on nonferromagnetic materials? This can only be resolved by considering the individual atoms of the ferromagnetic material. The individual atoms are actually tiny solenoids. The magnetic lines or ether flow out or into each pole forms a tubular configuration. There are few if any magnetic lines existing in the central portion of the tubes. This means that although most of the ether particles coming in opposite directions will be scattered and dispersed into random motions (as shown by iron filings placed over like poles facing each other) many of the magnetic lines will enter the central portion of these minute tubes. As a result there will be a greater ether bombardment on one side of the ferromagnetic atoms than on the opposite side. A so called diamagnetic atom has an outer magnetic configuration that is relatively uniform with no pronounced poles. Consequently incoming ether particles comprising the magnetic flow are diverted from their paths before they can get past the tight magnetic shield surrounding the "diamagnetic" atoms.

It should be kept in mind that the total number of ether particles per unit volume in a magnetic field is no greater than that existing outside the field. Therefore, the ether bombardment on any one side of a diamagnetic atom is not changed when it passes in and out of a magnetic field. Thus there is a random ether bombardment on the diamagnetic atom while in the case of the ferromagnetic atom this randomness is disturbed and there is a preferred direction of ether particle movement toward the atoms.

The accepted explanation of the ferromagnetic properties of atoms such as iron fails as usual to explain any of the facts concerning their magnetic properties. The valid explanation is almost selfevident. A significant percentage of the orbital electrons have either common orbital planes or move in planes that are nearly parallel. (As will be shown later, all the orbital electrons move in the same general direction such as clockwise or counterclockwise depending on the viewpoint. This is necessary in order for the electrons to orbit the nucleus.) This produces a net solenoid effect and thus the individual atoms behave like magnets. In the case of nonferromagnetic atoms all of the orbital electrons move in different planes, none of which are parallel. This cancels out all solenoid effects.

External magnetic fields cannot penetrate a material comprised of ferromagnetic atoms such as iron. The miniature solenoids are extremely mobile and readily align with an external field. This sets up a barrier which prevents the passage of the field through the material. It requires magnetic fields to affect magnetic fields. This situation is similar to that of two high speed jets of a fluid. When they encounter each other, the jet stream of the weaker one tends to be disrupted by any attempt to penetrate the stronger jet. The field set up inside a ferromagnetic material by an external field is generally stronger than this field.

The analogy of fluid mechanics as applied to magnetic fields can also be employed to explain the properties of bar magnets. When iron filings are used to show the configuration of magnetic lines around a bar magnet it becomes evident there is a direct flow of one pole into the other when the magnet is very short. The lines follow an oval or circular pattern. The configuration changes as the magnet becomes longer. The radius of curvature of the lines emanating from the poles becomes greater and approaches a straight line. There is a tendency for the lines to flow to the opposite pole but this is offset by lines flowing or leaking from the edges of the magnet between the poles. They tend to form their own oval patterns. The magnetic flux inside the magnet is virtually the same throughout its length. Therefore, the lines flowing out of the poles are diverted from their normal paths by the intermediate flows emanating from the sides of the magnet. The lines or ether particle flow out of the pole which corresponds to the south magnetic pole of the Earth cannot return or flow back to the opposite pole if the magnet becomes very long. The ether flow is rapidly dispersed by interactions with surrounding ether. However, a sink is produced by the alignment of the solenoid atoms of the magnet at the opposite pole. As a result surrounding ether particles tend to move in to fill the void. Consequently the flow of ether particles into this pole follows an identical pattern as that produced by the ether flow out of the opposite pole. It is significant that this ether flow into one pole is not the same flow as that which comes out of the opposite pole.

Since the ether flow out of the poles has no opposition from the flows out of the inner portions of the magnet, they will extend for greater distances beyond the magnet than the lines between the poles, because the ether flow inside the magnet between the poles tends to follow oval patterns, nodal points will form along its length by the ethers flowing out of one segment into another further down the magnet. There will be an even number of nodes. For example, a magnet of moderate length will have two nodal points. If the length becomes sufficiently greater, four nodal points will appear, etc. A picture of the magnet lines around a long bar magnet clearly shows these nodal points. This property of magnets will be employed later to explain the six belts of prevailing winds that exist between the magnetic poles of the earth.

Figure 11

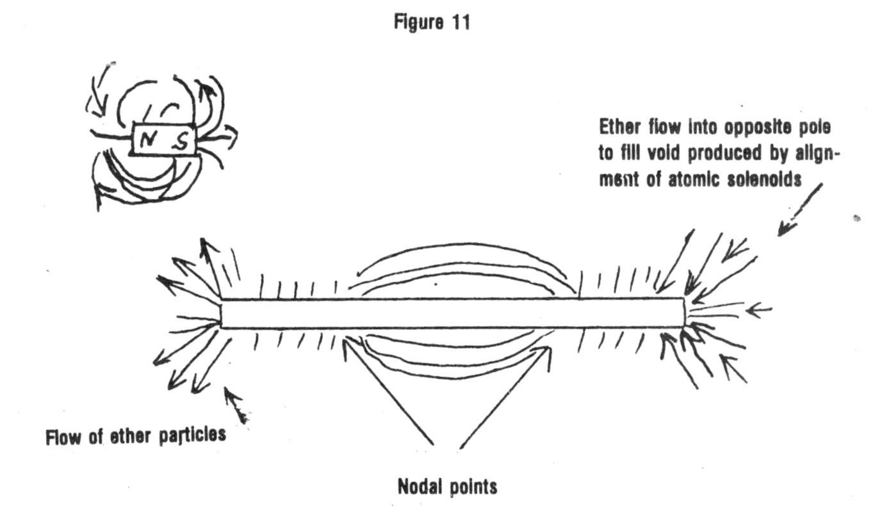

The magnetic permeability of ferromagnetic materials is always greater than unity, while the permeability of diamagnetic materials is always less than unity. Magnetic permeability of a substance is defined as the ratio between the magnetic flux within a material and that of the external field to which the material is exposed. Since the atoms of a so-called diamagnetic material have no fields of their own to be aligned when exposed to an external field, the resultant field inside the material will have a lower intensity than that of the external field. This is because the individual atoms disrupt some of the magnetic lines that penetrate the material. Ferromagnetic atoms align themselves with the external field. This results in a much higher magnetic intensity within the material.

Some experimenters have allegedly demonstrated that nonmagnetic metals, such as aluminum, can be converted into powerful permanent magnets by bombardment of certain kinds of energy. The permanency of the magnetic properties imparted to these metals depend on the length of time exposed. The induced magnetism was only temporary when the exposure time was brief. However, after a long exposure, the metals become permanently magnetized. This provides a clue as to what has transpired. The soft particles bombarding the material have carried hard electrons with them, thus permeating the material. The soft electrons, being able to penetrate the atoms, enable the hard electrons enclosed within the soft particles to enter the atoms and assume orbit. These additional electrons create the solenoid effect.

It is evident that the properties of these magnetic fields and the pinch effect they produce are the greatest factors in maintaining stability in the atom. The motion of the electrons in all directions produce low pressure effects causing the ethers to move in from all directions. This confines the electron movements to very restricted areas with overwhelming forces.

The concept of thousands of electrons comprising the atom and the omnipresence of camouflaged, hard electrons, resolves many questions concerning atomic structure, which cannot be properly understood on the basis of the idea of equal numbers of electrons and protons. Many physicists have toyed with the idea of an electron occupying many different places simultaneously, in order to make the facts conform with the accepted picture of the atom. An electron was looked upon as a cloud surrounding the nucleus. This concept, of course, was not compatible with the results of cloud chamber experiments. Once again, the ability to doublethink enabled them to live with the dilemma.

With this newly established viewpoint, the differences between a chemical bond and a cohesive bond, as well as the reason that a chemical bond is many times more powerful than the cohesive bond, becomes clear. Cohesion exists when the outer, electron shell of atoms and molecules are separated but are close enough so that the zonal effects become effective. In other words, the attractive forces are stronger than the repulsion forces. A chemical bond occurs when atoms are forced together close enough so that outer electrons are brushed aside by mutual repulsions, and the nuclei of adjacent atoms are separated by a relatively thin cloud of electrons. In this manner, atoms are bound together by the mutual attraction that their nuclei have for the same layer of electrons. This could not occur with the relatively few electrons previously attributed to atoms by orthodox science. Such a close proximity of nuclei is more likely to occur with dissimilar atoms. Under the right conditions, a similar pattern can be produced with atoms of the same element. This results in the allotropic forms of an element, such as carbon atoms, combining to form a diamond. It is interesting to note that diamonds are created only under conditions of extreme temperatures and pressure, conducive to forcing the atoms into more intimate contact with one another. The excessive heat and pressure tend to drive off many of the outer electrons. This gives the atom a higher net positive charge. As a result, the atoms are not only able to come closer together, but they have a higher specific gravity than carbon in the amorphous form.

The ionization process tends to break the chemical bond as well as other processes, such as electrolysis, and the concept of valences, which will be analyzed later.

THE CAUSE OF GEOMAGNETISM

The conventional theory of geomagnetism has about the same merit as some other theories already discussed. According to the accepted viewpoint, the major portion of geomagnetism is the result of electric currents in a molten iron core 2,000 miles below the surface. The theory is automatically destroyed, because an iron core doesn't exist. But even if one did exist, the conventional conclusion would be equally false. Scientists are somewhat vague as to how a magnetic field could extend 2,000 miles beyond an electric current. It requires a very powerful current to produce even relatively weak magnetic effects a very short distance above the flow. The electrical resistance of iron, at the alleged temperatures of the core, would be staggering. A steady flow of electricity requires constant potential differences. How are such potential differences produced and maintained in this hypothetical core?

The magnitude, width, and depth of such currents would have to be unbelievable to extend the magnetic field even a small fraction of the distance required, and the EMF required to produce it would be even more incredible. Where could such an EMF come from? So far, scientists seem reluctant about explaining this, especially since these currents are confined to a ball and would therefore follow closed paths.

GEOMAGNETISM

Another incredible demonstration of inconsistencies and contradictions in conventional physicists' thought processes is the case of Saturn and its magnetic field. For them, an iron core is essential for explaining a significant magnetic field around a planet. According to astronomical data, Saturn is supposed to have a very low mass in proportion to its size. Yet all the evidence, including probes sent to its outer atmosphere, shows it has a powerful magnetic field. To account for its relatively low mass, physicists conclude the core must consist of liquid hydrogen. Evidently, the art of doublethink has come to the rescue again. The threat of this speculation to geomagnetic theory has apparently been ignored.

A great wealth of evidence supports the conclusion that geomagnetism is produced by the earth's rotation. The intensity of the field is dependent on the concentration of negative charges in the atmosphere and the crust, and also the rotational velocity. As the earth rotates, it carries the charges along with it. This is equivalent to a myriad of electrical currents, all moving in the same direction. This effect is identical to that of a great solenoid. Interestingly enough, the polarity of the earth's field corresponds to that of a solenoid with a current flowing in the direction of the earth's rotation. The charges in the atmosphere and crust are predominately soft electrons. Soft electrons, without the specialized shape of hard electrons, have no preferred direction of spin. However, hard electrons are continually being released by the soft particles and, especially, at the magnetic poles where the giant egresses into the earth's interior are located. The hard electrons set the pattern of spin for all the other particles. Thus, the left-hand rule is followed by all the particles moving with the earth's rotation.

Physicists have always assumed a magnetic field is apparent only when a charge is moving relative to an observer. This is very bad reasoning. It actually violates the laws of electromagnetic induction. It is a well known fact that a conductor that moves perpendicular to the magnetic lines produced by a permanent magnet or a solenoid will have an EMF induced in it. The EMF is directly proportional to the velocity. Assume a conducto' is moved in the same direction as that of electrons flowing in a solenoid and that the velocity is the same as the velocity of the electrons. It will cut the magnetic lines produced by the flow of the electrons in the solenoid and, therefore, have an EMF induced into it. According to the above stated reasoning of the physicists, the conductor has no motion relative to the electrons, therefore, is not aware of any magnetic field. This means it could have no EMF induced into it.

Since the direction of the field is perpendicular to the direction of motion of the charges producing it, the field will be evident even if the observer is moving with the current, and there is no relative motion, as is the case at the earth's surface. Perhaps this oversight of the physicists is one of the main reasons this obvious cause of geomagnetism has escaped them.

Since the concentration of charges in the atmosphere fluctuates according to a 24-hour cycle, the magnetic field can be expected to fluctuate accordingly. This is an established fact. The field should increase during sun spot activity when the earth receives more charges. This is also a fact. The moon with less than one percent of the earth's rotational velocity and perhaps the same concentration of charges in its atmosphere should have less than one percent of the earth's field. The Apollo missions to the moon and moon probes have verified this. Jupiter and Saturn with their high rotational velocities should have fields much stronger than on earth, despite being further from the sun. NASA probes have detected fields in the upper atmospheres about eight times as great as at the earth's surface. Every available bit of evidence supports the above viewpoint concerning geomagnetism.

An enigma that may arise is that the earth has an orbital motion in addition to its rotation. Why doesn't the orbital velocity affect the earth's field? The earth's apparent field is produced by the hard electrons, released by the soft electrons as they approach the earth and enter the atmosphere. During their trip to the earth, the captured hard electrons are in the dematerialized state, therefore, have not acquired any kinetic energy by the time they reach the earth, since in this state they have no inertia. After they are released, they are accelerated to the earth's rotational velocity. Therefore, the only kinetic energy they display is that due to the rotational velocity of the earth. It is the collision of soft electrons bombarding the molecules of the atmosphere and particles contained in the atmosphere that cause some of the soft electrons to release the hard electrons responsible for the earth's magnetic field. The hard electrons are continually being released and recaptured again by soft electrons. As a result, there are always hard electrons present in the atmosphere.

How few man have ever lived who had mental capacity even to think of a first principle.—R. T. Trall

CHAPTER 12

THE NATURE OF GRAVITY AND RELATED PHENOMENA INCLUDING LEVITATION, MISSILE WEIGHT LOST IN SPACE, AND FASTER THAN LIGHT SPACESHIP PROPULSION

THE NATURE OF GRAVITY

The prerequisite for understanding the gravitational process is the realization that supposedly uncharged atoms and molecules are not electrically neutral, but possess a positive charge. It has always been assumed, since the days of Newton, that inertia is directly proportional to mass. This has been shown to be incorrect. Inertia is dependent upon total charge; therefore, independent of mass. It follows that an atom has less inertia than any of the fundamental particles of which it is comprised! The small, overall charge of an atom is the result of the balancing out of positive and negative charges. It s slight ability to generate a magnetic field for a unit increase of velocity is due to electrons following the left-hand rule, while protons follow the right-hand rule. Its inertia is limited because of the cancellation of magnetic fields of the constituent electrons and protons.

Stripping electrons from an atom will give it a strong positive charge. This means it will have greater inertia than before, although less mass. Adding electrons will also increase its inertial properties, if the total resultant charge is greater than the original positive charge. Otherwise, adding electrons will reduce the inertial properties, and in this case, increasing the total mass reduces its inertia.

After the author came to this conclusion, he was later gratified to learn a former Nobel Prize winner, Gabriel Lippmann, confirmed this principle in the late nineteenth century. Lippman found that bodies in the charged state offered a greater resistance to acceleration than in the uncharged state. He called it "the inertia of static electricity." It is not surprising this monumental discovery was ignored, since it threatened to topple cherished physical concepts. Ironically, Lippmann later received the Nobel Prize for another comparatively insignificant discovery.

Sufficient groundwork has now been laid for a complete understanding of the nature and cause of gravitational effects. Gravity has always been the most baffling of all the common physical phenomena. Until now, no theorist has ever come close to presenting a theory in any way plausible, or which fits the facts. It will soon become evident that nearly all of the basic concepts introduced thus far are required in order to properly explain it.

It has already been shown that gravitational effects are produced by a part of the electromagnetic spectrum, somewhere between the lower portion of the infrared and the radar frequencies. This knowledge is still insufficient to give one some insight into the mechanics of the forces involved. Since matter behaves like a positive charge, it follows that gravity radiations accelerate positive charges in a direction opposite to that of the direction of its propagation.

It has been stated that a gravitational field repels negative charges. This has been shown to be the case. The RCA laboratories in Princeton, New Jersey, allegedly demonstrated this in 1959. They supposedly discovered that negative charges tend to fall upward instead of downward, as had been expected. It is readily apparent why nothing more has been heard about it. Some of Reichenbach's experiments, to be discussed in Part IV, also indicate that such is the case. This effect was predicted on purely theoretical grounds by the author prior to the knowledge of these confirmations. A well known phenomenon also demonstrates the fact that negative charges are repelled by a gravitational field. When the hair on one's head is given a strong negative charge it will have a tendency to stand straight up. This becomes especially pronounced if one stands near a powerful Van de Graf generator when it is throwing out high concentrations of electrons. Many of the electrons become attached to the hair and tend to carry the hair with them as they are repelled upward.

This knowledge still leaves unanswered questions such as: "Why are the gravity-inducing radiations in this frequency range? How do they produce attractions and repulsions on positive and negative charges?" One important principle should be kept in mind before dealing with the mechanics of gravity. The more a given radiation, and the ethers with which it is associated, differ in frequency from other radiations and the matter and the ethers with which this radiation is associated, as well as the soft particles that permeate matter, the less it will be interfered with in its passage through matter. In other words, the more penetrating it will be.

The bulk of the radiations and soft particles of matter cover only a relatively narrow part of the electromagnetic spectrum. They are produced by the interactions of the fundamental particles of the atom, in addition to the interactions of the atoms themselves. This range extends from the upper end of the infrared to the lower end of the ultraviolet. Most of the remaining frequencies are in the higher ranges and are radiated by sun like bodies or created artificially in laboratories. Many of the particles resulting from higher-frequency radiations are absorbed by matter. It can be concluded from the principle mentioned above that infrared will be the most penetrating of the radiations mentioned.

Since infrared is at the lower end of the scale, the soft electrons associated with infrared will be less stable than harder electrons. This means the infrared will be more inclined to give up the harder electrons it contains when it penetrates matter. This and its penetrating ability are the reasons infrared is more heat producing than other radiations. It follows that the radiation's penetrating ability will increase as the lower range of the infrared is approached. Finally, the most penetrating radiation of all can be expected just below the lower infrared. Its frequency range and the ethers with which it is associated are further removed from the ethers associated with the particles of matter and the particles that interpenetrate matter, than that of any other radiation produced by physical matter. These are the gravity-inducing radiations.

At this point, a question that no doubt comes to mind is, "Why aren't the radar frequencies penetrating?" They seem to be in a range which should make this possible. Since radar bounces off matter, it shows that it encounters concentrations of soft particles consisting of photons somewhere in the approximate range. Along with the frequencies produced by the normal activities of atoms and molecules, harmonics and beat frequencies also exist. These comprise only a small part of the energy produced by such reactions, but it results in the release of soft particles comprised of photons in the lower frequency ranges, which interpenetrate matter at all times. This is the reason radar and still lower-frequency radiations in the radio band have a limited penetrating ability. Incidentally, it is the soft particles comprised of photons close to and in the visible range which permeates matter,and thereby renders matter visible. If only the hard particles were present, solid matter would be invisible, although completely tangible.

Now that the frequency range of the gravity radiations has been logically established, the next step is an analysis of the mechanics of gravitation. Basically, the nature of gravity radiations is the same as that of other radiations, with the exception that they are the most penetrating. They consist of photons and soft particles comprised of such photons, which accompany the photons. The photons travel at a higher velocity than the accompanying soft particles, as in the case of other radiations. It is apparent that the leading portion of the gravity radiation front produces negative charge effects, while the trailing portion which has passed a given body must have substantially reduced negative-charge effects. If this were not true, there would be no gravity effects. From the superficial standpoint, it would seem that an impasse has been reached. The negative charge of the leading portion of the "wave" front produces the necessary effects, and the rear portion should have the same effects, which would result in a cancellation, and therefore no gravity result. This means that in order for gravity to manifest itself, the trailing portion of the soft particle wave must either have little or no electrostatic field effects, or a positive field. There are two factors which make this possible: first, it is the spin of the particles which produce gyroscopic effect,and keeps the particles oriented in the same position. Second, the photons of this radiation have little tendency to scatter.

The cause of gravity effects is now becoming apparent. The faster moving photons overtake the soft particles, and tend to adhere to them in irregular patterns as they collide. This creates a perforated and extremely rough surface on this portion of the particle, not unlike that of a positive charge. This has a tendency to cancel out much of the negative field effects on this portion of the particle. The bombardments accelerate the particles to such an extent that no more photons can adhere to them. Therefore, the rear portion maintains the positive charge, or at least a badly impaired or reduced negative charge. Figure 11 illustrates this principle.

Now it becomes apparent that gravity effects are consistent with the picture presented earlier on the structure and differences of positive and negative charges. The reason for the limited penetrating ability of gravity effects also becomes evident. Since gravity radiations produce forces, it follows that there are interactions which eventually disperse the radiation. This is in accordance with the law of conservation of energy.

The intensity of the electrostatic field produced by the gravity radiations is extremely minute due to the fact that they are highly penetrating and produce slight interactions. The following analysis will give the reader some idea of the magnitude of this field. An electrostatic field of even modest intensity can give an electron sufficient acceleration so that in the distance of about a foot, as in a cathode ray tube, it is traveling 15,000 miles/sec of 2.5×10^9 cm/sec. Earth gravity could accelerate the same particle over the same distance to a velocity of about 8 feet/sec or about 250 cm/sec. The acceleration necessary to give a particle a velocity of 2.5×10^9 cm/sec is about 10^{17} cm/sec^2. This means that the accelerating force, or intensity, of even a moderate electrostatic field is about 10^{14} or 100 trillion times as great as the earth's gravitational field!

Three major reasons exist for this incredible disparity between electrostatic and gravitational accelerations: First, the gravitational radiation affecting matter comprised of soft particles is associated with the lower ethers. Therefore, soft particles in this range can interact with the overall positive charge of matter to only an infinitesimal extent. The other reason is that of the low field intensity around soft particles. It was shown earlier that the field intensity around a photon or a particle is directly proportional to the frequency. This means that the field intensity is only about $1/10^8$ or 10^{-8} that of a hard electron since a gamma ray has about 10^8 or 100 million times the frequency of the gravity frequencies. This relative field intensity disregards the slight additional effects produced by the harder particles camouflaged by the gravity-inducing soft particles. The combined effects of the soft photons and camouflaged hard electrons produce the field intensity around the gravity-inducing soft particle. These factors, combined with the very low net positive charge of atoms and molecules, result in the relatively minute acceleration gravity radiations imparted to ordinary matter.

A question which might arise at this stage is, "Why doesn't light passing through a transparent substance produce a gravity effect on it?" Light photons are quickly scattered and dispersed, even when passing through transparent substances. It is the soft electrons, continually disintegrating into light inside these transparent substances, that enable visible light to penetrate considerable thicknesses of transparent materials. When soft particles disintegrate, new photons are released. Even the most transparent substances soon disperse visible light completely. It is the complete scattering of photons, the disintegration of particles, and their scattering in all directions that render all radiations, except the gravity radiations, incapable of producing gravity effects!

It is not difficult to see how these concepts destroy the popular theory

Figure 13
GRAVITY-INDUCING RADIATIONS

Soft Electrons and Gravity-Inducing Radiations Passing Through Positive Matter

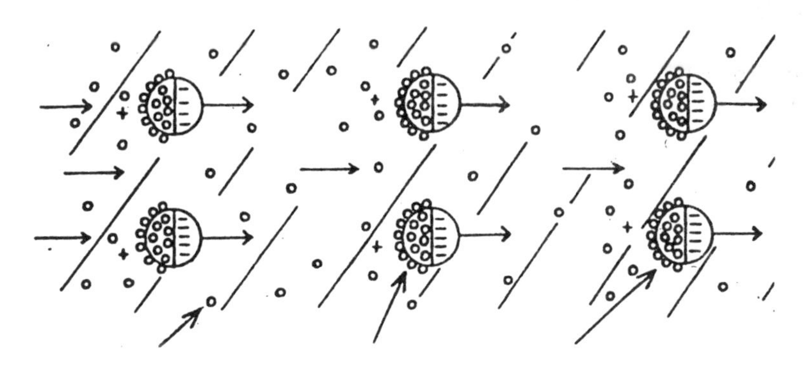

Photons of gravity-inducing radiations not scattered while passing through matter.

Soft electrons comprised of photons of gravity radiations.

Photons of gravity radiations colide and attach themselves to the rear portion of soft particles comprised of gravity radiations. This tends to nullify the negative charge on the back side of the soft electron which gives it a partial positive charge.

Enlarged Soft Electron Comprised of Gravity Radiations

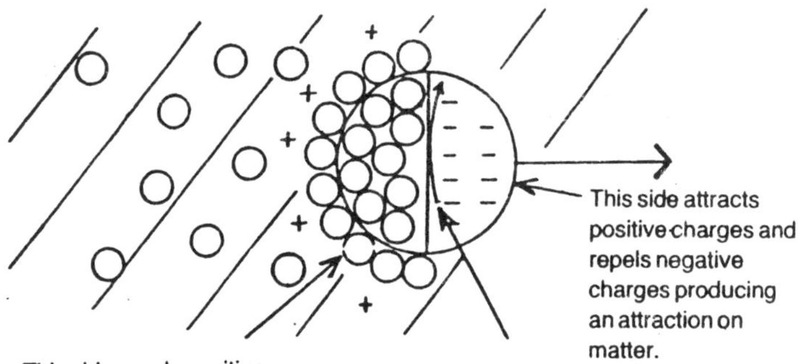

This side attracts positive charges and repels negative charges producing an attraction on matter.

This side repels positive charge and attracts negative charges creating a force in the same direction as the opposite side.

The spin of the soft electron produces a gyroscopic action which enables the particle to maintain its charge orientation with respect to its direction of propagation.

of black holes mentioned in Chapter 2 on relativity.

THE PHENOMENON OF LEVITATION

It is now apparent that gravity is an electrostatic effect, not some space warp or mysterious force with imponderable properties depicted by orthodox physicists. It follows that if matter is impregnated with sufficient quantities of negative charges, especially soft electrons, it will become weightless and even levitate. Some "adepts" in the occult arts have demonstrated this ability on occasion. In spite of this, and the experimental evidence showing that negative charges are repelled by a gravitational field, conventional theorists continue to ignore it, and assume that gravity reacts indiscriminately on all things alike. Once again, this is to be expected. If orthodox scientists recognized the reality of such things, they would automatically have to abandon nearly all the concepts they hold dear.

Some individuals seem to have the ability to do the reverse of levitation and impregnate their bodies with an abnormal positive charge by perhaps expelling large quantities of negative charges from their bodies. They make themselves inordinately heavy by this means. A certain dwarf who had a normal weight of 123 pounds could increase his weight to 900 pounds. He demonstrated this ability on television programs under rigorous fraud-controlled conditions. In fact, one famous strong man who lifted him up was unable to hold him, when he decided to increase his weight to 900 pounds. During this perilous turn of events, our scientists once again showed admirable composure and resourcefulness. They remained silent.

MISSILE LOSS IN SPACE EXPLAINED

The physics of levitation was demonstrated in part when missiles were found to have lost most of their original weight after traveling through the Van Allen Radiation Belt and returning to earth. The mystery deepened when this weight loss continued for a time, and containers in which pieces of the missile were placed also lost weight. This event was hushed up in keeping with standard policy concerning things which are damaging to orthodox concepts. The radiation belt contains high concentrations of negative charges of all kinds, from hard electrons to the very soft ones.

The missile became impregnated with negative charges as it passed through this region. Since they are of varying types, it was able to absorb an abnormal quantity. The more penetrating softer particles opened the door for the harder particles to enter. A similar principle is involved in the operation of a transformer and will be discussed later in Part III. Because the missile continued to lose weight, and was evidently losing particles that originally caused it to lose weight, a paradox arises. The loss of weight of the container, in which pieces of the missile were placed, which would mean that the pieces were discharging some of the negative charges they had picked up in the radiation belt, and were then absorbed by the container.

Paradoxes are actually a blessing, instead of being an annoyance to be kicked under the rug, as scientists have the bad habit of doing. They enable one to gain a better insight, if the brain is up to it. The first part of the above enigma is taken in stride. The absorption of the negative charges reduced the overall positive charge of the missile, and thereby reduced the gravitational attraction. Only one other conclusion can be derived from the subsequent phenomena. The number of negative particles expelled by the mass was small compared to the number of orbital electrons in the body. After it was impregnated with the conglomerate of particles, a readjustment of activity in the original particles began to take place. This had to continue until a new state of equilibrium within the atoms was reached. Although soft particles were being ejected continuously, those left behind were constantly disintegrating and depositing hard electrons within the atoms of the material. They, of course, assumed orbit around the nuclei of the atoms. The additional electrons captured by the atoms reduced the overall positive charge and, consequently, the weight, despite the particles being ejected. This process was actually producing allotropic forms of the elements comprising the material. This phenomenon is confirmation that there are thousands of electrons to every proton in the atom. Such a process could not occur on the basis of the conventional picture of the atom.

MISSILE WEIGHT LOSS IN SPACE POINTS THE WAY FOR DEVELOPMENT OF NEW MATERIALS OF EXTREME LIGHTNESS AND STRENGTH

Missile weight loss shows that a practical method of producing materials of unprecedented lightness and strength is entirely possible. A reproduction or simulation of the Van Allen radiations on the earth would demonstrate this. Evidently, the type of electrons required are combinations of such particles that are comprised of photons from gamma rays down to lower frequencies, but still far above those of ultraviolet. Softer particles comprised of X-ray photons and slightly above would readily penetrate matter and carry still harder particles with them into the atom. The tensile strength of cohesion between atoms and molecules could be increased with the right combination of particles locked between the molecules. They would have to differ slightly in degrees of hardness in a progressive manner so there is an interlocking and interpenetration. A method of generating large quantities of soft particles of any frequency will be presented later on in Part III.

THE POSSIBILITY OF FASTER THAN LIGHT SPACESHIPS BY MEANS OF GRAVITY-INDUCING RADIATIONS

In part I, it was shown that gravity-inducing radiations can be used as a highly sophisticated means of propulsion. In addition, such an application would account for the amazing performances of UFOs. It will be shown that this means of propulsion can produce almost unlimited velocities. The conditions of spaceships are different from those imposed on particles inside an accelerator since in this case the accelerating force travels with the mass being accelerated. There is also the consideration that atoms are accelerating instead of fundamental particles, which have a much lower velocity potential than atoms.

It was shown earlier that fundamental particles have far greater inertial properties than the atom. Therefore, when an atom is accelerated to a given velocity, a much lower quantity of electrostatic energy has been transformed than in the case of an electron or proton accelerated to the same velocity. The alleged reports about space visitors claiming that some of their ships can travel thousands of times the speed of light has a valid scientific foundation. By applying the gravity beam type of propulsion, a spaceship can easily exceed the speed of light with little change in its physical structure. At ultra-high velocities, or at a state where most of the electrostatic potential of matter has been transformed, cohesive forces will tend to break down and the material will become fluidic. It may be interesting to note that the late Gloria Lee, in her book entitled *Why We Are Here*, quoted one of the space beings as describing identically this phenomenon, when spaceships travel at velocities equal to hundreds or thousands of times that of light.

The velocity potential of a spaceship could be greatly increased by impregnating the ship and all the occupants with the right combination of negative charges. This could be carried to such an extent that the overall charge could be almost completely eliminated. The inertial properties would be greatly lessened and much higher velocities could be attained without transforming much of the electrostatic mass into magnetic energy.

When a body is traveling at such speeds, why don't ether particles attach themselves to the body in ever increasing numbers? How do they manage to escape? It is the very sudden changes in velocity which cause the particles to jam close enough together to combine with each other or anything else. As long as the acceleration is below a critical value, a mass of ether particles tends to form ahead of the moving object, closer together than normal, but not close enough to generate attractive forces. This mass affects other ethers in the path further ahead, but in lesser degrees. The result is that other ethers are moved out of the way. As the velocity increases, the region of affected ethers increases in extent.

At ultrahigh velocities, the closing forces on the rear no longer compensate for the forward resistance, so it requires a steady application of accelerating forces to mainain velocities many times that of light. This is probably the reason aliens have allegedly stated that some of their ships are much faster than others.

There are a number of reasons why a body traveling in free space at a steady velocity will encounter practically zero resistance. It has already been shown that ether particles of differing frequencies have little tendency to interact. This means the only ethers that could offer resistance to a body moving at a steady velocity are those associated with the fundamental particles of which the body is comprised. Such ethers are relatively rarified compared to solid matter and light. When this is coupled with an ultrahigh concentration of such ethers in a single body, a situation arises analogous to an extremely dense and massive body passing through an almost nonexistent atmosphere.

The tendency for the ethers to offer resistance to the passage of a body is reduced to the vanishing point by the extreme activity of the ether particles, whose average velocity is many times that of light. As a result, the trailing part of the body is bombarded by ether particles almost to the same extent as the leading portion. This means that a resultant force of near zero is exerted on a body traveling at a steady velocity.

The evidence concerning spaceship propulsion demonstrates that the famous Einsteinian equation $E = mc^2$ falls far short of representing the energy potential of matter. From the kinetic energy equation $E = \frac{1}{2}mv^2$, it follows that a body traveling only one and one-half times the speed of light, which isn't even a cruising speed for most spaceships, has a kinetic energy exceeding the value indicated by this celebrated equation. At this velocity, only a miniscule part of the energy potential of the mass has been released. The meaninglessness of the famous relation is also evident, because inertia is dependent only on net charge and not necessarily on mass or quantity of material. The mass factor in the equation is based only on quantity of material, with the ordinary uncharged atom as a standard.

ADDENDUM TO CHAPTER 12

As this book goes to press the author has uncovered another item which demonstrates the validity of concepts introduced in this chapter and elsewhere in this book. It is the fact that determinations of the so called gravitation "constant" G is always significantly higher when measured in mines than those made in surface laboratories. From what has already been shown, this is to be expected. The soft electron concentration below the surface of the ground is much higher than that above the surface for reasons already elaborated upon, therefore, the gravitating bodies used in the experiment will be impregnated with a higher concentration of soft electrons in mines than they would on the surface. This means they will radiate a higher concentration of soft electrons and thus a higher concentration of gravity inducing soft electrons. This effect is enhanced by the fact that soft electrons at these levels will also contain a higher percentage of gravity inducing soft electrons by the redistribution law. The overall positive charge of the masses is not affected because these soft electrons are not locked within the atoms. Otherwise they would not escape so readily. It is not surprising that the scientific community has been very quiet concerning these developments.

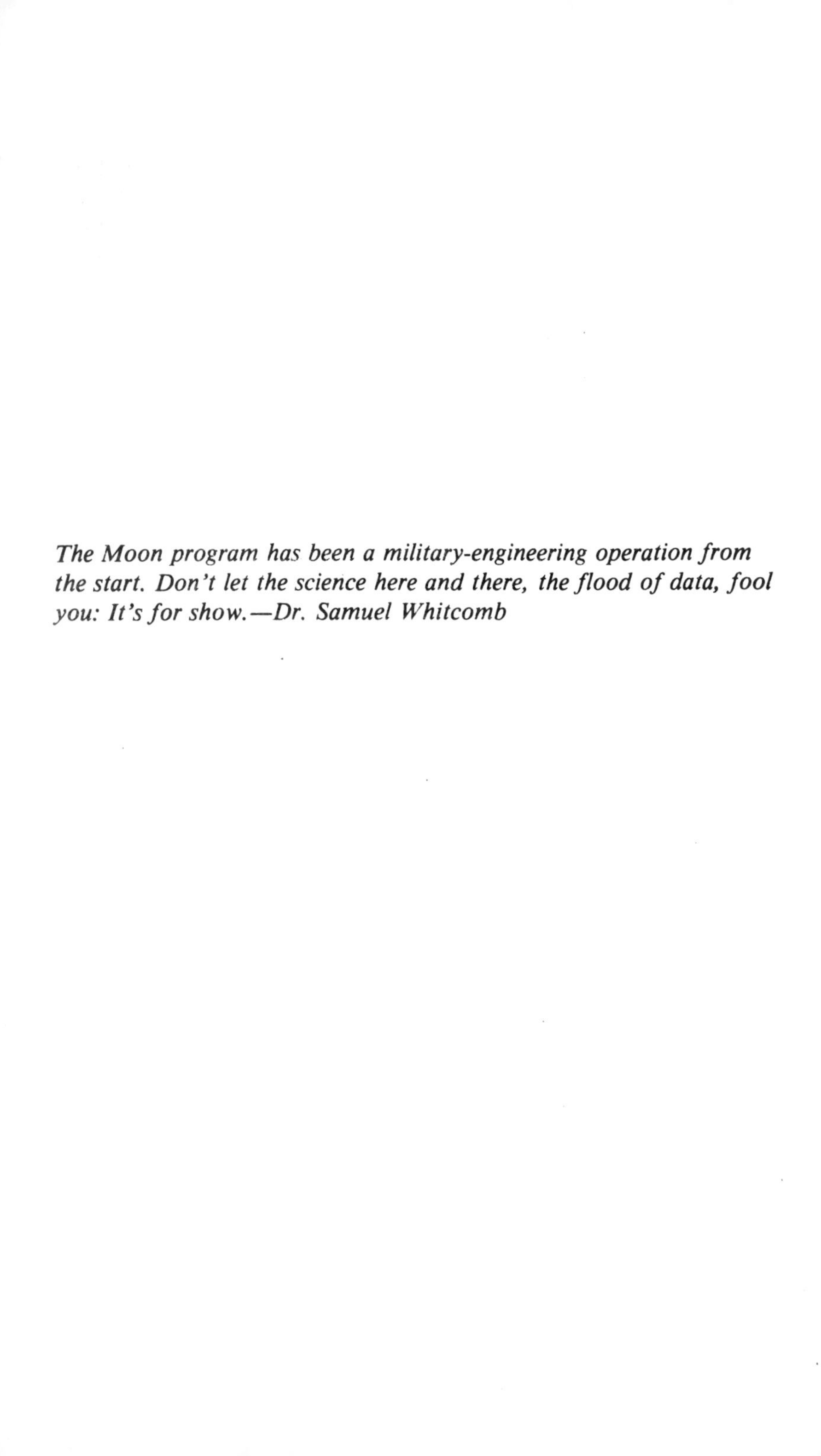

The Moon program has been a military-engineering operation from the start. Don't let the science here and there, the flood of data, fool you: It's for show.—Dr. Samuel Whitcomb

CHAPTER 13

A CLOSER LOOK AT THE PROPERTIES OF LIGHT

The fundamentals of physics have now been fairly well outlined; however, this presentation is still far from complete. There are still many details which need to be filled in. This is especially true concerning the properties of light, despite the fact that the real meaning of Planck's constant has already been presented and its relationship to light has become apparent. How does the law of redistribution of energy work? What are the real principles behind color perception? Why is the velocity of light independent of its frequency? Why is this velocity equal to the ratio between an electromagnetic and electrostatic unit of charge? The answers to such questions have never been given before. Great fluctuations occur in the velocity of electrons in their orbits when materials are subjected to high temperatures. This, in turn, creates interactions and interference effects between electrons moving in opposite directions inside atoms and between electrons in adjacent atoms. These interactions generate changes in the electrostatic field effects of the electrons, which will cause regular and distinct changes in their so-called orbits. This is because the charge on the electron varies with its velocity. Abrupt changes in the velocity of a particle disrupt the ethers, which, in turn, results in the formation of photons. In one respect, the theorists did make a lucky assumption, but the "quantum jumps" of the electrons were the effects, along with the light produced, and not the cause of the spectral lines.

The larger the atoms, the more complex the interactions, and consequently, the more intricate the spectral pattern. The photons comprising the electrons determine the range of the ethers that can be disrupted. These ethers are intimately connected with the electrostatic field intensity of the electrons. Thus it follows from this new definition of Planck's constant, just why this definition must be taken into consideration in all of the calculations concerning the frequency of light produced in interactions. This even holds for the discursive mathematical jugglings by mathematical physicists, and why they were able to account for some of the spectral lines from a quantitative aspect.

The definition can be clarified still more by keeping in mind the following: the electrostatic field effects around an electron are dependent upon the range and level of the ethers deflecting off the sides of the particles. This range is not necessarily the same as the range of ethers affected by sudden changes in the velocity of the electrons, but there is a direct correlation between the two. When electrons interact, some of the ethers deflected from the electrons will, in turn, interact directly or indirectly with other ethers that cannot contribute to the electrostatic field effects of the electron. In this manner, a tremendous range of ethers below that from which the electrons originated can be indirectly disturbed by the electrons, and Planck's constant plays a role throughout the procedure, since all ether particles have the same kinetic energy. Electrons cannot disturb ethers higher than those with which they are associated to the extent of producing harder photons and electrons, because of the ultra-high frequencies required. This is in accordance with the fact that energy cannot flow uphill.

THE LAW OF REDISTRIBUTION OF ENERGY

A more penetrating look at the law of redistribution of energy discussed earlier is now in order. Briefly, it states that when light interacts with matter, new light results with a lower average frequency than the original light. One of the simplest demonstrations of this law is done with the use of light filters. For example, a light beam in the blue or violet end of the visible spectrum, after passing through a series of filters, regardless of the types, will always emerge from the last one as red light, providing a sufficient number of them are used. These filters could be all blue, violet or any other combination.

It was shown in the previous section that when an electron or proton is activated, successively lower ethers are indirectly disturbed, resulting in the production of lower-frequency photons. This is in accordance with the universal law which states that energy can only flow from a high potential to a lower one. The law of redistribution of energy is based on this principle. When light interacts with matter, many of the photons scatter and are dissipated, while others recombine during reflections to form soft particles. These soft particles further interact with matter resulting in some of the original light being repropagated. It is the production of photons by the indirect disturbance of ethers that produces the lower frequency light resulting from the interactions of light with matter. The lower frequency light produced in turn interacts wtih matter to produce indirectly still lower frequency light. However, the intensity of such light rapidly decreases as the lower frequency levels are approached. It is the interactions of soft particles and their disintegrations which are the greatest factors in the direct and indirect disturbance of the ethers to produce new photons. The soft particles release hard electrons during disintegration and their interactions with matter and with each other disturb the ethers. In some instances the release of hard electrons can be violent enough to produce higher frequencies than those of the original light, as is indicated by the Raman effect.

It should be noted that the principles mentioned above are also responsible for inertia. This results when a change in velocity disrupts the normal flow of ethers around and through a body, which normally offers no resistance to steady motion below critical velocities, since the closing forces equal the forward resistance. The ethers are far more fluidic than anything experienced with matter. A disruption brought about by a change of motion tends to produce photons. This requires force or energy and inertia is an integral part of the manifestation of energy. It is natural for the ethers to resist any change in motion of an object, with just one exception. The exception occurs when a body has a net zero charge after being impregnated with a certain combination of energies. In this case, cancellation effects result and no magnetic field is produced when the body is accelerated; hence, there is no disruption of the ethers. As a result, the body will have zero inertia. This occurs during teleportation, which will be discussed in Part IV.

THE PHENOMENON OF COLOR

All of the colors we normally see are combinations of different frequencies of photons. This follows from the discussion in the last section. When light is produced, a wide range of ethers is disturbed. The soft particles vary considerably in the type of photons which combine to produce them. Each type is not uniform in size or stability, therefore, there is a continuous disintegration back into photons because of various interactions. This tendency for soft particles to group together is the primary reason for the difficulty in separating light into narrow frequency bands

As a result, a wide freqency range of soft particles and photons will tend to be grouped together. This means that bands of light in the blue, indigo, and violet ranges will contain other colors down to the reds, although the reds will make up only a very small portion. The eye sees only the dominant color and prisms cannot separate them. The famous color experiments of Edwin Land, about 20 years ago, proved this to be the case. This wasn't recognized at the time and different interpretations were placed on the results of these experiments.

An article written by Land, describing his experiments, appeared in the May, 1959, issue of *Scientific American*. These experiments destroyed a number of popular theories on color perception. Briefly, the Land experiments consisted of two black and white transparencies produced from black and white film, exposed to filtered light from two different parts of the spectrum. For example, one film might have been exposed to light in the upper part of the green portion, while the other was activated by a longer wavelength in the green. When the light which had exposed each film was passed through these transparencies, and the resulting images were then superimposed on a screen, the original scene which had been photographed by the different films appeared in full color.

Of course, it required certain conditions to produce the true color reproductions. For example, if the two wavelengths were too close together, the results would be different. If the longer wavelengths passed through the transparencies produced from the shorter wavelengths, and vice versa, the color reproduction would be reversed. In other words, objects that should have been red would be colored blue, green, etc. This shows these different colors were present in each part of the spectrum, and that the variations in the different parts of the transparencies did what normal attempts at separation of colors failed to do.

The experiments also show that it requires subtle combinations of frequencies for the eye to perceive color, when the light isn't in a narrow frequency band. Otherwise, the eye will see things in various shades of black and white. Shades of black and white contain all the colors, but in the wrong combinations to be seen as colors. This has its parallel and analogy in sound. The blacks and whites or shades of gray correspond to dissonance and noise, while the colors correspond to harmonies and tones. The ratios of frequencies producing colors in light are the same as in the realm of sound which produce the tones and harmonies in music. This is just another demonstration of the hermetic axiom. This is why certain musicians, composers of the past, and some connoisseurs of music experience music in terms of color. This is natural, since the same consciousness and awareness is involved in the interpretation of each medium.

The Land experiments were completely baffling to everyone, since they seemed to violate all the rules of color perception. Land attributed the results to previously unsuspected abilities of the eye, and to reactions of the psychological nature, rather than to something having physical reality. Physicists, of course, remained silent. Land should have received a Nobel prize for his work, which was of far greater significance than many other contributions for which this prize was awarded. This is no mystery. Nobel prizes are not awarded for work that is disturbing to the scientific community.

It is evident there are a myriad of colors in the near monochromatic category, never seen on this planet. It is likely many such colors are visible in the earth's interior. Many of the soft particles formerly bound together become separated and disintegrate during their passage through the earth's shell. Some particles in a cluster will disintegrate before others do. This would produce color effects not observed on the surface. In addition, this will occur to a slight extent during the passage of light through the atmosphere, but not to a degree that will be perceptible. The book, *Etidorhpa*, described such a phenomenon in the earth's interior. The term "primary color" is a misnomer. Each of the three primary colors covers a broad band of the spectrum, and is so situated that different combinations can produce all of the common colors of the visible spectrum. This is because each one contains all such colors in abundance.

THE NATURE OF LASER BEAMS

Light reflected from a mirror contains a higher percentage of soft electrons than the incoming light. When photons reach the reflecting surface, they are momentarily stopped. Some scatter and interact with each other to form soft particles. Others meet incoming photons to produce other soft particles before they can acquire light velocity again. If light from a given source were to be reflected back and forth a sufficient number of times, the result would be a beam that contains a very high concentration of soft particles. It would then display many of the properties of a laser beam. Such a beam would have little tendency to fan out, since the particles would be held together by mutual magnetic attraction. It would also be highly penetrating and quite lethal.

Decades before the advent of lasers, an associate of the author witnessed such an experiment with mirrors, using the sun as a light source. The resultant light, after being reflected back and forth about 35 times, blasted a hole in the side of a hill. Some laser beams are produced in a similar manner. The so-called light waves bounce back and forth between two plates and through some "excited" atoms. In any event, laser beams contain high concentrations of soft electrons, which tend to be bound together by mutual magnetic attraction. This is why they maintain their sharpness over great distances. The burning property of a magnifying glass is mainly due to soft particles' being concentrated to a focal point.

The insight just presented points the way to a device of revolutionary significance. Concave mirrors placed in the proper positions inside a box can transform the light from any source into a beam of soft electrons of any desired degree of intensity. The range of application for such a machine would be mind boggling. For example, soft electrons associated with colors known to be highly beneficial could be concentrated to produce rapid healing. This could render obsolete other healing devices proven to be effective. Any kind of beam could be obtained for any type of job, depending on the frequency range of the light used. The intensity of the soft electrons can be regulated by controlling the number of reflections. Figure 12 illustrates this principle.

WHY THE VELOCITY OF LIGHT IS INDEPENDENT OF ITS FREQUENCY

Here is another aspect of light which physicists have seen fit to ignore. It is implicit in the Maxwell equations, but it still isn't explained. When the ethers are disturbed to produce a photon, a fraction of them are compressed and a great number are forced close enough together to adhere. This is analogous to the cohesive forces of atoms. The higher the ethers affected, the more rapidly and suddenly this temporary displacement must occur in order to form a photon. Otherwise, the ether particles will escape this compression since they are very active. This momentary compression of the ethers quickly returns to normal, much like a compressed spring that is released. This rebound hurls the aggregate or photon forward at the speed of light. The distance of this rebound of the ethers is equal to the so-called wavelength, or the distance in which the photon is accelerated to the speed of light.

The same identical pattern occurs when still lower ethers are disturbed to produce a lower frequency photon, except that the rebounding of the

Figure 14
A DEVICE TO CONCENTRATE SOFT ELECTRONS

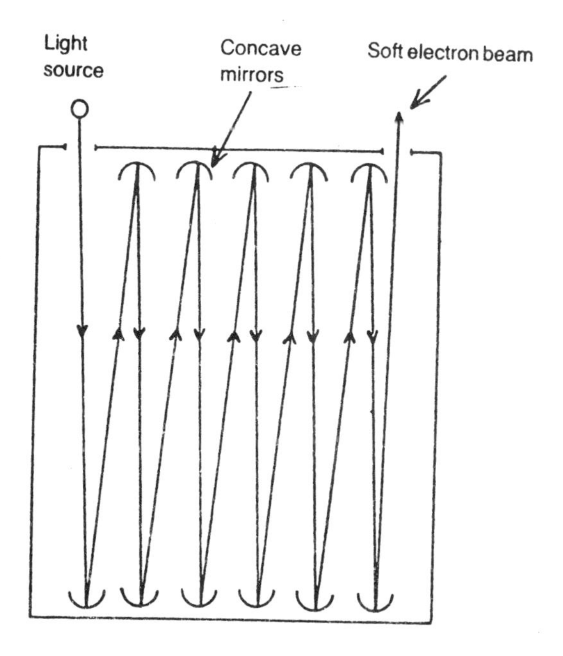

A soft electron beam is generated by positioning mirrors so as to create multiple reflections. As the number of reflections increases, a higher percentage of the original light is converted into soft electrons. The type of soft electrons produced depends on the frequency range of the original light source.

ethers takes place over a greater distance with a lower average acceleration of the photon produced. Since the warped condition in both cases follows identically the same pattern, the use of average acceleration can be applied in the following analysis to show that both photons reach the same velocity. Figure 11 shows the general pattern of a light beam and Figure 11 shows how a photon is formed and propagated.

In the following derivation, let (a) represent the average acceleration of the larger and lower frequency photon while (a') is that of the higher frequency photon. Let (t) be the time required for the larger photon to reach its maximum velocity and (t') the time required for the smaller or higher frequency photon. Now a' equals na where $n > 1$. From elementary mechanics, the distances through which the restoring forces operate in the case of both the lower and higher frequency photons are $\frac{1}{2}at^2$ and $\frac{1}{2}a't'^2$, respectfully. Since the average restoring force or acceleration is a linear function, the conclusion is that it is directly proportional to the frequency of the light produced; therefore, inversely proportional to the so-called wavelength. This of course is in keeping with Planck's constant. Now,

$$\frac{1}{2}at^2 = n(\frac{1}{2}a't'^2).$$

Substituting na for a' in this relation, it follows that

$$at^2 = nat'^2 \text{ or } t = nt'.$$

Since a't and at are the terminal velocities attained by the higher and lower frequency photons

$$t = nt' \text{ and } a = a'/n.$$

It follows that

$$a't' = at$$

which means that any two photons will always reach the same

velocity in free space regardless of their frequency.

THE BASIC PROPERTIES OF LIGHT

It was stated earlier that photons of light are produced when the ethers are disturbed in such a way that ether particles or molecules are forced close enough together and for a sufficient period, for them to adhere to each other. During the process, other ether particles in the vicinity are crowded more closely together than normal. The tendency for the ethers in the region affected to return to the normal state causes an imbalanced force on the photon just created. As a result, it is propelled at a high velocity. Since ether particles are extremely active, the action produces photons must be correspondingly rapid and of short duration. The more active the ether particles the higher the frequency required for the formation of photons.

In the external universe it is a well established fact that every object has a certain natural frequency. In other words, there is a certain frequency of vibration that it responds to. The greater mass, the lower the frequency of response. The same pattern applies to the ethers. The lower ethers, consisting of larger and more massive particles, will respond to a lower-frequency pattern than will the higher ethers. For a given force, the acceleration imparted to a given mass is directly proportional to the magnitude of the mass. Since the velocity of *light* is independent of its frequency or so called wave length, the realtive masses of the ether particles comprising photons of different frequencies can be determined. Light of a given frequency consists of moving photons separated by intervals of a certain length. The length of this interval plus the diameter of a photon is what is known as the "wave length." This is the distance through which the photon is accelerated by the restoring forces of the ethers which gives it light velocity. Since light is produced by the interactions of the fundamental particles of the atoms, the same in all cases, it follows that the average accelerating force disturbing the ethers is also the same. Therefore, the lower ether particles having a greater mass will be accelerated at a lower average rate than the higher ethers. From this fact, it follows the acceleration time is inversely proportional to the average acceleration of the photon. The distance through which the photon is accelerated is equal to $\frac{1}{2}\bar{a}t^2$, where $\bar{a}$ is the average acceleration and t is the time of acceleration. This means that if the mass of the photon is doubled $\bar{a}$ becomes half as great while t is doubled. Therefore, the "wave length" $\frac{1}{2}\bar{a}t^2$ doubles It can be concluded the frequency of light is inversely proportional to the mass of its photons or the mass of the ether particles comprising the photons.

WHY THE VELOCITY OF LIGHT EQUALS THE RATIO BETWEEN EMU AND ESU UNITS OF CHARGE

The behavior of electrons or protons in an accelerator shows that at the speed of light, all of their electrostatic potential has been transformed into magnetic energy. From the law of conservation of energy, it follows the total kinetic energy of the ethers producing the magnetic field is the same as the total kinetic energy of bombardment of the ether particles producing the electrostatic field, when the particle is at rest. Now it is possible to understand why the velocity of light relative to its source is the ratio between the EMU and ESU units of charge.

The electrostatic unit of charge (ESU) is a charge which will produce an electrostatic force of one dyne on a like charge one centimeter away. The electromagnetic unit (EMU) is a charge, which when traveling at a velocity of one cm/sec, will produce a magnetic field that will exert a magnetic force of one dyne on a unit pole or a similar charge traveling at one cm/sec at a distance one centimeter away in its equatorial plane. This is purely a hypothetical case, since two such charges one cm from each other would exert an electrostatic force of 10^{11} tons on each other.

It is evident the total energy of the magnetic field around one EMU of charge, traveling at one cm/sec is equal to the electrostatic energy potential around one ESU of charge; since they exert similar forces and are capable of doing the same amount of work. They are merely in different forms as has already been shown. It follows from the relationship between electrostatic and magnetic fields that the EMU charge, traveling at one cm/sec, will have an equivalent of one ESU of its charge transformed into energy. Since the electrostatic charge moves with the particles or mass of particles having the charge, the amount of electrostatic energy transformed will be directly proportional to the velocity attained.

This is analogous to a spaceship propelled by rocket fuel in free space. Assuming the mass of the fuel is negligible when compared to the mass of the ship, the fuel will be expanded at a constant rate to give the ship a constant acceleration. This means that the velocity attained at any moment will be directly proportional to the amount of fuel consumed.

As mentioned before, the behavior of particles in accelerators shows that when all their electrostatic energy is transformed into magnetic energy, they will be traveling at the speed of light relative to its source. This can also be deduced from the manner in which light is produced. At the moment the ethers that are disturbed to produce a photon start to rebound, they begin to accelerate the photon. The ether bombardments on the photon represent the electrostatic force. By the time the ethers return to normal, this electrostatic potential has been transformed into magnetic energy. This magnetic energy is manifested in the kinetic energy of the photon traveling at light velocity.

An ESU of charge, with all of its electrostatic charge transformed into magnetic energy, will be traveling at the speed of light. An EMU of charge with only one ESU of this charge transformed, will be traveling one cm/sec. Since the velocity attained is directly proportional to the amount of the electrostatic potential transformed, it follows that when two ESUs of its charge are transformed, it will be traveling two cm/sec. When c, or 3×10^{11}, ESUs of its charge are transformed, it will travel at the velocity of light, or 3×10^{10} ESUs of charge will equal the energy of one EMU of charge at light velocity. Therefore, the velocity of light relative to its source in cm/sec equals the ration between an EMU and ESU of charge or

$$\frac{\text{EMU}}{\text{ESU}} = c = 3 \times 10^{10} \text{ cm/sec.}$$

This highly interesting fact is an outgrowth of the relationship between electrostatic and magnetic fields and is one of the most important laws in the universe. It is indeed incredible that this conclusion was derived from Maxwell's equations in part based on an assumption diametrically opposed to the relationship between electrostatic and magnetic fields. It shows a theory can be wrong, yet still hit the truth occasionally, as quantum mechanics has in regard to atomic spectra. The Maxwell equations are perfectly compatible with the Lorentz transformation equations of special relativity. This is one of the major reasons relativity has been universally accepted by physicists. This compatibility is not surprising. Both the Maxwell and Lorentz equations conform with the idea that the charge on a particle is constant.

In the above demonstration it was stated the velocity attained during the transformation of electrostatic energy into magnetic energy was directly proportional to the amount of electrostatic charge transformed into magnetic energy. This is compatible with the principle that the kinetic energy of a moving body is manifested in the magnetic field developed around it. It is assumed a body of mass, m, has a certain amount of its charge transformed to give it a velocity, v. The velocity, of course, is directly proportional to the amount of charge transformed. For the sake of simplicity, it is assumed that the transformation is taking place at a constant rate meaning that the acceleration is constant. Let t, be the time required for this transformation. The velocity $v = at$ and the average velocity during this period is $at/2$. The distance covered $= (at/2) \times t = \frac{1}{2} at^2$. The energy or work required to accelerate the mass to velocity v, or to transform the electrostatic charge equals the force exerted on the mass m, acting through the distance $\frac{1}{2}at^2$. This force $= ma$. Therefore, the energy required is

$$ma\left(\tfrac{1}{2}at^2\right) = \tfrac{1}{2}m(at)^2 = \tfrac{1}{2}mv^2.$$

This is the kinetic energy of the mass, m, and it is also the energy of the magnetic field around it. In order for the energy conservation law to hold, it must be concluded the kinetic energy is manifested in the magnetic field.

This can also be shown from entirely different considerations. Within certain limits, the intensity of a magnetic field around a moving charge varies inversely as the square of the distance from the center of the charge. This distance is in a direction perpendicular to the direction it is moving. Let E represent the amount of charge transformed. Then the magnetic intensity at distance $r = \frac{E}{r^2}$. As E increases, how much does the extension of the field increase? Let r represent the outer limit of the field for the value, E. When E increases by a factor of h, we have $\frac{E}{r^2} = \frac{nE}{r'^2}$ where n' is the outer limit when E increases to nE

Therefore, $nr^2E = n'^2E$ or $n' = \sqrt{nr}$

As the body moves through the ethers; the vortex disturbance has a radius represented by the above relation. The ethers set into a vortex motion by the passage of the body do not return to normal immediately after it has left the region disturbed. There is a definite time lag. This means the length of the vortex is directly proportional to the velocity of the body. Therefore, as E increases by a factor of n, the volume of space affected or occupied by the magnetic field increases by a factor of $n(\sqrt{n}^2)$ or n^2. Since E is directly proportional to the velocity, it follows that the volume of the field varies as the square of the velocity.

The average field intensity within the volume is independent of the velocity since $\frac{E}{r^2} = \frac{nE}{r'^2}$. Since the energy of the field equals the average field intensity multiplied by the volume, it can be concluded that the total energy of the magnetic field produced by the motion of the body varies as the square of its velocity. This provides, for the first time, a graphic illustration of the mathematical formula for kinetic energy. When any mass is given an acceleration, all of its fundamental particles are given a certain additional spin perpendicular to the direction of motion of the body. This is compounded with their normal motions within the atoms and molecules of the mass. The additional magnetic field resulting permeates the entire mass.

It also becomes evident the rotational velocity of a particle producing a magnetic field is directly proportional to its translational velocity. The analogy represented above regarding the rocket-ship and fuel expended to give it a velocity represents a paradox impossible to resolve with conventional science. During the acceleration of the ship, kinetic energy is increasing with the square of the time, while the amount of energy expended to produce the kinetic energy varies directly with the time. From the standpoint of orthodox science, there is a definite violation of the law of conservation of energy. A lot more energy is derived from the kinetic energy of the ship than was used to generate it. This paradox has never been resolved, and physicists cope with it by ignoring it.

When an electrostatic field is transformed into a magnetic field, the total energy of the ether particles involved is not changed. All energy in the universe is a result of the motion of ether particles. The energy of motion of the ether particles, before the spaceship is accelerated, is the same as the total energy afterwards. Only the direction of motions has been changed. Therefore, there is no violation of the law of conservation of energy. The reader can see this paradox substantiates the existence of the ethers described, and also the nature and relationship of electrostatic and magnetic fields.

The principles regarding the relationship between an EMU, an ESU of charge provide a means of calculating the ether pressure exerted on a single hard electron at rest. Obviously, the percentage of total, ether pressure on the particles transformed into an electrostatic force is dependent on their relative distance from each other. The inverse square law for electrostatic force is valid only within certain limits. More than likely, a single electron will induce zero force on another electron one centimeter away.

An EMU charge traveling at one centimeter per second will have one esu of its charge transformed into magnetic energy. This is equivalent to an esu charge traveling at the velocity of light. In this case, the normal ether pressure or ether bombardment has been entirely transformed into a rotary motion around the particles comprising the charge. This means that ratio $\frac{\text{esu}}{\text{EMU}}$ of the total ether pressure exerted on the charges comprising the EMU charge traveling at one cm/sec has been transformed to produce a magnetic force of one dyne on an e s u charge one centimeter away traveling at light velocity. The energy involved is identical to the electrostatic force an e s u charge exerts on a like charge, one centimeter away. From the law of conservation of energy it follows that the ratio $\frac{\text{e s u}}{\text{EMU}}$ of the total ether bombardment on the particles comprising an e s u charge has been transformed into the electrostatic force! This means that the ratio $\frac{\text{EMU}}{\text{e s u}}$ dynes, or approximately 3×10^{10} dynes total ether pressure is exerted on the particles comprising the e s u charge. The charge on a single electron has been measured at 4.8×10^{-10} esu. This means that there are 2.08×10^{9} electrons in an e s u charge. Therefore, $\frac{3 \times 10^{10}}{2.08 \times 10^{9}}$ or 14.4 dynes totalpressure is exerted on a single electron by the surrounding ethers. This represents a pressure beyond normal compreshension when the minute size of an electron is considered.

CHAPTER 14

THE ROLE OF SOFT ELECTRONS IN PROMOTING CHEMICAL CHANGES AND MAINTAINING LIFE, AND THE PYRAMID PHENOMENON

SOFT ELECTRONS, MAGNETIC FIELDS, AND CHEMICAL CHANGES

Much has already been said about the importance of soft particles in all phases of our existence. However, a more extensive treatment of this subject needs to be given. It has been repeatedly confirmed that magnetic fields have considerable healing properties and will stimulate plant growth.(28) What has not been realized is that it is not the magnetic fields themselves which are responsible, but the soft electrons they capture and concentrate. Another phenomenon of magnetic fields puzzling many is that one pole of a permanent magnet has beneficial effects on organisms, while the opposite pole produces deteriorating effects.(28) The effects of magnets are not difficult to understand. The magnetic flow out of one pole carries beneficial soft electrons with it, which are forced into the area to be treated. The opposite pole draws the vital energies or soft particles out.

One of the most significant properties of soft electrons is their ability to promote chemical changes. As mentioned previously, the electrostatic zonal effects around atoms and molecules determine, in part, their chemical and physical properties. A change in a molecule is not likely to take place without lessening the chemical bond or attraction among its constituent atoms. Soft particles interpenetrating the molecule will bring about this condition by carrying harder electrons in with them, which in turn will weaken this bond by offsetting the positive charge effects of the nucleus. Soft particles tend to camouflage a variety of harder particles. This is a vitally important property because, in this manner, other atoms, which are going to take part in the chemical change, also have their zonal effects temporarily altered, so they can come into more intimate contact with the reaction. The soft particles tend to act as catalysts for the reacting particles. This has a tendency to disintegrate the soft particles involved. The release of energy then expedites the reaction. The disintegration of the soft particles also allows the normally powerful electrostatic field effects within the atom to return to their original state.

For any type of charge, the right kind and concentration of soft particles can accelerate the reaction hundreds, even thousands of times faster than the rate at which it would normally take place. The disintegration of soft particles involved in chemical changes and the release of hard electrons is the source of much of the heat produced during chemical reactions.

THE PROPERTIES OF WATER

Special types of particles radiated by catalysts, such as platinum, are responsible for their ability to promote chemical changes. It should be mentioned that the chemical properties of atoms and molecules are, in part, governed by the soft particles they radiate. Water is a universal catalyst, because of its unique ability to collect and concentrate an enormous quantity of soft electrons of all kinds. This is the reason water has the highest specific heat of any known substance.

The great amount of energy contained in water, in the form of soft particles, has been unwittingly demonstrated by experimentors on many occasions. For example, there are a number of reports of internal combustion engines running on water treated with a minute quantity of some undisclosed chemical. The engines in each case performed as well as they would have on gasoline. Such a demonstration was supposedly witnessed under controlled conditions by the Navy Department during World War I. F.D. Roosevelt was also allegedly involved. The man who had the secret was named Andrews. He disappeared after the demonstration under mysterious circumstances. There have been many rumors of others. It doesn't require much imagination to realize what happened after such discoveries were made known. The universal application of such discoveries would have wrecked the petroleum industry.

Of course, no reasonable explanation could be given for this phenomenon, since it seemed to be contrary to all the rules of chemistry. The explanation is apparent in light of the principles involved. The chemical was the deciding factor in triggering the disintegration of the more unstable soft particles contained in the water when the atomized solution was subjected to compression and ignition inside the engine.

A seeming paradox may come to mind, concerning the properties of water. Since water contains a high concentration of these particles, then why isn't the weight and inertia of water affected? The concentration of soft electrons fluctuates considerably, yet the weight and inertia don't. This question is appropriate, and once again the answer is simple. These particles are extremely mobile and act independently of the water, since they are not locked in the water molecule, nor are they actually attached to it. When water is exposed to a gravitational field, the soft electrons are repelled, while the water molecules are attracted. Since the soft electrons are not bound to the molecules, their repulsion does not affect the force of attraction exerted on the water molecule. Each is affected independently of the other. Yet the water molecule can still attract the soft electrons. This will affect the weight of the water, but not to a significant degree. A different situation occurs when an "adept" charges his body with an excess of soft electrons so that he can levitate. Such charges are locked temporarily into the cells of his body and become an integral part of it.

A paradox seems to exist with regard to clouds. They consist of small water droplets that do not fall. From the standpoint of the properties of water just presented, they should fall. Every water droplet is attached to a dust particle. This dust particle absorbs a high concentration of negative charges from the water. The particle would levitate upward, were it were not for the water droplet holding it down. If the amount of water around this dust particle exceeds the critical amount, the droplet will fall as rain. Outer space is permeated with fine dust that continually replaces the dust taken out of the atmosphere by precipitation. This dust is vital to sustaining life on a planet. Without it, there would be little or no precipitation.

Under certain conditions, water can lose weight and even levitate. Experiments have shown that water, when ejected in the form of fine jets, will start to levitate after falling a certain distance. Also, the fine spray resulting from waterfalls often has a tendency to levitate upwards. This phenomenon has puzzled many observers. By now the reason is obvious. Such conditions cause the water droplets to be impregnated with an inordinate concentration of soft electrons. Also, the turbulence causes a greater number of hard electrons to be released within the water.

The reason water has a great affinity for soft electrons must be made clear. Water is a unique substance. It is comprised of two elements among the most chemically active and are gases. In fact, it is the only stable compound which is a liquid at normal temperatures, and whose molecules consist exclusively of gaseous elements. The fact that three oxygen atoms can magnetically combine to form an ozone molecule indicates that the oxygen atom is extremely magnetic. This means that a higher percentage of its orbital electrons are moving in approximately the same plane. This leaves fewer orbital electrons tending to offset the positive charge of the nucleus and other portions of the atom. Consequently, two sides of the oxygen atom possess an inordinately strong overall positive charge. When the hydrogen atoms combine with an oxygen atom, the electrons on the side of the hydrogen atoms adjacent to the oxygen atom are brushed aside. (This is on the segment of the oxygen atom where most of the electrons of the oxygen atom are orbiting.) The normal flow of electrons around the proton of the hydrogen atom are diverted to a flow which encircles the oxygen atom and the outer periphery of the hydrogen atoms. This results in a powerful bond between the hydrogen atoms and the oxygen atom which is both electrostatic and magnetic. The electron flow around the hydrogen atoms is extremely rapid. As a result, the overall positive charge of the hydrogen atoms in this case is very high. Since there is a very strong mutual repulsion between them, they will line up on opposite sides of the oxygen atom. Thus the water molecule has the structure H-O-H.

The molecule created from this combination has strong and extensive positive zones. The attraction zone is consequently a considerable distance from the molecules relatively speaking. This is why the specific gravity of water is low despite the strong positive charge of the molecules.

The great affinity of water for soft electrons is now apparent. The large, positive zones between molecules are havens for soft electrons, drawn there by the attenuated, but significant, attraction of the hard electrons captured by the soft electrons. Although soft electrons are large compared to hard electrons, they are still very small compared to an atom. Therefore, the spaces between water molecules can harbor large quantities of soft electrons, without their being bound to the water molecules.

Other properties of water can be more readily understood, when the conditions determining whether a substance is a gas, liquid or solid is analyzed. Two given atoms or molecules will attract each other, when the electrostatic forces favoring attraction overbalance the repulsive forces. At any relative position, there are repelling forces tending to counteract the attractive forces. It follows there is a position in which the resultant attractive force is at its zenith. This means there is a zone around any two atoms or molecules where the attractive forces are greater than the repulsive forces. All other areas are repulsive zones. A substance is in the gaseous state when the average kinetic energy of all the molecules is sufficient to carry them past the zone of attraction, regardless of their relative positions. The molecules of a substance which is a gas at normal temperature have attractive zones that are relatively weak and of limited extent. When the substance becomes a liquid, the average kinetic energy of the molecules is not great enough to take them beyond the zone of attraction when they are grouped close together. The attractive zone, however, is not great enough to confine them to a small area and, as a result, they have a relatively wide range of movement. Due to the Maxwell distribution law, a certain percentage of the molecules, at any instant, have a velocity that enables them to escape from the surface of the liquid, and evaporation is the result. In the completely solid state, the kinetic energy is too low to allow any molecule to move a significant distance after it enters the zone of attraction, and its motion is confined to an extremely limited area. Evaporation can, and does, take place under certain conditions when molecules occasionally reach sufficient velocity to escape from the surface, as in the case of ice.

At extremely low temperatures all substances, especially under pressure, become solid and brittle; since practically all molecular activity ceases. A slight displacement of molecules at any portion of the substance, due to stress, produces a break; since the molecules at this point of stress are not moving far enough or fast enough for a significant portion to stay in the zone of attraction, before a break can occur. Any substance, regardless of how brittle it may be, will stretch a certain amount before a fracture occurs. The distance of stretch depends on the extent of the zone of attraction. A ductile and flexible substance consists of molecules with relatively large zones of attraction, and the molecules have a wide range of movement.

If a substance receives no soft electrons from the exterior, those contained within it either escape or disintegrate. Soon all molecular activity dampens, and finally ceases, as the temperature is reduced to absolute zero. The soft electrons produced by the activity of the fundamental particles leave the material without disintegrating, therefore do not contribute to any molecular activity.

Perhaps the property of water that has been the most baffling, is that it expands as it freezes. It is unique in this respect. The principles introduced above easily resolve the mystery. The high concentration of soft electrons greatly weakens the repulsive and attractive forces between the molecules. Therefore, the average kinetic energy of the molecules at the freezing point are still of sufficient magnitude to enable the molecules to move in and out of the zones of repulsion and attraction, without being confined in the attraction zone. The cooling process must proceed until the soft electron concentration reaches the stage where the attractive forces become strong enough to confine the molecules to the attractive zone. When this occurs, the water becomes a solid. Since the attractive zone is an inordinate distance from the molecules, the average distance between molecules becomes greater than it was when the water was in the liquid state. At the freezing point, the molecular activity is low enough to permit soft electrons to enter or leave the substance without disintegrating. This means, in order for the water to be transformed from a solid back to a liquid, the same quantity of soft electrons must be injected into it as were removed, when it changed from a liquid to a solid. Both processes occur without a change in temperature, because the disintegration of soft electrons is minimal at this stage. When the concentration becomes greater, the disintegration rate increases sharply, and the temperature rises as a result.

There is another phenomenon concerning water and other substances, which has not been widely discussed or written about, let alone explained. It is that the melting and freezing points are not constant, but fluctuate considerably, depending on conditions. For example, water can still be a liquid at temperatures considerably below 0° Centigrade, the temperature which nearly everyone believes is the freezing point. As a matter of fact, this temperature was accepted as the official freezing point, because it was found to be the maximum temperature at which water freezes without being subjected to high pressures

The soft electron concentration in a given area can vary without the temperature changing. A residual pocket with a high concentration of stable, solt electrons can reduce the normal repulsive and attractive forces between the molecules of water at 0 centigrade and below to the extent it is still a liquid. This means the thermal agitation of the molecules must be reduced further in order for the water to freeze.

Another phenomenon concerning water, never explained and thus ignored by science, is that in cold weather, hot water pipes have a greater tendency to freeze than cold water pipes. The heating of the water drove off the majority of the soft electrons, normally harbored within the water. Due to the low temperature of their surroundings, the soft particles were not replaced. Therefore, when the water in the hot water pipes approached the normal freezing point, it did not have to go through the process that the unheated water had to, in order to transform from a liquid to a solid at the freezing point.

Of all the strange properties of water, its expansion as it freezes is something conventional science has been unable to ignore. The accepted "explanation" is that as the water freezes, the molecules arrange themselves to form crystals. This particular arrangement is in a geometrical configuration, supposedly resulting in fewer molecules per unit volume. As usual, the conventional explanation consists only of descriptions without any consideration of the causes.

The properties of water as a solvent, ionizer, and catalyst have now become understandable. When a soluble substance is placed in water, the cohesive bond between the molecules is broken by the presence of the high concentration of soft electrons carried in the water. The zones of attraction disappear, and the individual molecules are free to move around like the molecules of a gas.

A similar condition exists when a compound is ionized by water. Not only is the cohesive bond broken, but a chemical bond is also broken. With the two portions of a molecule separated, one part has a stronger affinity for orbital electrons than the other. Potentially, it then has an overall negative charge, while the other part losing some of its electrons to the other has a potentially positive charge. These charges are camouflaged by the high concentration of soft electrons in water. The condition is similar to the capture of hard electrons by softer electrons. Electrostatic attraction and repulsion between ions is almost completely nullified.

As mentioned previously, soft electrons make chemical changes possible. It then follows that a catalyst supplies soft electrons necessary for chemical reactions. Therefore, water which contains soft electrons of many different kinds should be a great catalyst. In fact, the property of water to capture and concentrate these soft electrons renders it the most versatile of catalysts. It is this property of water that gives its life-sustaining ability. In fact, any living organism can survive and actually thrive without water if it is continuously bombarded with the right type and right concentration of soft electrons. The capture of hard particles by softer particles has been discussed throughout this treatise. This fact is of transcending importance. It is deeply involved in a wide range of phenomena, from the transmission of heat and electricity to the formation of clouds. A detailed analysis of this process will now be presented.

Ether particles have zones of attraction and repulsion, as do atoms and molecules. This is in accordance with the hermetic axiom, and makes possible the formation of photons from ether particles. Since photons are comprised of ether particles, they will in turn possess zones of attraction and repulsion. In the case of ether particles, these zones will be correspondingly smaller in proportion to the diameter of photons. When photons combine to form electrons or protons, the same zones are present between these particles. However, the zones of attraction are minute, when compared to the diameter of the electron or proton, and like particles seldom, if ever, get close enough together at sufficiently low velocities for the attractive forces to become effective. The situation is entirely different when two like particles comprised of photons approach each other with widely differing frequencies. Electrostatic repulsion or attraction is considerably lessened, because each is associated with ethers which differ considerably from each other. When they are in direct contact with each other, electrostatic repulsion tends to vanish, since there can be little or no ether bombardments on the sides facing each other. Since each particle associated with ethers is somewhat different, they will tend to interpenetrate. This means they will be completely within the ether attraction zones of one another. As a result, the harder particle is captured by the softer one.

In like manner, the captured harder particles will, in turn, capture still harder particles, and they will likewise capture still harder particles. This process continues until the hard electrons normally associated with electricity are confined. This combination of particles tends to nullify the electrostatic forces which are normally produced by the confined particles. This tendency to nullify electrostatic forces will tend to camouflage the captured harder particles, so that their presence is not readily apparent.

The ether particles normally bombarding the hard electrons and protons which produce electrostatic field effects tend to be diverted from their normal paths by the presence of softer particles, or mediums between the repelling like charges, or the attracting unlike charges. The interpenetrating softer particles produce an ultra-high concentration of ether particles around the hard particles. The motion of these ether particles is greatly restricted. This offers a barrier to the higher ether particles that normally bombard the hard particles. This has a tendency to slow them down, and those that do collide with the hard particles do so with considerably less impact than normal. Therefore, they tend to become electrically neutral and their motion nearly slows to a halt. Soft particles also permeate matter, as well as the spaces between matter, yet they do not to any great extent neutralize the electrostatic field effects of the fundamental particles, because they are more concentrated, and also their rapid motion tends to prevent capture. However, additional concentrations of soft particles of the right kind, injected into matter, can render the elementary particles within the atom electrically neutral and the matter becomes what is known as "dematerialized". This is discussed in more detail in the chapter on teleportation in Part IV. The conglomeration of soft and hard particles, also by the above process, renders the soft particles electrically neutral.

It should be noted that only hard particles or the fundamental particles of the atom are hollow. All other particles, including photons, do not have this tendency because of the nature of their formation. If the softer particles were hollow, they would be unable to capture harder particles. Hard particles entering a hollow, soft particle would, of course, maintain their charges and force a mutual repulsion. Therefore, they would immediately escape. Photons, if hollow, would tend to be less stable, and the probability of forming other particles would be lessened.

When a soft particle disintegrates, a chain reaction ensues. The disintegration releases the confined, harder particles. The energy released during the disintegration is generally sufficient to disintegrate the weaker hard particles it originally captured. This, in turn, results in the disintegration of still harder particles, until the very hard and stable electrons of electricity are released. It was mentioned that the hardest particles were directly created by the great mind power of the logos. They, therefore, possess far greater stability than do the other particles, and will not disintegrate during the process which started with the disintegration of soft particles. Figure 12 depicts the capturing process.

Highly interesting experiments performed in Poland during the summer of 1927 by two scientists, Howsky and Groot, demonstrated the ability of soft electrons to house and camouflage harder electrons, and to release them under certain conditions. These experiments also were a great confirmation of other principles which have been elaborated upon in this treatise, and especially those involved with levitation.

A small quartz crystal was attached to an oscillator which transmitted radio frequencies of several kilowatts. During the transmission, the quartz crystal lost its transparency and increased its volume 800 percent.

The crystal then levitated and carried the oscillator, as well as a 55 pound weight suspended from it, to a height of two meters above the floor of the laboratory. An account of this incident appeared in an issue of *Science and Invention* magazine. A photo showing the experiment and the levitating process was included.

The levitation occured when the crystal was subjected to vertical oscillation pressure, via direct electrode contacts and transverse oscillation, via non attached electrodes, broadcasting radiation, with the crystal interposed between them. The experiments were performed at low temperatures.

The properties of a crystal are discussed in Chapter 21. A crystal is essentially a glorified condenser. When the small crystal, mentioned above was bombarded from all sides by low frequency photons and soft electrons from the oscillator, it was impregnated with an overcharge of hard electrons associated with a wide range of ethers. These electrons resulted from the disintegration of the soft electrons, penetrating the crystal. The overcharge forced the molecular layers of the crystal further apart, causing it to expand. At the same time, the crystal was given an abnormally high negative charge throughout its structure. As a result, the earth's gravity would repel it with considerable force. Conceivably, this force could be as much as about 1000 Gs. The crystal originally weighed one ounce and the gravitational force would enable it to lift a 55 pound weight. More than likely, the weight itself was also impregnated with a high concentration of very soft electrons which, when disintegrating, would give it a gravity nullifying, negative charge.

The impregnation with hard electrons would tend to produce high temperatures. Undoubtedly, Howsky and Groot found this to be the case. Therefore, in order to prevent overheating, the parts involved had to be subjected to low temperatures. Attempts to explain the results of the experiment, as expected, were pitifully vague and inept. The reader can see that all aspects of these results were in perfect harmony with concepts already presented.

Experiments involving similar principles, which were promoted by the Chicago College on Gravity Research, show that a 60 cycle alternating current, imposed on a solenoid, will cause an aluminum plate to levitate nearly a foot when placed over the solenoid. It is significant and expected that the plate was heated during the process. A solenoid subjected to AC will radiate very low frequency and unstable photons and soft electrons. They will, of course, penetrate an aluminum plate and disintegrate, releasing a high concentration of hard electrons in the material. Naturally,

Figure 15
THE MANNER IN WHICH SOFT PARTICLES CAPTURE HARDER ELECTRONS

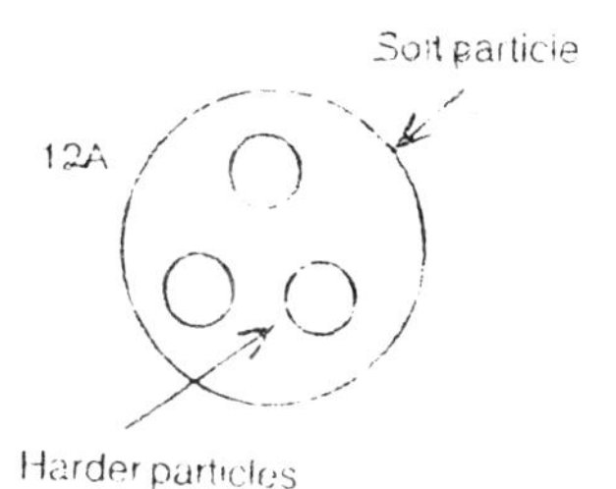

Two particles differing greatly in the frequency range of the photons of which they are comprised have little tendency to repel or attract each other. Therefore, they tend to interpenetrate as shown in 12A

Since there are zones of attraction and zones of repulsion between ether particles, it follows that when two like or unlike charges are close enough together, they will attract each other. Charged particles have the same properties as other particles because they are comprised of photons which are in turn comprised of ether particles. Normally, particles comprised of the same frequency photons never approach each other close enough for a long enough time to attract. However, particles which differ considerably in the frequency range of the photons of which they are comprised satisfy the conditions for entering the zones of attraction. There is a slight attraction upon reaching this zone which increases as the particles interpenetrate. Finally, the softer particle tends to capture and hold the harder one. If the frequency difference is too great, the soft particle is unable to hold on to the harder one, and the harder particle passes readily through it without being captured. 12B depicts this condition.

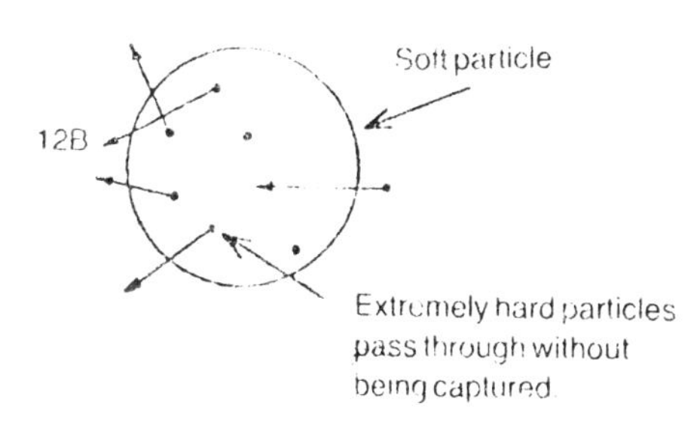

Figure 15 (continued)

If the hard particles shown in 12B encounter particles which have already been captured by the soft particle, they will tend to be captured because the frequency difference of the constituent photons is not as great. 12C depicts this process.

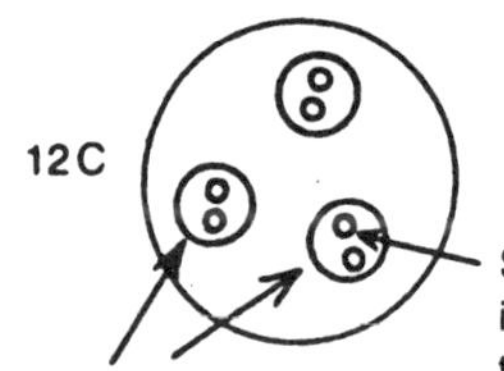

The process in 12C continues with the capture of still harder particles until a conglomerate of particles within particles exists as shown in 12D

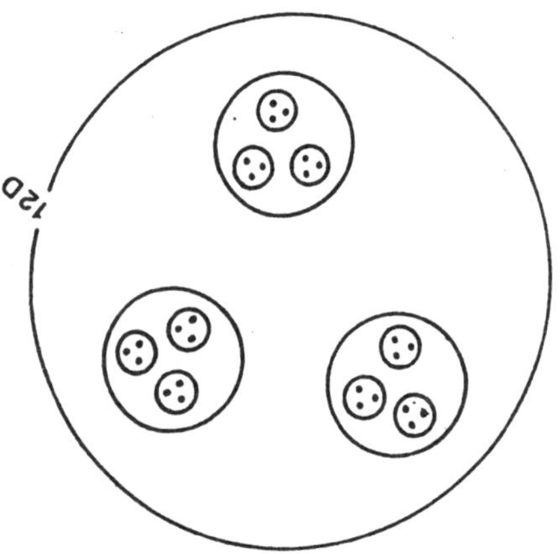

The capturing process tends to nullify the electrostatic field effects of the captured particles. Electrostatic forces are the result of a disruption of the random movements of ether particles. The combination described above partially restores this randomness in the vicinity of the particles. When the disintegration of a soft particle occurs, a chain reaction generally takes place. The soft particle destruction releases the captured particles and the energy released results in their destruction. In turn, still harder particles are released and so on down the line.

Figure 12 (continued)

it would tend to levitate and heat at the same time.

THE PYRAMID POWER PHENOMENON EXPLAINED, USING THE CONCEPT OF SOFT ELECTRONS

Pyramid experiments are gaining wide publicity. So much has been written on the subject that little space will be devoted herein describing the effects produced. Perishables placed inside a pyramid generally show little, if any, tendency to decay or spoil. The energies experienced are extremely beneficial to humans, and prolonged stays over extended periods of time have resulted in some degree of rejuvenation. In many instances, plant growth has been accelerated, and so on. It is not surprising that satisfactory explanations have not come to light. Physicists steeped in orthodoxy have remained silent. The mystery vanishes in light of the new insights already presented.

Soft particle bombardments from outer space, and especially from the sun, concentrate inside the pyramid. Some, passing through the surface of the pyramid, are slowed down to such an extent that the earth's gravitational field, repelling the negative charges, tends to keep them inside, until collisions from other particles drive them out. Most of the particles collected by the pyramid concentrate along the edges. This is to be expected. Electricity on any charged body tends to do much the same thing with concentration at points and along edges. In fact, pyramid frames have been found to be nearly as effective as the closed pyramid if, and only if, there is a continuity in the framework or no breaks in any of the joining parts. This is also to be expected, since a break in the framework is similar to an open circuit. Figure 13 depicts the pyramid phenomenon.

The soft electrons collected on a pyramid frame or closed pyramid soon reach a saturation point, and continuous bombardment causes the excess to drop down inside the pyramid. This, coupled with the gravity repelling forces, results in a high concentration inside.

The proportions of the pyramid are apparently a factor in its performance. If the sides are too steep, many of the soft electrons will move along the edges into the ground outside, instead of being forced inside the pyramid. If the slope is gradual, the angles are too obtuse to allow many particles to collect. Also, the particles will tend to strike the surface at nearly a right angle and pass straight through, with only a small reduction in velocity. If they strike at a sharper angle, there is a greater tendency for them to be retained by the material.

Figure 16
THE PYRAMID PHENOMENON

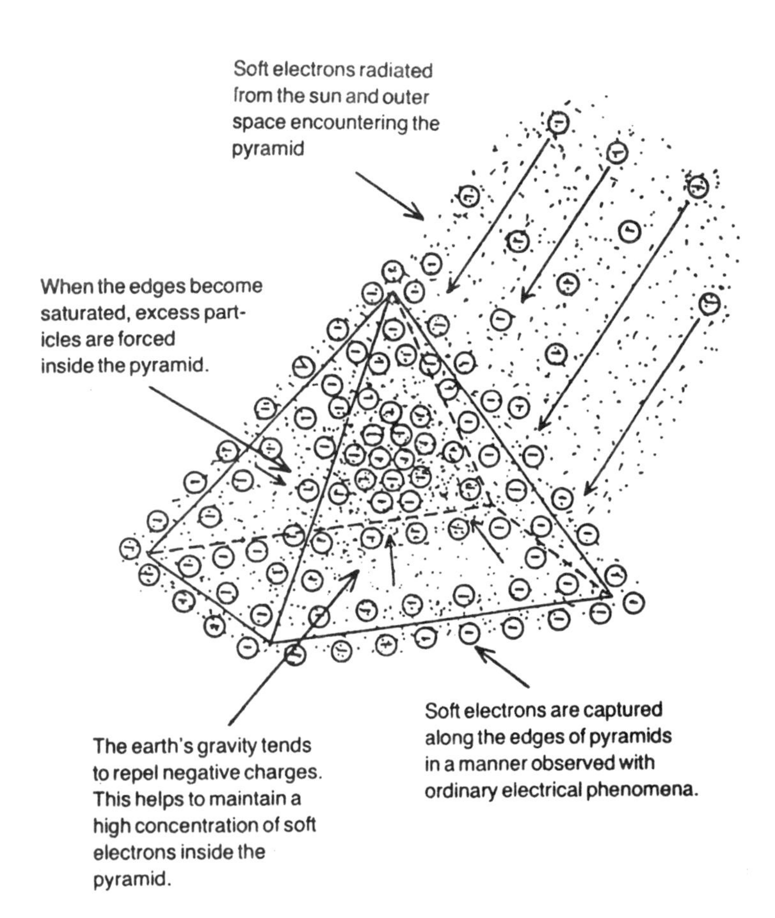

If two sides of the base of a four-sided pyramid are aligned with magnetic north, it is more effective. Since particles tend to travel down magnetic lines of force, the flow of soft particles inside the pyramid is directed more towards a side than an edge. This reduces the tendency for the particles along the edges to be dislodged before a sufficient quantity accumulates. At the same time, particles attached to the sides tend to be forced to the edges, allowing a greater charge to build up.

If a razor blade is placed with its edges pointed in the direction of the earth's magnetic field, a slow honing action occurs along the edge. The soft particles affect the cohesive forces of the molecules of the blade, and render it more plastic for a short distance below the surface. The constant flow redistributes the molecules which will be more affected at the thinner part of the blade. The blade, being metallic, will also attract and concentrate soft electrons along its surface. It has also been found that this honing action can even take place outside a pyramid, but at a much slower rate.

Although frame pyramids are nearly as effective as those with sides, pyramids can be rendered more potent by lining the interiors of a nonmetallic, enclosed pyramid with metal foil of good conduction, such as aluminum or copper. The foil allows a greater quantity of soft electrons to accumulate around the nonmetallic outer portion because the soft particles do not pass through the metallic substance as easily. This causes a backup of soft particles. During the process, the foil absorbs large quantities of soft particles, before many of them can enter the pyramid. Pyramids also radiate soft electrons upward from the peak. Many of the soft particles that are momentarily stopped on the outside of the pyramid are repelled upward by the earth's gravitational field. After the pyramid becomes saturated, a greater quantity of soft particles than ever will concentrate inside. The foil will continue to radiate a high concentration of soft particles during the night, when the number of particles bombarding the pyramid is considerably reduced.

It is found pyramids work better during the summer than any other time of the year. They are also more effective in the lower latitudes than similar ones located in the higher latitudes. This is because most of the energy concentrated by the pyramid comes from the sun. There are conflicting opinions as to the effectiveness of pyramids because of this, since there is little understanding of the principles involved. For example, those who experiment with pyramids in Canada may claim they don't work, while those in Southern California will contradict them. Hypersensitive people have found the energy around a permanent magnet has the same "feel" as that inside a pyramid. This is understandable, since they are both concentrating the same kind of energies.

CHAPTER 15

THE NEW COSMOLOGY THE SOURCE OF THE SUN'S RADIANT ENERGY, AND THE CAUSE OF NOVAS AND SUNSPOTS

One thing that all suns seem to have in common is their great size in comparison to planets. The astrophysicists speak of white dwarfs of planetary size and less. It is apparent from the evidence that has been presented throughout this treatise that any claims made by astronomers or astrophysicists pertaining to celestial determinations have about the same degree of merit as the other scientific claims that have been mentioned previously. There is nothing to justify the existence of a white dwarf. For one thing, due to its small size and its limited gravitational influence, it could only hold very small bodies of asteroid size in orbits, and then only for a short distance away. According to the fallacious theories of orthodox science, a white dwarf consists of atoms with practically all their electrons stripped away, and hence possesses enormous gravity. It will be shown that astrophysicists have no way of accurately determining the distance away or the size of stars.

The larger the body, the greater its mass or volume in proportion to its surface area. This means that as the size increases it is less probable that the energies produced by the normal activity of the atoms in the body's interior will escape from the surface, without a resultant increase in the temperature of its surface. The energy radiated from the surface will be in the form of photons and other particles of all types. Below a critical size, the surface area is sufficient to allow all of the radiant energy created in its interior to escape without an increase in temperature. In fact, such a body will lose heat unless it receives sufficient energy from its surroundings.

As a body increases in size, its surface area becomes increasingly inadequate to allow the radiated energy in its interior to escape without a buildup of heat at and below the surface. The surface will radiate the heat or energy outward as quickly as it is created in the interior. The rate at which energy is radiated from a surface increases rapidly with a resultant increase in surface temperature. This varies as the fourth power of its absolute temperature. For example, within a certain temperature range, if the temperature is doubled, the rate at which energy in the form of photons and soft particles is radiated increases by a factor of 16.

The critical size of such a body will depend on its composition. For example, if it contains a high concentration of mildly radioactive substances, this critical size will be less. If the body has a hollow condition, the outside dimensions would have to be greater. The red giants, if they are even close to the dimensions claimed, would have to be hollow with relatively thin shells; otherwise, they wouldn't be red. Their surface temperatures would be astronomical.

The actual source of the energy that is finally radiated into outer space is the soft particles and photons normally radiated by the atoms of the material inside a sun, this is due to the activities of the fundamental particles. Because of the great mass of the sun, an abnormal concentration of these soft particles is always present in the nterior. This concentration is greatest near the surface. There is a steady increase in intensity from the center toward the outside. This results in a continuous disintegration of a high percentage of those particles near the surface, which is accompanied by a great increase in temperature, which in turn results in a greater rate of disintegration. At the same time, the rate at which the soft particles are created increases. A state of near equilibrium exists when the rate at which the soft particles are created in the interior approximately equals the rate at which they disintegrate. It would follow, then, that the highest temperatures exist at the surface and steadily decreases with the distance below the surface. This means that any sun has a relatively cool interior.

The principle that size is the major factor in a celestial body's ability to radiate is confirmed by the behavior of very large planets such as Jupiter and Saturn. An application of this principle indicates that bodies of such size should start radiating more energy than they receive from outside sources. Recent determinations indicate that both Jupiter and Saturn do, in fact, radiate more energy than they receive from the sun. A recent probe showed a surprisingly higher temperature in Jupiter's upper atmosphere than was formerly believed to exist.

It now becomes apparent that the conventional theory which states that the radiant energy of the sun is produced by thermonuclear reactions is complete nonsense. One thing to consider is that if this were the case, the sun's radiation would be so lethal that no life could exist on any of the planets in the solar system. The deadly and highly radioactive radiations resulting from this kind of reaction would be simply too much for nature to cope with on a daily basis. The high concentrations of ultraviolet rays are potent enough, but this has been mitigated by the atmosphere and the law of redistribution of energy.

The very simple, but vitally important, mathematical law concerning the relationship between volume and surface area is the governing factor in the source of the sun's radiant energy and has been overlooked by scientists in other scientific fields.

Although the interior of the sun is relatively cool, the temperature gradually builds up over eons of time. The effects of the disintegration and dispersion of soft particles, generated by the activity of the fundamental particles, slowly increase the temperature throughout the interior. Much of this effect is contributed by less stable particles that don't travel very far from their point of origin before disintegration occurs. As the temperature increases, the rate of disintegration of particles increases. This greater activity also results in more particles being created. The more stable particles concentrate near the surface because they travel further before disintegration. When this concentration reaches a critical state, an explosion results, causing an abnormal quantity to be ejected from the surface. This is the cause of sunspots, which function as relief valves. This condition has its parallel on earth in the form of volcanoes.

Occasionally throughout the universe this heat buildup in stars is much greater than normal due to a combination of factors which might include an increase in the quantity of radioactive elements in the interior caused by transmutation. In such cases, relief valves in the form of sunspots no longer take care of the excess energy increase and large portions blow apart, releasing astronomical quantities of radiation. After the explosion, the supernova becomes a burned out body in comparison to its former state. Considering the countless billions of stars within our vision, and that only a few supernovas have been observed down through history, it is logical to conclude that it is not the fate of the great majority of stars.

One of the phenomena concerning the sun which completely baffles all of the scientists is that it seems to rotate faster at the equator than it does in the higher latitudes. The sunspots in the vicinity of the equator make a revolution about the sun in less time than those in the higher latitudes. This is an annoying paradox which can't be pushed aside by these scientists because it is out there for all to observe.

The part of the sun that we see is a highly fluidic blanket. The portion around the equator could rotate faster if, and only if, a steady external pull is exerted on this region of the sun. Otherwise, internal friction would eventually produce a uniform motion. This means that bodies in orbit near the equator and close to the surface are generating a high concentration of gravity-inducing radiations. It becomes evident that such bodies could not consist of normal matter. If they are not a group of UFOs, or special satellites comprised of unique materials, then they must be composed of atoms and molecules made up of softer particles which are affected very little by the sun's radiation. Such bodies could generate a concentration of gravity radiations considerably out of proportion to their masses. Being constructed of this kind of material, they would be practically invisible.

ASTRONOMICAL ERRORS IN DETERMINING PLANETARY SIZES AND DISTANCES

Charles Fort cited many instances of fiascos that belied astronomers' claims of extreme accuracies in determining stellar and astronomical distances. In the process, his revelations did little to enhance their reputations as paragons of integrity. He also presented evidence indicating that the stars and planets are much closer than is commonly believed. The following discussion will show that Fort was right and the source of error in astronomical determinations will be analyzed.

The principles employed by astronomers in their measurements are essentially the same as those used by surveyors in measuring elevations and distances. Some of the surveyor's instruments are scarcely less sophisticated than those of the astronomers. Yet, according to Fort, some of the experts admit that they are unable to determine the height of mountains with any degree of precision and, in fact, their calculations can be off by as much as ten percent. This is reflected in the inconsistent heights attributed to various mountains over periods of time. There are significant fluctuations. Different surveys give different results. Evidently, altimeters are far more accurate and are, no doubt, the basis by which the elevations of large areas are found. The author recently had an opportunity to check the above with an altimeter. It was adjusted for sea level, and then a trip was made which finally culminated in a drive to the top of a lookout mountain, which is supposed to have an elevation of 9,269 feet. It rises abruptly out of a plain that has an elevation of about

4,300 feet. The altimeter agreed very closely with established elevations along the way such as those of towns with elevations varying from 1,000 feet to over 4,000 feet. At the top of the mountain, however, the altimeter registered only 8,800 feet. The author then readjusted the altimeter to register the 9,269 feet, which was the height attributed to that mountain and returned. At every spot on the return trip, the altimeter consistently indicated elevations more than 400 feet higher than before. Even after several months, the altimeter still shows an elevation more than 400 feet higher than it should. It is significant to note that all phases of the trip took place during fair weather.

The fact that the altimeter was accurate at all places except at the top of the mountain whose height was found by triangulation shows that the methods employed by surveyors and astronomers are far from being accurate. The altimeter showed that there was an error of about ten percent in the measurment of the height of the mountain. If surveyors with their fine instruments cannot determine the height of a mountain only a few miles distant, one can only marvel at the discrepancies that would occur when one is observing an object at planetary or stellar distances.

There are several factors which astrophysicists and astronomers have not taken into consideration in their calculations. Perhaps the most important of these is the fact that all electromagnetic radiaitons, including gravity in free space, suffer an attenuation affect, well beyond that due to the inverse square law. It has already been shown that all space occupied by the material universe is permeated with soft and hard particles of all kinds that have been radiated by planetary systems for countless ages. This principle is demonstrated by fluctuations in the velocity of light to be discussed soon and the gravity attenuation that prevents the roofs of giant caverns deep inside the earth from caving in, as mentioned earlier. It also follows that there is a steady decline in the velocity of light as it travels through space. The reasons become apparent from the following considerations.

Normal light, or light which has traveled relativey short distances from its source, immediately resumes its original velocity, after passing through a dense medium, such as glass or water. As shown earlier, this is due to the close bunching of photons and soft electrons in any given ray. The concentration of particles in a ray of light tends to decrease after traveling great distances. The farther it travels, the more attenuated the ray becomes. This means that its ability to increase its velocity after passing from a medium of a given density, to one less dense will be reduced. This, of course, is due to the scattering and dissipation of particles within the ray, as it encounters the conglomeration of particles, moving in random directions throughout space.

Since conglomerations of soft particles permeate all known space, and the distribution is not uniform, it follows that light will experience refraction effects, even when passing through free space. Therefore, even under the best conditions with observations beyond the atmosphere, astronomical observations cannot be made with any degree of accuracy. The difficulty, of course, is compounded when they are made inside the atmosphere. It is a small wonder that Charles Fort found a wealth of evidence that completely debunked the astronomers' claims of great precision.

The fluctuation in soft particle distribution and the refraction effects of the atmosphere rules out the possibility of averaging out errors by making many observations and applying the mathematical method of least squares, developed by the mathematician Gauss. Conventional statistical theory obliterates actual small variances and distorts data by such averaging out processes. The gross errors that crop up despite these methods speak for themselves.

In order to measure the orbital distances of the various planets, it was first necessary to find the distance of the earth from the sun. Originally, this was allegedly found by measuring the angles that two widely separated observation points on the earth made with the sun. It is known as the parallax method. The distance to the sun was calculated from these angles and distances between the points. The size of the sun could then be determined and, knowing the orbital period of the earth about the sun, the sun's mass and surface gravity were calculated, by applying the Newtonian concept of gravitation.

More recently, the distance to the sun known as the "astronomical unit" was supposedly determined with a high degree of accuracy, by measuring the distance of the body Eros by the parallax method when it was closest to the earth. Knowing the period of Eros' orbit, the distance to the sun was calculated by the use of Kepler's third law, which states that "the square of the periods of any two planets are proportional to the cubes of their mean distances from the sun." Since the orbital periods of the planets are known with a reasonable accuracy, most of the other unknowns within the solar system could be calculated by knowledge of the sun's alleged mass and surface gravity. By now, it should be apparent that it would be a miracle, or at least one of the strangest coincidences ever, if the actual distances coincided even approximately with the calculated values.

If the Newtonian concept were valid, and the planets were held in orbit by only the effects of the sun's surface gravity, then the orbital periods of the planets would be a reliable means of determining planetary distances. Since it has been proven that the concepts on which these calculations were made are false, it can be safely concluded that the size of the orbits is considerably different from what the astronomers claim. As a result of dissipation effects of radiation, well beyond that which can be expected from the inverse square law, it follows that planetary distances are much less than the accepted values.

This excessive attenuation of the gravity effects of the sun is reflected in the alleged rapid increase of orbital distances of the outer planets. For example, the earth is one orbital unit from the sun. Mars is supposed to be 1.52, the Asteroids 2.76, Jupiter 5.2, Saturn [illegible].58, Uranus 19.16, and Neptune 30.24. It is interesting to note the manner in which the orbital distances increase. From earth to Mars the difference is .52 units, Mars to Asteroids 1.24, Asteroids to Jupiter 2.44, Jupiter to Saturn 4.38, Saturn to Uranus 9.68, Uranus to Neptune 11.08.

Planetary systems are a result of intelligent planning. This means that orbital distances will be kept to a minimum. The orbital differences will be great enough to prevent excessive perturbations when planets are in conjunction with each other. The larger the planet, the further removed it must be from adjacent orbits. Even with this taken into consideration, a big discrepancy in the alleged planetary distances becomes apparent. The outermost planets Uranus and Neptune have the greatest orbital difference, and they are not the largest planets.

It does not even follow that, the longer the orbital period, the greater the planetary distance. For example, the larger and more massive the planet beyond a certain critical amount, the slower it must move in order to stay in a given orbit. This is because the total gravity effects of the sun are unable to permeate and affect the entire mass to the extent that they would a smaller planet. For example, a planet like Jupiter or Saturn could be placed in a stable orbit inside that of earth. Yet it would have to move so slowly in its orbit that its orbital period would be much greater than that of the earth. This means that orbital periods are not necessarily a reliable gauge for relative orbital distances.

A satellite too small to transform the sun's higher frequency radiations will depend only on the sun's surface gravity to be held in orbit. This means that such a body would have a much lower orbital speed than that of the earth in order to maintain an orbit comparable to that of the earth. The situation is similar to that of a body of extreme mass.

An interesting question arises in regard to the Asteroid belt. It supposedly consists of thousands of fragments, ranging from less than a mile in diameter to over 500 miles in diameter, in orbits between Mars and Jupiter. Any object over about thirty miles in diameter could transform a significant portion of the sun's higher radiations into gravity effects. Astronomers have no way of measuring either the distances of these objects or their sizes. Also, it is not likely that the orbital periods of more than just a few of the larger ones have been determined with any degree of accuracy. Therefore, in regard to the principles just introduced, the Asteroid Belt offers no paradox.

Another factor that would help resolve any paradox that might develop in regard to the outer planets is that there is overwhelming evidence our sun is binary, as most stars happen to be. The earth-moon system is in such an orbit that our visible sun is always between us and its twin. The other planets in the solar system would then be exposed to the entire binary. Some of the more intelligent members of the scientific community have long suspected that our sun is a binary. The other planets seem to be much brighter than they should be, on the assumption that our visible sun is the only one in the solar system. Also, the solar prominences and outbursts seen during total eclipses seem much to violent to be coming from just the sun we are aware of. Other strong evidence is the case of Mars. The great polar caps melt during the summer months and patches of green advance toward the equator. This shows vegetation. This means that the temperature in the polar regions gets well above the melting point at times. If our sun were not a binary, the temperature on Mars would never rise above subzero temperatures at any time or place on its surface.

Assume that Mars is 1.3 times as far from the sun as the earth is. This is much closer than the distance claimed by the astronomers. This means that Mars would receive only $1/1.3^2$, or 59 percent of the heat from the sun, that we do. The highest temperature recorded on the earth is about 135° F or 64.3° C or 337.3° absolute. On this assumption, the temperature on Mars should never rise above .59 (337.3) degrees absolute or 199 degrees. This is 74 degrees centigrade below freezing or -101.2° F! Even if Mars were only 1.2 times as far from the sun as the earth, its temperature at any place on the surface would never rise above -38° F! These calculations are based on the principle that the heat content of a body is directly proportional to its absolute temperature. A picture sent back from Mars on June 7, 1979 by Orbiter 1 shows a landscape covered with snow. The snow had obviously drifted in places, which belied statements that we were only observing extremely thin coatings of ice on the rocks and soil. It was admitted that a similar coating, one Martian year previous to this, was observed and that it lasted 100 days. This had to have been taken during the late winter or early spring on that portion of Mars. It is extremely significant that it melted before the summer months. It is apparent from this that the temperatures on Mars are about the same as those on earth. This can only be accounted for if it were based on the conclusion that our sun is a binary. Further evidence that Mars has a warm climate will now be given.

An incredible contradiction that appeared in an article on Mars was contributed to the 1978 edition of the *Encyclopedia Americana*. Articles on subjects of a scientific nature are not likely to be solicited by such publications unless the contributors have a high standing in the scientific community. Therefore, it is safe to conclude that the author of this article was such an individual. He stated that Mariner flights have shown that the north and south polar caps on Mars consist of very pure dry ice or frozen carbon dioxide at a temperature of -128° C or -198.4° F. Yet, further on, he also stated that the temperature at the south pole may, on occasion, rise to 32° F (0° C), but that the average temperature is about 20° F (-7° C). The north pole is supposed to be colder, where the temperature may get down as low as -120° F. From this information, it would appear that the polar regions of Mars, experiences about the same temperatures as the earth's polar regions. Yet they are supposed to turn vast areas and quantities of carbon dioxide into dry ice at -198.2° F! Where all this carbon dioxide could come from on a planet devoid of vegetation, with an atmosphere of about one percent of the density of ours, was not made clear!

If this author is not an academic scientist, then we are faced with a real paradox. He has demonstrated an ability for doublethink that one should expect only from an honored member of the scientific community.

According to NASA, recent calculations have shown that the Martian atmosphere has only about one percent the density of the earth's. This contradicts other findings concerning cloud formations. Dense and very extensive clouds are often detected on Mars. Pictures of the volcano Olympus Mons have shown clouds hovering close to the summit of the mountain, which is supposed to rise 15 miles above the surrounding countryside. It is claimed that clouds are often found at an elevation of 90,000 feet! This is much higher than any water vapor and ice clouds found on the earth. The fact that they move shows that the air is sufficiently dense at such altitudes to produce winds capable of moving clouds. This indicates that Mars actually has an atmosphere denser than that of earth.

Another factor that confutes the claim of a thin atmosphere is the tremendous dust storms that often occur. Some of them dwarf any that have ever experienced here on earth. The experts try to surmount this difficulty by assuming wind velocities of over 300 miles per hour. How sustained wind velocities of this magnitude could be achieved has never been made clear. In addition, extensive areas of fine dust necessary to produce such a condition could not exist in an atmosphere as thin as that which has been attributed to Mars.

Another of the alleged findings of NASA that is open to question is the claim that the magnetic field of Mars is about the same as that of the Moon. Mars has a relatively high rotational velocity and therefore should have a strong field. There are two possible reasons for this discrepancy. First, it is likely a recent attempt to discredit the geomagnetic theory of planetary rotation, which is in direct conflict with orthodox concepts and is gaining favor, or the weather conditions on Mars are such that the negative ion content in the atmosphere is often very low. It has been found that in many areas of persistent winds the negative ion count is very low. The measurable field of a planet is dependent on the concentration of hard electrons in the atmosphere. There is also the possibility that the atmosphere contains a large number of free protons or highly ionized hydrogen atoms. The first possibility given is the one most likely to be correct. The integrity of NASA officialdom has consistently proven to be much less than impeccable.

Radar pictures recently taken of Venus show two almost perfectly round depressions that are antipodes of each other. One has a diameter that is 40 percent as great as that of the planet itself. The other has a diameter nearly 30 percent as great. Incredibly, these were explained away as being impact craters. It is difficult to believe that even the scientific community has any members of sufficient mental vacuity to endorse such an explanation. Yet the author knows an honored member intimately who insists this is what they are. As anyone who has even a modicum of intelligence should realize, an impact crater will have a depth that is a reasonable percentage of its diameter, especially if the missile does not bounce off and sinks below the surface. An impact capable of producing a crater with such a diameter would completely shatter even a solid planet. The impossible coincidence that a planet would have two such craters nearly the exact antipodes of each other has been cheerfully ignored.

The only possible explanation is that these "depressions" are giant openings into the hollow interior. The energies being radiated from these openings would deflect radar to the extent of creating the illusion of their being shallow sinks. Venus, being closer to the sun and in full view of the binary, would require much larger openings to dissipate the heat that would build up in the interior.

Other claims by NASA with regard to Venus which are steeped in contradictions are those of the dense clouds surrounding Venus consisting of sulphuric acid, and that the surface temperature is about 1000° F. Early pictures of Venusian terrain sent back by a probe which soft landed on the surface show a landscape very similar to that of the earth or the Moon. Rocks were shown with sharp edges and there was the usual evidence of normal ground erosion. The type of erosion that would be produced by a combination of high concentrations of sulphuric acid and 1000° F would reduce everything on the surface to a blob. The clouds on Venus undoubtedly consist of a tremendous mantle of water vapor and droplets, which would protect the surface and promote earthlike conditions.

Evidently, NASA has been unable to get its act together properly. In addition to the above, some reports have indicated that the Martian polar caps are a mixture of dry ice and frozen water, while others give the impression that they are comprised only of common ice. Such inconsistencies on the part of NASA could be attributed to the fact that NASA officials consist of various kinds of prevaricators. Apparently, few, if any, of them are clever enough to be consumate liars. If it were not for the double and triple thinking ability of academic scientists, the credibility of NASA might be seriously questioned by more individuals.

Another factor that leads astronomers astray is the fact that higher frequency light is refracted more by a lens than the lower frequencies. As a result, an image is magnified to a greater extent if the object is illuminated with higher frequency light. Light that is attenuated, in the manner described earlier, such as losing velocity, being scattered, and being brought to lower frequencies by the redistribution law, will have a tendency to be refracted less, the farther it travels. Each of these three factors is by itself sufficient to produce this effect. Together they compound it. Consequently, the image of a distant planet will not be magnified by a telescope, to the extent that the power would indicate. As a consequence, the planet will seem to be more distant than it actually is.

The eye, which contains a lens, will play the same kind of trick and produce the same effect, but to a lesser extent, than with a telescope. A telescope then will only perform up to its expectations when closer objects are being observed.

Since electromagnetic radiations have a tendency to lose velocity after traveling great distances, it follows that the method of bouncing radar off planets is not reliable. This, including the determining of the earth's velocity in its orbit by the alleged precise measuring of the aberration of light from stars, has supposedly enabled astronomers to calculate the astronomical unit to an extreme degree of precision. Allegedly, all of the various methods of determining this unit were in close agreement with each other. One can only speculate as to how much juggling of figures has taken place during the process in order to achieve such confirmations, since the integrity of the scientific community has proven to be less than impeccable. All that can be said about all of these distances is that they are less than the accepted values.

Although planetary and stellar distances are completely unknown and there are no reliable means available (at least at the present time) of determining them, the diameters of some of the outer planets can be calculated far more accurately than any of the other values in the realm of astronomy. Such planets are those with satellites and whose orbital distances in proportion to planetary diameters, as well as their periods, can be measured. The determination of these constants are not affected to any significant degree by the dissipating factors of light mentioned above since a planet and its satellites are about the same distance from the earth.

When a planet is viewed through a powerful telescope its diameter, and the relative distance of a satellite from its surface can be laid out along a scale. The main factor that renders it possible to approximate the diameter of any of these planets is the knowledge that they have practically the same surface gravity as the earth. Another is that the orbital period of a satellite is approximately commensurate with the surface gravity as is the orbital period of the moon in regard to earth gravity. This method is not completely reliable for satellites of any appreciable size because of the attenuation of gravity effects and the transformation of radiations as they penetrate matter.

As an example, the moon is actually about ten percent smaller in diameter and about ten percent closer to the earth than is claimed. Since Mars has very small satellites its diameter can be calcuated with a higher degree of accuracy than the other planets. The calculation of the diameter can be made from the following relations:

$$\left(\frac{c^{-}}{d}\right) g = \frac{v^2}{d} \qquad \frac{2\pi d}{v} = t$$

Where d is the radius of the orbit, r is the radius of the planet in miles. The diameter is 2r; g is the acceleration of earth gravity in terms of miles per hour per hour; t is the period of the orbit in hours; v is the velocity in miles per hour, and d is the radius of the orbit in miles. From the two known values, g and t, the others can be readily determined. The results are quite astonishing. Mars turns out to have a diameter of about 11,300 miles. Jupiter only about 33,000 miles with a probable error of more than ten percent, and coincidentally, Saturn has about the same diameter as astronomers have claimed, or about 75,000 miles, with a probable error of more than ten percent. Therefore, Saturn is, by far the largest planet and Jupiter is next with two close rivals, Uranus and Neptune.

When the earth is between both Mars and Jupiter, and the sun. Jupiter on the average has an apparent diameter of about 2.57 times that of Mars. The actual diameter of Jupiter, according to the above figures, is only 2.92 times Mars' diameter. This would indicate the orbit of Mars as being only very slightly inside Jupiter's orbit. This is not likely. Since the calculated diameter of Mars has a far greater probability of being correct than the 33,000 miles indicated for Jupiter, it is safe to conclude that there is a disparity between the total gravity effects Jupiter has on its satellites and that due to its surface gravity alone. Because of its size, it will radiate more per unit surface area than a smaller planet such as Mars or the earth. This means that there is more radiation transformed into gravity radiations. As shown earlier, the great disparity between the surface gravity effects of the sun and its total gravity effect on planets is because of the tremendous amount of radiation per unit area emanating from the surface. Unfortunately, Jupiter and Saturn do not have tiny satellites such as Mars; therefore, their orbital periods are dependent on more than just the surface gravity of these planets. As stated earlier, it has been found that Jupiter and Saturn radiate more energy than they receive. Therefore, the value for g in the above equation must be increased slightly more than ten percent in order to conform with reality. As indicated above, the total gravity effects of the earth on the moon is about ten percent greater than its surface gravity effects alone. A more likely figure for the diameter of Jupiter would be 36,000 to

40,000 miles. This would place the orbit of Mars far enough inside the orbit of Jupiter to prevent excessive perturbations when they are in conjunction with each other. Likewise, the diameter of Saturn must be somewhat greater than 75,000 miles. Since Saturn is a much larger body than Jupiter, the intensity of its radiation must also be greater. Consequently, there will be a still greater disparity between its surface gravity effects and the total gravity effects on its satellites. Therefore, its diameter could be over 90,000 miles as based on these concepts.

Recent confirmation that the 11,300 mile calculated diameter for Mars is realistic has been unwittingly supplied by NASA. Measurements of surface detail show that the diameter of the giant volcano Olympus Mons at its base is 375 miles. Pictures of the entire planet which show this volcano, belie the claimed diameter of 4,200 miles. According to such views, the diameter of Olympus Mons is only about three to four percent that of the planet, instead of the nine percent it should be if astronomical calculations were valid.

Since astronomers have no reliable means of calculating planetary distances, it is charitable to consider any claims of accurately determining stellar distances as merely supposition. The distance of the closer stars is allegedly found by measuring their parallax with the diameter of the earth's orbit as a baseline. Two observations are made with six-month intervals. There is supposed to be a slight apparent displacement of the stars as the earth moves from one part of the orbit to the opposite side. The nearest star is supposed to be four light years away and the diameter of the orbit is allegedly about 185 million miles. This would produce a displacement of about 1.5 seconds of arc. It is like viewing a nickel from a distance of two miles. The margin of error is compounded because the observations are six months apart. The variation in concentrations of soft particles in outer space is sufficient to render the measurement of any parallax an impossibility, even if the observation could be made from the two points simultaneously. This is to say nothing of the fluctuating refraction effects of our atmosphere. The parallax of mountains only a few miles away are made with a surprising margin of error, as has been shown above.

Even without consideration of the disrupting factors in outer space and the atmosphere, the degree of precision required to determine such minute displacements as claimed by astronomers is truly astounding. One can only marvel at the type of magic astronomers must employ in their profession. It is the author's opinion that the moral character attributed to them by Charles Fort transcends their intellectual integrity.

It seems that, according to a logical cosmic plan, star systems should not be any further removed from each other than is necessary. That is to say, the radiation effects from each have minimal effects on any of the others. It does not require separations of light years. One need only look at constellations and star clusters objectively and logically to realize that they are relatively close together. For example, two stars about the size of our sun, one light year apart, would be about 10,000,000 diameters from each other. Consider two fairly close stars in a given cluster or galaxy that are about the same distance from the observer. Could they possibly be much over a few thousand diameters apart, let alone ten million?

Early astronauts reported that the stars are not visible above the atmosphere. They are made visible in the atmosphere because their light is diffused, producing greatly enlarged and distorted images of their discs. Diffusion of such magnitude does not occur in outer space, and geometric optics would apply. As a result, the stars are too distant for their outlines to be resolved by the naked eye. This does not mean that they are light years away. They can be seen easily with moderate sized telescopes. This has been demonstrated by small observatories placed in orbit above the earth. If they were as far away as is claimed, none could be seen by even the most powerful telescope in the world.

It is evident that there are minimum and maximum sizes a star can be. They cannot be much larger than our sun. A reasonable estimate of a maximum diameter would be about 1,000,000 miles. At four light years away such a star would have an apparent diameter of about .0075 seconds of arc. About 1.5 minutes of arc is the minimum resolution of the human eye. This means that a telescope would require a resolving power 12,000 times that of the eye to make such a star visible at a distance of four light years. This is supposed to be the distance of the nearest star. No telescope at the present time has this much power. The above considerations did not take into account the attenuation effects already discussed, which would drastically reduce the resolving power of a telescope for such distant objects.

With the principles which have been introduced in this chapter, the maximum distance of many of the stars can now be very roughly estimated. The apparent diameter of a given star as viewed through an orbiting telescope of known power can be determined. With the knowledge that its maximum diameter is about 1,000,000 miles, the distance can then be approximated. This is based, of course, on the assumption that light follows only the inverse square law.

THE ROLE OF GIANT UFOs IN COSMOLOGY

Some of the "stars" astronomers have thought to be solar systems are no doubt giant space ships of planetary sizes relatively close to us. As mentioned in Chapter 1, Fort cited instances of stars suddenly changing positions and even vanishing. A notable case of the present day is a "star" that has been observed for decades by many observers including the author. It is of the first magnitude and continuously fluctuates in color. Its position in relation to other stars has changed considerably on numerous occasions during the past 25 years. As is to be expected, astronomers have conveniently ignored this phenomenon. The most notable case of a giant UFO mentioned by Fort occured during the last century. A spindle-shaped object, perhaps larger than the planet Venus, passed through the solar system. During its passage it came close to the sun and seemed to be immune to the gravitational field of the sun or of any of the planets. After it was reported by some astronomers, the incident was treated in the same manner in which all such anomalies are treated by the scientific community. Large spaceships passing close to the earth would account for large areas on the earth which have been blacked out for hours during the day. There have been several such occurences recorded. Fort even mentioned a few cases.

It is more than likely that giant UFOs have been deeply involved in notable events of the past which have never been explained. For example, the great flood of Noah's day seems to defy all the rules of elementary physics and common sense. It was supposed to have been produced by a rain that pelted the earth for 40 days and nights. How could such a rain cover entire mountain ranges? The hardest rain on record, going continuously for 40 days and nights, could not account for more than about 200 feet of water. Yet this flood covered Mt. Ararat, which rises three miles above the surrounding country. In any event, where would all the water come from that could produce a violent rainstorm lasting for 40 days? Interestingly enough, records kept by other peoples on other parts of the globe mention a similar flood, and geological evidence confirms it. Rain could account for only a small percentage of the water involved in the flood. Where did this extra water come from and where did it go after it receded?

The only answer is giant spaceships, with levitation beams that can move planets from one place to another and to different orbits. A levitating beam or beams of sufficient magnitude to move the earth to a different orbit would displace large portions of the oceans, causing land masses to be inundated. After the moving process was completed, the displaced oceans would return to their former positions.

No doubt prior to the flood the earth was in a different orbit, in full view of the binary sun, and perhaps closer to the sun than it is now. Its surface would be protected by a great mantle of water vapor as is the case with the planet Venus. When the earth was moved into its present orbit, this mantle of water vapor quickly condensed as rain.

There are other types of catastrophic events that cannot be explained by natural means. These include polar shifts, earth upheavals that produce mountain ranges and earth magnetic polarity shifts due to changes in the direction of the earth's rotation and changes in the axis of rotation. The evidence is overwhelming that these changes took place in a very short time. All of this has been adequately covered in the books written by the great scholar Emmanuel Velikovsky such as *Worlds in Collision* and *Ages in Chaos* and *Earth in Upheaval.* He researched ancient literature in various parts of the world and found consistent accounts of global catastrophe, as a result of the earth tumbling on its axis. This included records of the sun and moon rising in the west and setting in the east. The annals of ancient Egyptians state that the course of the stars had changed direction four times since they had kept records. They also mention that the sun set twice in the sky where it now rises.

There are also accounts of the sun and moon standing still for periods of time. There are other records of the remote past that state that the night did not end for four days. In other words, there is corroborating recorded evidence in various parts of the world that there was either a prolonged day or a prolonged night.

From the explanation already given for geomagnetism, such changes would reverse the polarity of the earth's magnetic field. This has been confirmed by polar magnetic records in rocks which show magnetic reversals. Other evidence of sudden polar changes is that of preserved ancient mammoths unearthed in Siberia in a standing position. They had undigested food between their teeth and in their stomachs which consisted of temperate flora. Also, much tropical coral is found in arctic regions. As would be expected, evidence of glacial deposits are also found in tropical areas near the equator. There is also a great deal of geological evidence that some of the higher mountain ranges such as the Himalayas were formed very quickly. Mayan literature tells about the face of the earth changing, mountains collapsing, and other mountains growing. Velikovsky also found evidence that the Himalayas did much of their growing in historical times.

The logic employed to explain polar flips and changes in the direction of the earth's rotation is not only tenuous but infantile. The standard explanations involve meteor impacts, great earthquakes and the thickening of the ice caps in the polar regions. The analogy of the spinning top with melted wax dropped on it to produce a wobble has been given. The gravitational pull on the earth by the sun is much too feeble to cause even a relatively slight unbalanced condition brought about by increases in ice caps to cause polar flips within billions of years. If it did occur in this manner, then a rotation on a new axis would be mandatory. Otherwise, one part of the earth would always face the sun while the rest of it would experience permanent darkness. A change in rotation on a new axis would require a great coupling force. It is indeed incredible that none of the distinguished writers and authorities who recognize the reality of such earth changes in the past have not seen the gross inadequacies in these explanations.

Once again, the only manner in which the earth could have been manipulated to produce these recorded earth changes is by giant gravity-inducing beams emanating from spaceships. Great precision is required in such an endeavor. Due to the limited penetration of such gravity beams, the forces needed to move the earth in the above manner would be concentrated only in the outer layers of the earth's crust, and only on a small percentage of the surface area. The stresses produced in such areas of the crust would be colossal. It is analogous to throwing a bull around by only grabbing its tail. The tail and areas around the base would take up all the stress. The source of the tremendous earthquakes and great movements of land masses to form mountains now becomes apparent.

The question remaining is why there are periodic manipulations of the earth with accompanying cataclysmic events. According to geologists, magnetic polarity has changed at least 171 times in the past 76 million years. When farm land is overworked, it must lie fallow for awhile, in order to recuperate. Was this same pattern applied to the earth in general? The inhabited portion of the earth and the temperate zones that support vegetation become depleted after thousands of years, much in the manner of overworked farm land. The desert areas, land covered by ice and portions of ocean bottom were once inhabited and supported a great deal of vegetation. They are now like a field lying fallow, slowly being rejuvenated and cleansed by radiations from the sun and outer space. Not only is the land depleted in inhabited areas, but pollution in various forms including inimical energies and thought forms accumulates in intolerable amounts.

There are other reasons for manipulating planets and even changing their orbits on occasion. Ancient records, including testimony from outer space aliens, tell of a planet in the solar system that was destroyed in interplanetary war. It was in the orbit occupied by the asteroid belt. Debris from this blown-up planet has imperiled the entire solar system. Since a planet would scatter debris in all directions after it blew up, the asteroid belt would represent only a fraction of the material that comprised the original planet. The rest of the fragments would be orbiting the sun in a myriad of orbits and orbital planes. If a planet happened to be on a collision course with some of the more dangerous concentrations, it would have to be moved out of the way and its orbit changed; very likely such an incident with Mars and Venus, as described by Velikovsky in his book *Worlds in Collision* occurred. This book gives an account of these planets coming dangerously close to the earth and both of them almost colliding with each other before they assumed their present orbits. Prior to this, Venus was not seen as a morning and evening star. It was described as a comet that came from outer space. If the gravitational field of Venus had captured some of the debris from the destroyed planet as it was towed out of its previous orbit, it would have given the illusion of being a comet.

According to old records dug up by Velikovsky and others, it is indicated that we didn't always have our present moon. It is a comparatively late arrival and was likely a moon of the planet that was disintegrated. This planet, incidentally, was known as "Maldek".

RESOLVING OLBER'S PARADOX, THE RED SHIFT AND RELATED PHENOMENA

There is a paradox associated with cosmology which has never been resolved by conventional scientists, despite their claims to the contrary. It is known as Olber's paradox and is based on a principle of elementary mathematics. It assumes that the average distribution of stars remains about the same throughout the universe. Although the distribution is not uniform, the average number of stars in space within a certain distance of us varies directly as the cube of the distance, since the volume of the space involved varies in this manner. From a conventional standpoint, the light intensity from any star varies inversely as the square of its distance from us. This means that the amount of light received from the stars within a given distance varies directly with that distance. For example, the total amount of light received from all of the stars within 100 light years will only be one-half as great as the amount received from all the stars within 200 light years. If the universe extended beyond the four billion light years in which astronomers claim to have recorded stars, the sky should actually be blinding in all areas, instead of being black. Scientists have been consistent and provided a solution to this dilemma, which shows the same bad logic as many of their other theories.

Their explanation is that the more distant stars are receding from us at higher velocities, as indicated by the red shift. Even if this were true, the implications of Olber's paradox still hold. The most distant stars photographed still project as much light to us as before. While the visible frequencies are shifted toward the red, the ultraviolet must be shifted toward the visible and, therefore, the red shift does not resolve the paradox.

Some of the principles already discussed resolve Olber's paradox and explain the red shift at the same time. Space is permeated with soft and hard particles of all kinds, which stars have been continually radiating for millions and even billions of years. Light continually interacts with these particles when passing through space and the law of redistribution of energy takes over. In this manner, light from any star is steadily brought down to ever lower frequencies. It follows that the more distant the star the greater the average frequency decreases. The astronomers guessed right in this instance. The more distant the stars, the greater the red shift. Their conclusion was correct, but their explanation was wrong. The red shift is merely due to the law of redistribution of energy. At the same time the light is dispersed and attenuated to a degree far more than can be attributed to the inverse square law.

Therefore, light from the more distant stars is either dispersed or transformed into frequencies below the visible range. The starlight, which barely shows up on photographic plates, has been so thoroughly dimmed, which is in accord with the redistribution law and normal dispersion, that an illusion is created in that the stars are far more distant than they appear to be. It now becomes apparent that Olber's paradox is no longer a paradox.

As stated earlier, stars are made visible in our atmosphere by the diffusion of light, which forms greatly enlarged but distorted images of these disks. Light from distant objects, which subtend very small angles, is diffused outward from the original light rays after they enter the atmosphere by an amount which deviates very little from a certain constant. For a closer body such as a planet, whose disk subtends an angle much greater than that of a distant star, this constant does not magnify or distort the diameter by nearly as great a factor as that same constant added to a very minute apparent diameter.

The fallacies of the "big bang theory" and the conventional interpretation of the red shift have come into evidence by an enigma known as the quasar. Quasars are celestial objects with abnormal red shifts. If they were as far away as the red shift indicates, then in order for them to be visible to the extent they are, some of them would have to be 1000 times as bright as the entire Milky Way galaxy! An astronomer by the name of Halton C. Arp, with obviously better mental acumen than his illustrious colleagues, has shown by a brand of logic and intelligence uncommon for a man in his profession that quasars must only be a minute fraction of the claimed distance from us. He has found a surprising number nestled in the spiral arms of some spiral galaxies which are relatively close. Statistical analysis shows an overwhelming probability they are a part of such galaxies. To assume otherwise would be stretching coincidence much too far. As is to be expected, this has not endeared Arp to most of his fellow astronomers. It is indeed refreshing for a professional astronomer to finally appear in modern times with at least a modicum of intelligence coupled with integrity. Charles Fort would have been rendered speechless. The exact antithesis of Arp is an astronomer who has received a lot of publicity in recent years. He is a "famous" popularizer of the fallacies and dogmas of academic astronomy and cosmology. He is to these subjects what Asimov is to the other realms of orthodox science. The reader already knows his identity. He is, of course, none other than Carl Sagan.

A quasar is undoubtedly a moderate sized radiating body of a size approximating that of our own sun. The abnormal red shift can be attributed to an inordinate concentration of soft electrons or rarified gases of great thickness surrounding that body. The light from such a body would consequently experience a considerable red shift as a result of the redistribution law.

Spectral lines by which the red shift is determined do not experience as great a change in frequency as does the rest of the light radiated by such a star. This is because the light comprising a spectral line is more concentrated than the other frequencies. The rays of light of which a given spectral line is composed are far more numerous. Consequently, the light from a star will travel a greater distance before all of the rays of that line experience a drop in frequency. The laws of probability play an important role in this process.

FLUCTUATIONS IN THE VELOCITY OF LIGHT

It was shown earlier that light passing through concentrations of soft particles will tend to lose velocity, as it does when going from one medium into a denser one. The concentration of soft particles throughout space, and especially around planetary bodies such as the earth, is not uniform. Therefore, measurements of the velocity of light will fluctuate. This fact was unwittingly demonstrated by physicists with the Massbauer effect, which they thought was a confirmation of general relativity. Accurate determinations of this velocity will find not only 24 hour fluctuations, but also seasonal ones and significant changes during sun spot activity. The velocity will be found to be less during the day than at night and also during the summer and, especially, during sun spot activity. This, of course, is because the concentration of soft particles is greater during these periods.

Countless determinations made during the 1930s with a mile long evacuated tube indicated that there were fluctuations much greater than could be attributed to experimental error. Reports were not explicit in stating whether the velocity fluctuated according to the rule mentioned above, but they did state that there were daily and seasonal variations. This fact was too damaging for the world of official science to tolerate, since the velocity of light heretofore was supposed to be the universal constant. What have the physicists done about it? Perhaps the reader has guessed it.

Present day encyclopedias do not mention these embarrassing deviations. The list of measurements and their dates in chronological order suggests ever more precise determinations over the years, which have been progressing toward the final exact measurement of this "universal constant". They conveniently left out all the data which occurred between these dates, which don't fit this pattern. One might wonder how soundly physicists sleep at night. Perhaps not as well as the astronomers Charles Fort wrote about. An older physics textbook on optics which was used about thirty years ago, entitled *Physical Optics*, by Robertson, mentioned these various discrepancies. Robertson disposed of the anomaly by suggesting that the fluctuations were probably "more instrumental rather than real". What the author meant by this nebulous and contradictory statement was not made clear. He had already stated that these fluctuations were greater than those which could be attributed to experimental errors, which naturally includes instrumental errors. Evidently, Robertson was one of the great masters of the art of doublethink.

It would seem that if the Michelson-Morley experiments were to be performed on the outside of a small spaceship traveling in free space at a very high velocity that positive results could be obtained. It would not show ether drift, but it would show soft particle drift. A large body like the earth with a dense atmosphere and a far greater concentration of soft particles at its surface than exists in outer space would prevent such a result. The earth tends to carry all of the soft particles in the vicinity along with it. Therefore, no soft particle drift would be detected. As mentioned in the chapters on relativity, no ether drift would be detected because the ethers offer no resistance to the passage of light.

As indicated earlier, faster moving light produces effects similar to that of higher frequencies moving at a lower velocity. Conversely, light traveling at lower velocities behaves in a manner similar to that of lower frequencies moving at higher speeds. This is what creates the Doppler effect of light. For example, the rotation of the sun produces the red shift on the side of the sun moving away from us, and the blue shift on the opposite side which is moving toward us. In the latter case, the light is moving faster, because it has the rotational velocity added to its velocity relative to the source. In the former case, the rotational velocity is subtracted from the velocity relative to its source and therefore it is moving at lower velocity, since the light source is moving away from us.

The reasons on the basis of concepts introduced earlier is not difficult to understand. The higher frequency light is comprised of photons and soft electrons associated with the higher ethers than that of lower frequency light. For a given velocity the photons and electrons of the higher frequency light will interact with matter more readily than those of the lower frequencies. So, within certain limits, the lower frequency photons and soft electrons will interact in a manner similar to that of the higher frequencies, when they travel at a higher velocity.

THE ORIGIN OF MOON CRATERS

The concensus seems to be that moon craters are caused by the impact of meteors. This is consistent with the quality of logic displayed in other areas of orthodox cosmology. The diameter of most of these craters is disproportionally great compared to their depth. A true impact crater has a depth commensurate with its diameter. An impact great enough to produce a crater with a diameter of some size on the moon would shatter the entire moon, since it is hollow with a relatively thin shell. To wit: some craters have a mountain in the center. It is significant that, in all cases in which the crater has a mountain, the mountain is always in the center. How did it ever escape destruction?

The only logical answer is that the craters were produced by particle-beam weapons during the great interplanetary war. This, no doubt, was the one mentioned earlier, when the planet Maldek was destroyed. Other planetary bodies show similar craters, for instance, Mercury, Mars and the moons of Jupiter.

A concentrated beam of high speed positive charges, preferably protons, can have devastating effects, if directed against a specific target. The beam by itself does relatively little damage. It is the after effects that are destructive. While in motion, the positive charge effects of the particles comprising the beam are minimal. After they strike the target, they lose their velocity and a tremendous positive charge is concentrated at the point of impact. This charge is maintained by incoming particles. A high concentration of soft and hard electrons converges on the area from all directions, creating a void in the regions originally occupied by these particles. Others rush in to fill the void and a chain reaction, or domino effect, is produced which affects the regions of space at ever increasing distances around the target area. The number of electrons that converge on the area is far out of proportion to the number of protons concentrated in the area.

The ramifications are not difficult to imagine. The soft electrons congregating there disintegrate and release the hard electrons they contain. An inordinate concentration of hard electrons is the result, and is far more than can be absorbed by the protons. First, an implosion and then an explosion of electrons of colossal proportions are created. Most of the energy of the explosion is directed outward, since it follows the lines of least resistance. The number of particles involved and the amount of energy released can far exceed that of any nuclear device. Since the energy is directed outward, extremely wide but relatively shallow craters in a planet's surface result. The principles involved in such destructive forces are similar to those employed by Wilhelm Reich's cloudbuster, which will be discussed later. The center of the craters produced would experience a relatively small disturbance and, consequently, any mountain in the path of the proton beam would be left standing.

The fallacies in universally accepted cosmological dogmas have now been made apparent. One fallacy which has been gaining some popularity and acquiring a wider acceptance among astronomers and astrophysicists in recent years is the big bang theory. According to this misconception, the universe began with a giant explosion billions of years ago and the universe which resulted has been flying apart and expanding ever since. Of course, all life came about by the chance combinations of various atoms and molecules. The outermost portions are receding from the center of this explosion at a higher velocity than those which are closer to the center.

The famous red shift is the main basis for this concept, which is a very worthy concept, and as such capable of taking its place among the other celebrated theories of academic science such as relativity, tidal theory, concepts in particle physics and other products of the "fertile" minds of modern physicists. The big bang theory at least demonstrates consistency in the quality of thinking among orthodox scientists.

ADDENDUM TO CHAPTER 15

As mentioned in this chapter, the evidence that Mars has an extremely dense atmosphere (in fact much denser than that of earth) is overwhelming. This would account for its red color. Much of the visible light reflected from its surface that reaches us is brought down to the lower frequencies by the redistribution law since it must pass through a dense and extensive atmosphere. Its color will resemble that of its sky. It is interesting to note that astral travelers who have visited Mars (and the author knows one personally whose integrity is impeccable) claim that its sky is red. This principle would also account for the moon's yellow appearance. There is sound evidence as will be shown further in Chapter 18 that the moon has a much denser atmosphere than the earth. Howard Menger claimed that the moon has a yellow sky. Interestingly enough the earth has a blue tinge when viewed from outer space. Its sky of course is blue.

We sedulously inculcate in the coming generations exactly the same illusions and the same ill-placed confidence in existing institutions and prevailing notions that have brought the world to the pass in which we find it.—Prof. James Harvey Robinson

CHAPTER 16

AN EXPLANATION FOR CONDUCTIVITY OR THE RULES GOVERNING THE TRANSMISSION OF HARD AND SOFT ELECTRONS THROUGH VARIOUS MATERIALS

CONDUCTIVITY AT NORMAL TEMPERATURES AND ATOMIC FIELD ZONES

Hard electrons travel through metals more readily than through non-metals. This indicates that they encounter more extensive positive electrostatic fields between atoms and molecules than in nonmetals. At the same time, the atoms in metals are usually more mobile or free to move around than is the case with solid nonmetals. This is why the best conductors of electricity are also the best conductors of heat. It is significant that all of the heavier atoms are metals with the exception of radon, which is a gas. This means that such atoms have a higher net positive charge, which causes a stronger mutual repulsion for greater distances on atoms which are not directly attached to each other. This greater extension of the positive zone around such atoms gives them more freedom without breaking the bond which holds them together. The repulsive forces of nearby atoms increase the mobility of any given atom.

The heavier atoms contain more protons and neutrons bunched together. The outside pressure necessary to hold a group of mutually repulsive particles together is independent of the number of particles present. This principle can readily be demonstrated from a one dimensional standpoint. Consider a group of identical springs of a given length. Let F represent the average force applied over the distance L in order to compress a spring completely. Assume there are N springs independently distributed over a surface. The amount of work required to completely compress all of the springs is NFL. All of these springs are now arranged in tandem or along a line in order to represent N mutually repulsive particles. The average force required to compress all of the springs is the same as that required to compress only one spring since this force is transmitted equally to all of the springs. This time the force acts over a distance of NL. In accordance with the law of conservation of energy the work required to compress the springs in this case is still FNL. This means that the pressure required is independent of the number of springs. The same analogy can be extended to three dimensions.

From the above argument, it is apparent that large numbers of protons are as easily contained in a group as are smaller numbers. This becomes even more evident with the consideration that the larger groups generally contain a higher percentage of neutrons. This means that the activities of most of the protons in the heavier atoms are restricted. This in turn indicates that a lower percentage of their electrostatic potential is transformed into magnetic energy, resulting in a higher net positive charge of the atom. Generally, the elements with the higher atomic weights have a higher specific gravity. There are slight deviations from this rule, however. Smaller atoms probably generate fewer soft electrons which tend to remain locked in the atom or among large numbers of such atoms, than is the case with larger atoms. They would thereby be affected more by a gravitational field.

One might conclude that the heaviest atoms make the best conductors, but this is not the case. Silver, copper, and aluminum are the best conductors. Although their positive field zones are not as extensive, they have less inertia and thus are more easily pushed out of the path of a flow of hard electrons. The arguments presented thus far are not the only factors involved in accounting for small variations from the general rules outlined. The overall atomic pattern is too complex to be covered in full by this treatise.

Electrons which flow along conductors are continually colliding with atoms moving about. Therefore, it requires a steady application of force of EMF at the ends of the conductor to keep them flowing. The atoms of nonmetals are more firmly locked into position and therefore do not have much of a tendency to move out of the way. This is why they make good insulators. Electrons, which follow the lines of least resistance, tend to move on the surface of the conductor where there is less tendency to collide with atoms.

The rules concerning the conductivity of soft electrons are somewhat different from those of hard electrons. Soft electrons are enormous when compared to hard electrons. This is apparent when considering that the average diameter of a particle is directly proportional to the so-called wavelength of the light comprising it, or inversely proportional to the frequency. The ethers associated with atoms and their fundamental particles are much higher than those associated with soft particles. This means that atoms will offer little resistance to the passage of soft electrons. However, the magnetic fields resulting from thermal agitation of atoms and molecules are involved with ethers which are closer to the ethers directly associated with soft electrons. Therefore, soft electrons will interact with these fields. This explains why metals in general offer a greater resistance to the passage of soft electrons than nonmetals. The atoms or molecules of metals have a greater range of motion.

SUPERCONDUCTIVITY

The conditions for superconductivity are not difficult to ascertain. The atoms in a superconductive metal no longer move about to any extent at very low temperatures. Under such conditions, the electron flow pushes atoms out of the way which block the path, thus forming straight and clear channels for other electrons to follow. Uniform positive fields are encountered in these cleared passage ways produced between rows of atoms in the material. The atoms or molecules are practically stationary, therefore, no magnetic fields impede the flow of electrons. It doesn't necessarily follow that the best conductors at normal temperatures become superconductors at low temperatures or even reach the superconductive stage, except at perhaps absolute zero. Their general mobility may be a liability where superconductivity is concerned.

It is interesting to examine the stumblings of theoretical physicists on the subject of superconductivity. This was considered one of the great unsolved mysteries of physics until about twenty years ago. A physicist by the name of John Bardeen allegedly removed the annoyance when he committed the atrocity of bringing quantum mechanics into the picture. Of course, his supposed explanation was nonexplanatory and consisted of a vague and inexplicable mathematical description. He was showered with nearly every scientific honor available for this speculative malfeasance. Even though this gaudy adornment to physics was "understood" by only a handful of quantum mechanics experts, the faith shown in it by the adherents of science is truly phenomenal.

The simple and obvious approach to a problem seems to be abhorrent to a modern physicist. It is clear just why physics has reached such a deplorable state of abstruseness. Physicists and their followers seem to think that an alleged solution which is hopelessly complex shows great profundity, when it actually displays a badly confused state of mind. There is actually nothing difficult to understand about the phenomenon of superconductivity, yet modern theorists have somehow managed to make something incomprehensible out of it. There are many more complicated than simple solutions to a problem. In actuality, the number of solutions is generally in direct proportion to their complexity. This means that it is more difficult to find a simple solution because there are fewer of them. The degree of intelligence required to find a solution to a given problem is inversely proportional to the amount of additional information needed, over and above the minimum number of facts which are necessary in order to solve the problem. Therefore, the simplest solutions are generally the most difficult to find unless one is lucky. In any event, the simple solution has the greatest likelihood of being correct since nature's laws are basically simple.

THE PARADOX OF THE TRANSFORMER AND THE SOURCE OF ELECTRICITY IN ANY CONDUCTOR

The ordinary electrical transformer presents an enigma. The secondary of the transformer continues to pour out or eject electrons indefinitely from a seemingly unlimited source. There is a limited quantity of free electrons in conductors which should be quickly exhausted. The standard argument used to account for the source of current is that free electrons in the circuit supply the electrons and are used over and over again. A simple calculation demonstrates that free electrons in conductors are not the source of electricity.

Consider a wire two millimeters in diameter which carries about 10 amperes of current. The electron flow is concentrated near the surface of the wire. Since the electricity in a conductor travels at about the speed of light, such a wire 186,000 miles long would have 10 coulombs of electricity distributed over its surface at any instant. The surface area of this wire is 1.84×10^6 square meters. A parallel plate condenser having a plate of this area with a separation of one millimeter would have a capacity of

.016 farads. Even with a potential across its plates of 100 volts, it would still only be able to concentrate an equivalent of 1.6 coulombs, and a good part of this electrostatic charge would be due to the displacement of the electrons and protons of the atoms. This voltage is far more than enough to concentrate all of the free electrons in the plates on the surface. Similarly, all of the free electrons in the wire example would be involved if the current were maintained with 100 volts. Of course, a wire this long would have too much resistance to carry any appreciable current with 100 volts, but this has nothing to do with the argument just given. As a matter of fact, even 6 volts is much more than enough to produce a current of 10 amps in a wire 2 mm in diameter. This can be demonstrated by connecting the poles of a large capacity 6 volt battery with such a wire. Therefore, there aren't enough free electrons in any conductor to supply an appreciable current. This means that the source is from other than free electrons. Since the secondary of a transformer or any insulated wire continues to furnish electrons, the conclusion is that the hard electrons somehow manage to get through the insulation from the outside.

Since a current has inertia, any change in the primary current of a transformer produces a force in the opposite direction in the secondary by the law of action and reaction. This reactive force is manifested by a disturbance of the ethers which produce the EMF. The voltage or EMF is the result of an increase of ether bombardment which has been shown to be the source of electrostatic forces. The EMF induced in the secondary creates a temporary electric void in the wire. This draws negative charges of all kinds to the wire. The softer electrons quickly penetrate the insulation and stop at the surface of the wire since they do not travel as readily through a hard electron conductor. These softer electrons absorb most of the electrostatic forces in the insulation which impede the flow of hard electrons. This opens the door for the hard electrons to pass through the insulation and enter the wire.

Electrical charges, comprised of photons in nearly all the frequency ranges, permeate all space, since they are continually being radiated by stars throughout the universe. They are not so easily detected since they are in the form of conglomerates in which the harder particles reside inside the softer ones. The resulting combinations are highly penetrating and it takes something like an EMF induced in a conductor to separate the harder particles from the softer ones. The performance of a transformer can be greatly impaired by completely shielding the secondary with a good conductor of electricity such as copper or pure aluminum.

An associate of the author has performed this experiment, which verifies the principles just outlined. The shield tends to impede the flow of soft particles to the secondary.

The terms EMF (electromagnetic force) and voltage need further clarification. The true nature of the phenomena associated with these terms has never been fully understood. All that has been known is that if a conductor is exposed to an EMF a flow of electricity is produced. Also voltage is associated with the amount of energy or work a current is capable of producing. An EMF of a given value can induce a current with a definite voltage. The voltage produced is directly proportional to the EMF impressed on the conductor. Also the energy of the current is directly proportional to its voltage. The amperage of a current is a measure of the number of electrons passing through each segment of a conductor per unit time. Since wattage, or the total kinetic energy of this current flow, is equal to the amperage multiplied by the voltage, it follows that the amperage is also directly proportional to the energy of the current flow. Therefore, voltage is a measure of the average kinetic energy of the electrons flowing along the wire. This in turn is directly proportional to the square of the average velocity of the electrons. This simple definition of voltage is sadly lacking in all standard textbooks.

An EMF induces an accelerating force on an electron. What is the nature of this force? Basically there are two methods of producing an EMF. One is by subjecting the conductor to a fluctuating magnetic field or by having the conductor cut through magnetic lines of force. The result is the same. The other is by exposing the conductor to a difference of potential such as connecting it to the opposite poles of a battery. In this case one pole has a negative charge while the opposite pole is positive. The flow of electrons is the result of an electron concentration at one point tending to flow to an area where there is a shortage. The EMF is produced by direct electrostatic force, which in turn is of a dual nature. There is the tendency for negative charges to be attracted to positive charges as well as the mutual repulsion of negative charges. The voltage attained is directly proportional to the difference of potential existing between the poles of that battery.

The EMF produced by a fluctuating magnetic field gives the same results but the process is different. When a conductor is subjected to a fluctuating magnetic field, as with the secondary of a transformer, the "free" electrons of the conductor and the outer electrons of the atoms which are not as intimately associated with the atoms are exposed to differential ether bombardments. It is equivalent to an electrostatic force.

When a magnetic field changes, the change does not take place simultaneously throughout that volume of space occupied by the field. It progresses from one portion to another. This creates differential electrostatic ether particle bombardments on electrons within the field. When a conductor cuts magnetic lines as with an AC generator, the electrons are subjected to the same conditions experienced by electrons moving between the poles of a magnet described in Chapter 11. The accelerating force will be in a direction perpendicular to the direction in which the electrons in the conductor are found to move.

If there were even a small fraction of the free electrons existing in the matter as is believed by our physicists, the negative charge effects of matter would be so great that these bodies would be unable to get close to each other. Much of the charge on condensers comes from outside the condenser, as is the case with the flow of electricity in conductors. Actually, free electrons in a conductor are practically nonexistent. Hard electrons which are not a part of the atoms are captured by soft particles which permeate matter. The soft particles release hard electrons when subjected to the EMF in a current, or the voltage across the plates of a condenser.

The current in a straight wire is evenly distributed along the surface where the electron flow encounters the least resistance. The released hard electrons that are directly affected by the EMF tend to move as a unit partially held together by mutual magnetic attraction. This unit leaves a temporary void behind it which is quickly filled by surrounding hard electrons. Many such groups are started simultaneously in a conductor by an applied EMF.

The source of electricity flowing in power lines as well as that produced by generators comes from soft particles which permeate and surround the area has been proven during auroral displays. When aurora activity is unusually high, large transformers in Canada have been known to burn out and even explode. At the same time, increase of current flow in power lines has been great enough to trip circuit breakers as far south as Texas. As explained earlier, the concentration of soft electrons in the atmosphere is greatly increased during auroral phenomena. Some areas, of course, receive much higher concentrations than others at the same latitude.

A loop of wire, or coil, offers impedance to an alternating current. This property of loops or coils is known as inductance. Since a single loop of wire has inductance, it follows that it can be explained in terms of one loop.

Electrons tend to travel along the surface of a conductor. This is the path of least resistance. The major source of this electricity is the high concentration of soft electrons that gather around a conductor and permeate the material. This is due to the relatively high positive charge of the conductor. The greatest concentration is found at the surface and a short distance below the surface. When an EMF is applied to the conductor, free electrons are set into motion. During this process, soft electrons concentrated at and below the surface tend to disintegrate and release more hard electrons. This is enhanced by the concentration of soft electrons, which in turn causes an agitation of the soft particles which causes them to become highly unstable.

In a straight wire, most of this disintegration and nearly all the electron flow take place below the surface. This condition greatly shortens the mean free path of the electrons and the flow stops immediately after the applied EMF is shut off. Consequently, an alternating current will encounter the same ohmic resistance in a straight wire as will a direct current. However, the situation is different when the conductor is looped.

When an EMF is applied to a loop, the free or released hard electrons below the surface are forced to the outside by centrifugal force, whence a still greater disintegration of soft electrons occurs because the greatest concentration is at the surface. The mean free path of the electrons is greatly increased and the flow continues for a brief period after the EMF traveling in the direction of the flow ceases. When the EMF continues in the opposite direction, as in the case of an alternating current, the force must oppose the momentum of the electron flow in the direction opposite to that of the applied EMF. The explanation of the impedance or inductance that a coil offers to an alternating current is now apparent. It follows that this impedance will be directly proportional to the number of turns and to the frequency of the AC. It is logical to assume that the deceleration rate of the electron flow is a constant when the EMF is zero. This means that the more quickly the EMF is applied in the opposite direction of flow, the higher the velocity of flow that will be encountered. It will be a linear function.

It would now seem evident that when the AC is rectified or has been changed to a pulsed DC, the coil will produce an increase in amperage where a straight wire will not. Experiments have proven this to be the case. It was found that the input amperage of a current was greatly increased after it passed through a coil. The increase was greatest during the initial stage of the applied EMF and soon dropped to a lower value as the concentration of soft electrons around the wire was reduced. It follows that a coil will offer impedance only to an AC current!

A steady direct current experiences the same resistance in a coil as it does in a straight wire of the same length. The fluctuating EMF produces extreme agitation of the soft electrons around and inside the wire resulting in the disintegration of a high percentage of them, and the release of a high concentration of hard electrons. This does not occur during the flow of DC. There is more of a flow outside the wire where less resistance is encountered. This is offset by the fact that it requires more force to divert the electrons from their tendency to flow in straight lines. During the initial application of the DC, there is a surge of additional current during the buildup of the EMF for those reasons already given. When the current is shut off, there will be a momentary surge of current in the opposite direction. The excess of electrons, on the surface of the conductor and in the coil, will naturally flow toward the void outside the coil and in the opposite direction to which the current was flowing. The concepts just outlined can be applied when building a self-sustaining electric generator, which will be presented in Chapter 21.

When an alternating current is applied to a coil, the EMF must overcome the impedance each time the EMF changes direction. The greatest amount of resistance occurs at the beginning of each change, and steadily decreases as the current builds up. The resistance will be at a minimum when the current reaches its maximum. This is because the EMF changes direction more frequently and encounters the maximum resistance for a higher percentage of the time.

The magnetic characteristics of a solenoid will now be explained. The flow of electrons in a wire results in a circular magnetic flow around that wire. As mentioned previously, the magnetic effects between electrons moving together tend to cancel each other out. They are drawn together and the resultant ethers, or magnetic flow, encompass the entire group. This also occurs between adjacent wire segments in a coil. The magnetic effects are cancelled out between the segments and a continuous ether flow, encompassing the entire coil, perpendicular to the direction of the current flow, will result. The solenoid then will behave like a bar magnet with continuous lines of force moving into one end and out of the other.

The earth's atmosphere produces geomagnetism in much the same manner that a solenoid produces a magnetic field. Charges in the atmosphere move along with the earth in a circular motion. Although there is little motion of the charges relative to the surface, a magnetic field is still created. Magnetic lines, or ethers, flow from the south magnetic region to the north magnetic region as the result of these rotating charges.

I am in earnest—I will not equivocate—I will not excuse—I will not retreat a single inch—AND I WILL BE HEARD.

—Wm. Lloyd Garrison

CHAPTER 17

PECULIAR AND UNEXPLAINED ANOMALIES OF NATURE

THE PROPERTIES OF HELIUM AT LOW TEMPERATURES

Helium at low temperatures exhibits strange properties which have never been explained by science. The assertions of quantum mechanics experts are contrary and highly misleading. They have never explained anything satisfactorily, despite all of their vaunted claims. Such efforts are no better than the practice of tacking a name on some phenomenon and thereby claiming that it has been explained.

Liquid helium below 2.2 degrees Kelvin is known as helium II. It demonstrates the characteristic of superfluidity at such temperatures. It readily passes through extremely narrow slits and capillaries with no evidence of retardation in the process. The well-known "creeping film" effect is displayed when it is in this condition. The liquid tends to climb up the walls of a container and if that container is not partially submerged in a liquid helium bath, it is soon emptied.

Helium I also shows dualistic properties. It will deflect vanes submerged in a moving liquid while demonstrating superfluidity, or a lack of viscosity, at the same time. Yet, the deflection of the vanes indicates that there is viscosity. These and other paradoxes of helium actually demonstrate the validity of some of the principles already introduced in this treatise.

The interactions of protons and neutrons in the nucleus of helium result in greater activity of the protons, with the consequent transformation of a greater portion of their electrostatic potential into magnetic fields. The number of protons and neutrons in the helium atom is the optimum number for the greatest amount of proton activity. As a result, the net positive charge of helium extends farther beyond the electron zone of activity than normal and is consequently weaker. Therefore, helium has little tendency to combine with other atoms. The zonal effects practically disappear when helium is reduced to temperatures below 2.2° K, because none of the soft electrons produced by interactions of the fundamental particles are disintegrated by thermal agitation of the molecules. This results in higher negative charge effects throughout the mass. Helium atoms have no affinity for each other in this state, and helium at 0° K will remain a liquid unless it is subjected to high pressures.

The near absence of zonal effects means that the negative field around the atoms extends for greater distances. This readily accounts for the creeping film effect. Since the walls of the container holding helium II behave like a positive charge, the helium atoms acting like negative charges under these conditions will distribute themselves over the walls in a manner similar to that of a conductor. If the container is out of the bath, the mutual repulsion of the atoms will cause nearly all of them to be ejected from the container, since the repulsions are stronger than their affinity for the sides of the container. There is, however, a weak positive field which exists a considerable distance beyond the confines of the atoms of helium II. This and the almost complete absence of kinetic energy of the individual atoms enables helium to remain a liquid. The overall positive charge also enables helium II to be affected by gravity.

Some of the molecules of helium II have appreciable velocities at any temperature above absolute zero or 0° K. Such atoms have magnetic fields around them. This completely resolves the mystery surrounding the dual properties of helium II. The helium molecules of low velocity display the superfluidic effects, while at the same time the molecules with the higher velocities have stronger magnetic fields around them. These higher velocity molecules interact with the outer molecules of the vanes immersed in the liquid causing them to be deflected. It is to be expected that the portion of helium II which passes through narrow slits and capillaries is at a lower temperature than the rest of the liquid. This has been confirmed. Here is an actual demonstration of Maxwell's demon separating the low velocity molecules from those of a higher velocity!

Helium II exhibits a property which even the quantum mechanics experts surprisingly admit they have no means of explaining. The superfluidity of helium II is lost if it is allowed to flow too rapidly. When helium has a rapid flow, significant magnetic fields develop around all the atoms which are extremely feeble, but are strong enough to produce interactions with each other and with the magnetic fields generated by the kinetic energy of molecules of other substances. This consequently destroys superfluidity. It should be kept in mind that the magnetic fields, due to the thermal agitation or motion of the helium atoms, are similar to the magnetic fields produced by the motion of the atoms of other substances. This fact makes the interactions possible. Superfluidity is a very delicately balanced condition which is easily upset.

An isotope of helium, called helium 3, having fewer fundamental particles, produces fewer soft electrons than normal helium. In addition, the presence of fewer particles in the nucleus causes the protons to be less active. As a result, helium 3 has more pronounced zonal effects around the atoms, and, due to this fact, it was not expected that helium 3 would exhibit superfluidity at any temperature. This has since been proven to be the case. There is an optimum number of particles in the nucleus of the helium atom which produces the greatest proton activity. If that number is high, the protons are restricted and mutual repulsion cancels out. If the number is low, the interactions are greatly reduced.

"MYSTERY SPOTS" INCLUDING THE FAMOUS OREGON VORTEX

There are a number of well-known areas called "mystery spots" or "magnetic anomalies", where unusual phenomena occur and nature's laws are said to have gone awry. The best known of these is called the Oregon Vortex, located near Gold Hill in southern Oregon. It is situated near the fault line which runs along the West Coast, and still another vortex in southern Oregon and one in southern California. The following analysis will be restricted to the Gold Hill, Oregon Vortex. Most of the peculiarities of this particular vortex are confined within an area 165 feet in diameter. Within this area, sudden changes in a person's height seem to occur. It is also significant that gravity effects fluctuate within that area. Gravity may be as much as ten percent below normal in some cases. This means that a 200 pound man would weigh only 180 pounds.

These phenomena do not occur uniformly within the vortex area, but follow lines or tubes which run north to south and east to west. These lines or tubes are called terralines and are about five feet wide. They also seem to exist outside the vortex area, in a regular grid pattern covering many thousands of square miles. However, the effects of these terralines above the surface are more pronounced and warped within the vortex. Smoke blown in the path of a terraline tends to move spirally along the terraline. A pendulum consisting of a heavy iron ball suspended by a chain swings abnormally when the direction is along the terraline. The swing is much longer in one direction past the point of rest than it is in the opposite direction. A broom inside the vortex stands upright with little persuasion. Everything in this area, including the broom, tends to lean toward magnetic north.

According to John Litster, in a pamphlet entitled *The Oregon Vortex*, the vortex area expands and contracts periodically.(77) He also indicates that although the terralines outside the vortex do not oscillate, the portions which intersect the vortex do. The following passage is taken from this booklet on page 3: "The lines within the area move, or oscillate, with a period of 22.329 seconds." Litster failed to divulge his method of determining this period to such a degree of refinement. Atomic clocks weren't readily available at the time he wrote the booklet.

A valid explanation for the vortex will now be presented. The vortex and terralines consist of beams of soft electrons traveling at very high velocities. Figure 14 illustrates the phenomenon. The types of particles cover a wide ranges with a significant percentage comprised of high frequency photons in the upper ultraviolet range. The conclusion that they have a high velocity and a wide range of frequencies is the only way to account for the phenomena observed.

The apparent sudden increase in size when a person walks from one region to another is due to refraction effects of light. Photographs verify this effect. This is the only explanation offered by scientists for any of the phenomena observed which shows any degree of rationality. Of course they are somewhat vague as to what produces the refraction effects. It is the ultrahigh concentration of soft particles and the associated variations in their intensity resulting from the terralines and the main vortex shell which cause the light rays to bend. When light encounters a terraline, it is refracted and lens effects are produced. The beams of soft particles contain a high percentage of particles which are comprised of photons whose frequency range is not far removed from the photons of visible light. The distribution of particles in these beams is such that the bending of light rays is not sufficiently abrupt to indicate the outlines of the terralines or the changes in intensity.

When an object enters the vortex, it immediately becomes impregnated with these soft particles. This reduces the weight to some extent, because of the reduction in the overall positive charge. Another factor contributing to the weight reduction is the bombardment of high speed particles, flowing upward in opposition to the earth's gravity. Two of the well established phenomena have now been accounted for. Several more aspects remain. Objects in some parts of the vortex tend to roll uphill. This is due to a terraline running parallel to the ground. The bombardment of the particles produces a force on the object in the direction of flow. This is also responsible for the behavior of pendulums or plumb bobs in some parts of the vortex. The direction of swing is along a terraline. The swing in one direction is moving with the flow, while in the opposite direction the bob or pendulum moves against the flow.

The force of bombardment of these high speed particles is demonstrated when smoke is blown into the vortex or terraline, or when small pieces of paper are released. They tend to move around in spirals, traveling down terralines and moving upward in the vortex, as though they had encountered a whirlwind. This phenomena is responsbile for the term "vortex" being applied to the area. A flow of the charges assumes a vortex pattern This is due to the configuration of magnetic fields resulting from the motion of these charges. The magnetic field, as previously mentioned, assumes a corkscrew motion. This corkscrew pattern of magnetic fields is the pattern for the general motion of these particles as a group since these particles have a tendency to move down magnetic lines of force. It will be noted that this vortex motion will follow the left hand rule since the particles are predominately negative.

The author does not know whether magnetometer measurements have been made in the area. It is probable that they would show a substantial increase in the earth's field since standing objects tend to lean toward magnetic north, indicating a strong, concentrated field. This is in accordance with the principles of terrestrial magnetism. The tendency to lean toward magnetic north is a result of the increase in the earth's field and, more importantly, that objects placed in the vortex are saturated with the particles. This renders the body more susceptible to the earth's field since the particles occupying the body tend to travel down magnetic lines of force toward the north. There is no tendency to fall over because of the tremendous bombardment of particles moving up from the ground, which accounts in part for the gravity reduction. It also explains why a broom in the area can be made to stand upright without support.

The behavior of these terralines, at the point where they interest the vortex, and the tendency for the network to assume a hemispherical shape, is also to be expected. The influence and bombardment of the great flow emanating from the ground forces the terralines upward and distorts them at the same time. The lines are moving in a horizontal direction while the vortex moves in a direction perpendicular to them. The concentration of the charges in the vortex should increase from the outer edge toward the center. This pattern would produce a displacement of the terraline network in a hemispherical configuration.

It is probably apparent to the reader at this point that phenomena observed in the vortex confirm principles and concepts already discussed. All that needs to be done now is to account for the origin of the energies in the vortex. A powerful clue is already at our disposal. The intensity of the energies in the vortex greatly lessened immediately following the great Alaska earthquake of 1962. A broom could no longer be made to stand upright. Whether or not the terralines were affected is not clear. It was not until some time later that the vortex resumed its old behavior. This seems to eliminate the possibility that some manmade device, placed underground in the distant past, is the cause.

The apparent conclusion, is that the vortex energies are somehow connected with the bombardment of energies from the sun. There are great fault lines in the region of Alaska and the Aleutian Islands which have also been a region of great volcanic activity. The solution is not difficult considering the discussion of the origin of earthquakes and related phenomena. It is possible that the alternate charging and discharging of energies in underground faults creates the oscillatory pattern. The presence of giant underground caverns may also contribute to the periodic discharge of soft particles through certain relief points on the surface. The discharged particles are readily conducted away by underground channels which come close to the surface in the vortex area. Apparently, the entire earth pulsates in response to the cyclical pattern of the sun, much like the nature of the fundamental particles. The hermetic axiom necessarily connects the phenomena.

Many scientists have visited and studied the area over a long period of time. A variety of theories has been advanced by them to explain the phenomena. As the reader should expect by now, such theories have varying degrees of merit ranging all the way from the idiotic on up to the moronic.

The most recent attempt to explain away the phenomena in the Oregon Vortex was described in an article entitled, "Magic Man," by Scott Morris which appeared in the May 1981 issue of Omni Magazine. The protagonist of this article was the famed magician Jerry Andrus. As a master of illusion, Andrus has no peers among his fellow magicians. He is able to create illusions that baffle all of his colleagues. Recently Andrus and Morris visited and studied the phenomena in the Oregon Vortex. The final conclusion of this illustrious gentleman was that the phenomena in the vortex was an illusion and nothing else.

To support this conclusion, the author apparently falsified some of the findings. Consider the case when the height of an individual suddenly changes when he moves from one area to another. There is a line of demarcation where the change is instantaneous as soon as the line is crossed. A plank is centered at one of these lines. Wheh a camera is placed such that it is centered between the two ends and at right angles to the base line it

Figure 17
THE OREGON VORTEX

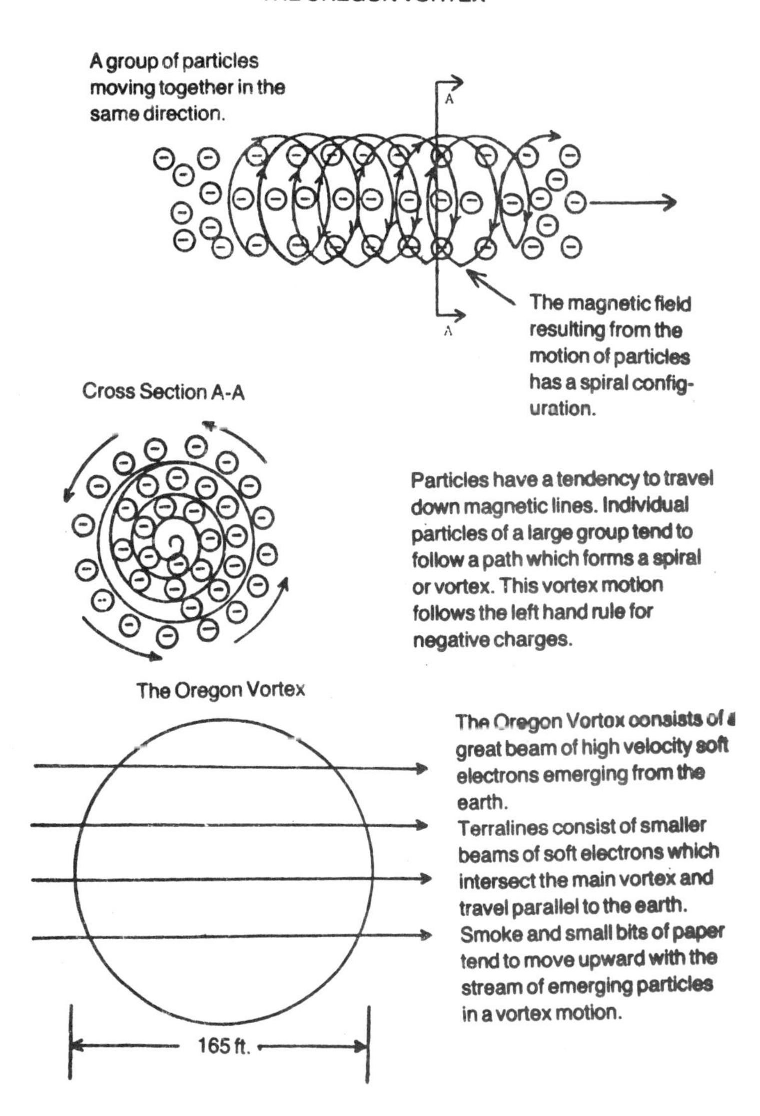

will definitely record a change in height of at least four inches when a person moves from one end of the plank to the other. The pamphlet, "The Oregon Vortex" by John Lester, shows a series of photos which prove that this phenomenon is real. One can measure the change from these photos. Perhaps the most interesting of these photos is that of three levels placed at the line of demarcation. Two are in a vertical position a certain distance apart at their bases and the other is in a horizontal position. According to the bubbles, they are all level, yet the ends of the vertical levels appear to be (and measurments confirm this) farther apart at the top than at the bottom, and according to the photos, they are also wider at the top. They appear to be badly warped.

It is highly significant here that the apparent change in size is not readily apparent when viewed from all directions and under the same conditions in any of these areas. This shows that the phenomenon is produced by light being refracted as it passes from an area of high soft electron concentration to one of a lower concentration or vice versa. This produces what is known as a lens effect.

According to Scott Morris, his camera did not show a change when it was placed in the manner described above. He did mention the heavy weight suspended from a chain. From its normal position at rest, as described earlier, it definitely swung further in one direction than it did in the opposite direction. It does require less force to move it in the direction of greater swing than in the opposite direction. This author personally confirmed this. Yet Mr. Morris denied it. He stated that the force required was the same in each case. Andrus and Morris ignored other significant facts such as the broom standing without support, which at the same time leans away from the vertical. This was determined by a plumb bob, the change of weight in various parts of the vortex, the strange curving of Madrona trees where they come in contact with the terralines, and other phenomena.

This illustrates once again the devious tactics to which many individuals will resort in order to support their pet dogma, and that they will conveniently ignore certain facts that are a major threat to that dogma and often difficult to explain away. No doubt Andrus is a very clever man along certain lines of endeavor, but his cleverness seemed to desert him when he was confronted with facts outside his domain. How often has this pattern been repeated among the members of the scientific community? It seems that lack of intellectual integrity is not confined to this group. It is left up to the reader to decide to which portion of the scale mentioned above the Morris-Andrus theory of the Oregon

Vortex belongs.

GRAVITATIONAL ANOMALIES

There are a number of little publicized gravitational anomalies which seem to refute the Newtonian and Einsteinian dogmas. One of the most baffling of these is that the force of gravity over oceans and large bodies of water is greater than over land masses. In addition, the deeper the water, the greater the force. This is the opposite of what should be expected. The new concept of gravity easily resolves this paradox. Water contains high concentrations of soft electrons of all kinds, some of which correspond to the lower infrared range, and are not far removed from the gravity range. These soft electrons are more readily affected by gravity radiations and many of them tend to be repelled and move upward in the same direction as the gravity radiations. Some of the photons associated with the gravity radiations attach themselves to the trailing portion of these very soft electrons. This promotes a slight nullifying effect on the negative charge effects on that trailing portion of these particles. This enables some of the soft electrons in the lower infrared region to produce weak gravity effects in addition to the normal gravity. The result is higher than normal gravity over oceans than over land masses.

The behavior of matter ejected by explosions on the sun's surface defies all of the popular laws of gravity. This matter occasionally rises to altitudes of several hundred thousand miles. It does not follow a trajectory in descending as it is supposed to. Also, its speed of decent does not follow the law of falling bodies at any time. In fact, the velocity of fall is much lower than should be expected. One of the reasons is the low surface gravity of the sun. Another reason is the variable quantity of negative charges which impregnate these masses.

THE ORIGIN OF THE VAN ALLEN RADIATION BELT

The Van Allen radiation belt consists of high concentrations of charged particles and is centered around the earth's equator. It has a crescent shaped cross section. The upper fringes extend to about 60° north and south latitude. The lower limits of the inner portion are several hundred miles above the earth's surface. The outer portion extends to about 28,000 miles above the earth. The highest concentration of charges is in the inner portion at an average distance of several thousand miles above the earth. It is confined to the lower latitudes. *Figure 18* depicts the Van Allen belt.

As usual, the conventional explanation is totally misleading. The claim is that the Van Allen belt consists of electrons and protons, which are captured by the earth's magnetic field. This shows the usual bad logic. Particles captured by a magnet have their greatest concentration around the poles. The opposite is the case here. Also, if they were captured by the earth's field, why are they so far above the earth? If geomagnetism were produced according to conventional theory, its highest intensity would be close to the earth's surface. Therefore, the Van Allen radiation belt, instead of being a great distance above the earth, would concentrate near the surface, if its presence were due to particles captured by the earth's magnetic field.

Since the Van Allen radiation belt does not consist of charges captured by the earth's magnetic field, why do they assume the configuration of the belt? Nearly all of the particles in the belt are particles which have been ejected by the sun. These particles consist mainly of soft electrons of various kinds. Their penetrating ability, as is indicated by their effects upon satellites, have given the false impression that they are high energy particles. Soft particles which penetrate solid matter release hard electrons and protons in the process. It was assumed that these hard particles could only have penetrated matter if they had extremely high initial kinetic energy. The earth's magnetic field must be already saturated with particles since its field is of limited intensity and can capture no more. Additional particles coming in tend to be repelled by the field back toward outer space. The highest concentration of particles in the earth's field is in the higher latitudes. Therefore, the greatest repulsive forces must exist in that region. That is why the belt is concentrated closer to the equator.

Cosmic dust, which permeates all of the space occupied by the physical universe, plays an important role in the formation of the Van Allen belt. Were it not for the presence of these dust particles, the earth's gravitational field would prevent a belt from forming around the earth. Particles ejected by the sun tend to lose much of their initial velocity due to collisions as they approach the earth. The lower velocity, negatively charged particles tend to collect around dust particles, which have a net positive charge. This produced a neutralizing effect by which the combination is neither attracted nor repelled by the earth's gravitational field. Charges with a much higher velocity reach the earth and penetrate it. This neutral combination is not stable and particles are continually being dislodged from dust particles by collisions with other particles. The

Figure 18
THE VAN ALLEN RADIATION BELT

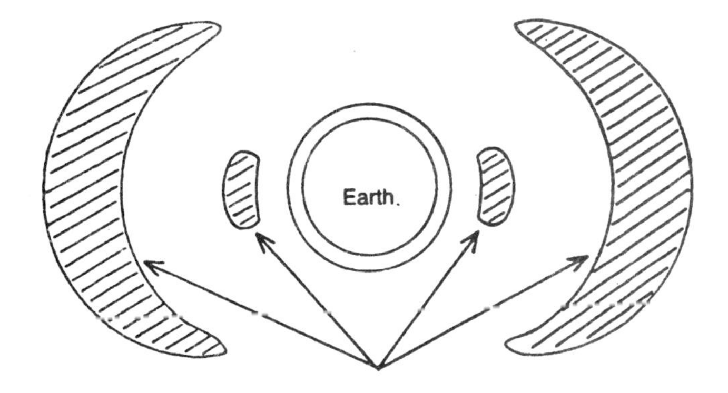

Zones of highest concentration of
electrons and protons

The positions and distances of the Van Allen belt from the earth demonstrate that the particles are not captured by the earth's magnetic field.

lower portion of the radiation belt encounters the zone of particles captured by the earth's field. This is one reason that it does not get closer to the earth. The presence of the cosmic dust enables a very high concentration of these particles to be near the center of the belt.

Many of the soft particles permeating the cosmic dust tend to demate rialize it. This accounts for the dust which always collects on completel enclosed surfaces in a supposedly dust-free atmosphere. When the dema terialized dust encounters a surface, some of the dematerializing energies tend to be drawn out or disintegrate, leaving materialized dust on the surface.

CHAPTER 18

NEW INSIGHTS INTO THE RESEARCH OF WILHELM REICH

Wilhem Reich is one of the few men in this century who is completely worthy of the appelation "scientist". His contributions to various fields of science are staggering. He has been pilloried by the world of science for his efforts. His persecution by members of the AMA, its henchmen in the U.S. Government, as well as some others eventually brought about his demise in a federal prison in 1957. Although his books were burned by government agents, fortunately most of his work escaped their attention, and some of it is now being reprinted. This chapter is mainly concerned with Reich's research on what he termed "orgone energy" and related phenomena. As will be shown, his discoveries in this field are a marvelous confirmation of principles upon which we have already elaborated. In fact, the author has learned about some of the more important details of Reich's experiments after much work had already been completed on this book.

ORGONE ENERGY, BIONS, AND SOFT ELECTRONS

Reich first became aware of a mysterious radiation he later called "orgone energy" while experimenting with bions. Reich's definition of a bion, taken from his book entitled *The Cancer Biopathy* on page 15, is as follows:

> Bions and energy vesicle designate one and the same microscopically visible, functioning formation. The term "bion" refers to vesicles into which all matter disintegrates if made to swell. These vesicles represent transitional forms between nonliving and living matter. The bion is the elemental functioning unit of all living matter.(99)

He even produced bions by heating substances to incandescence such as coal, earth crystals, and ocean sand, and then subjecting them to chemicals which induced swelling in completely sterile containers. Living matter such as bacteria emerged from these sterile preparations! This, of course, violates all orthodox biological concepts, and was one of the discoveries which led to Reich's persecution.

Reich experienced a tendency for his eyes to smart while examining bions under a microscope. The longer the period of observation, the more his eyes hurt. In *The Cancer Biopathy*, on page 86, one of his experimental subjects exposed to the same radiation stated, "I feel as if I had been staring in the sun for a long time."(99) This energy also fogged photographic plates through shielding. In a dark room, the bion cultures emanated blue and violet light. The room also became saturated with these energies, and it seemed to come from the walls and objects around the room. This energy even produced a reddening of the skin like a sunburn. A deep tan eventually developed over the entire body under constant exposure, although there was no exposure to the sun.

Reich later performed experiments with electroscopes in the presence of high concentrations of this energy. he put on a pair of rubber gloves which had been exposed to the sun. When he moved his hands toward the electroscope, there was a strong deflection of the leaves. The rubber gloves had not been charged in a conventional sense. When the gloves were placed in the shade for a time in the open air, they no longer influenced the electroscope. It is extremely significant that after the gloves had been exposed to the sun, they influenced the electroscope again! Other objects such as paper, cotton, wool, etc., exposed to the bion cultures, also influenced the electroscope. This was also the case when an organic substance was placed in contact with living tissue, such as the human body. The more active or healthy the individual, the greater the reaction on the electroscope. It is also significant that when the electroscope was exposed directly to the radiation from the bions there was no reaction.

Reich later found this energy was everywhere, but in varying concentrations. It would readily penetrate everything, including lead shielding, but was more easily absorbed by organic and nonmetallic substances than by metal. He built orgone accumulators consisting of boxes with alternating organic and metallic material for its siding. He also found the immediate source of this energy was the atmosphere, which in turn received it from the sun. The concentration of energies in these boxes, or accumulators, depended on the time of day and weather conditions. The concentration was at its lowest during the night. It was somewhat lower on cloudy days than on clear days.

The nature of the energies with which Reich was dealing is probably growing apparent to the reader from what has already been revealed. The greatest portion of the transformed energies from the sun, reaching the lower levels of the atmosphere, is still in the lower ranges of the ultraviolet and the blue and violet part of the visible range. Much of the radiation is in the form of soft electrons, comprised of photons, in these frequency ranges. This is the orgone energy Reich discovered. The blue and violet light Reich observed in the dark room was the result of the more unstable of these particles breaking up into their constituent light. This is also the reason for the blue sky. The disintegration of soft particles in the atmosphere produces scattered photons moving in all directions. The concentration is much lower at night, and there is a lessened tendency for disintegration by collision with air molecules, since none are being radiated from an external source. As a result, the sky becomes black. During the day, a lower percentage of the radiation from the sun has been transformed into the lower frequencies in the upper atmosphere, according to the law of redistribution. Consequently, the photons of violet light outnumber the blue photons. This explains why the sky takes on a violet shade in the higher elevations.

It is also interesting that the sky is a deeper blue at the zenith than near the horizon. The radiation from the sun is transformed into the lower frequencies at the lower elevations. Therefore, there is more visible light and a greater quantity of other light frequencies which tend to blend into white light, mitigating the blue. When one's line of sight is along the horizon, only the lower portions of the atmosphere are viewed where these transformations are taking place.

According to physicists, the blue results from the scattering of blue light by dust particles in the atmosphere. If this idea were valid, then all dust particles would have to be nearly uniform in size to be so partial to blue. This would be a most extraordinary coincidence, violating all of the rule of probability. At any rate, why doesn't the remaining light from which the blue was extracted create odd color effects, and why doesn't the spectrum produced by rainbows and prisms indicate a shortage of blues? Of course, there is the other difficulty in explaining the process by which light can collide with any particle and scatter only the blue light.

Reich's conclusion was that orgone energy is responsible for the blue sky, and he gave a logical argument to support this idea. He noticed on clear days distant mountain ranges and hills were blue. Yet right after a rainstorm or during extremely cloudy conditions, the blue disappeared. Most of the orgone energy in the atmosphere between the viewer and the hills had been washed away by the rain or absorbed by the clouds. As was pointed out earlier, soft electrons have a tremendous affinity for water. It is because of the orgone absorbed by water. The blue is the light released by the disintegration of a portion of the orgone.

Before continuing with Reich's researches, the present trend of thought concerning the color of the sky in relation to the density of the atmosphere at or near the point of observation should be discussed further. If the quantity or density of earth's atmosphere were to increase, it follows that the color of the sky would change from blues to colors associated with the lower frequencies. A point would soon be reached at which the sky would become yellow and the horizon would take on a saffron hue. Much of the blue of the lower atmosphere of the earth is a mixture of the yellow and green. As the atmosphere becomes denser, the yellow, being lower in frequency, starts to dominate. It is highly significant that Howard Menger in his book *From Outer Space* described such a sky on the moon. (It was suggested in Chapter 1 that large areas on the moon have a considerably denser atmosphere than is experienced anyplace on earth.) According to this book, Menger was taken to the moon and allowed to walk around on its surface. All aspects of Menger's book have a ring of truth. They are in harmony with what the author knows concerning the subject matter discussed in the book. For example, Menger encountered a highly advanced alien known as a space master who made the following statement concerning the nature of time: "There can be no time without motion nor motion without time and neither without thought". This is essentially the same definition already presented in this book, which the author formulated long before reading Menger's book.

There have been others prominent in the UFO controversy who claim to have been taken to the moon and who became aware of earthlike conditions on the moon. These include the late Buck Nelson and George Adamski and also Edward M. Palmer. Their claims have all been in agreement with each other. In fact, as early as 1950 Buck Nelson claimed the moon had earth gravity. The author apologizes for this digression.

Reich's experiments with the electroscope demonstrated the nature of soft electrons and the nature of light presented earlier. They also demonstrated the presence of high concentrations of hard electrons existing everywhere, camouflaged by softer electrons. It was shown earlier how soft electrons create electric currents in conductors and make other phenomena possible. Organic materials absorb large quantities of orgone energy and at the same time absorb significant quantities of hard electrons, which are carried into the material by the orgone. This creates electrostatic field effects around the material, and hence strongly affects the electroscope. Since sunlight produced a similar charge on organic substances, it is apparent that light consists of negative charges, mostly soft electrons, moving with the photons. It has yet to be explained why the direct radiations from bions did not affect the electroscope. It has been shown previously that the intensity of the electric field around a particle is directly proportional to the frequency of the light photons of which it is comprised. This means that the electrostatic field intensity around soft particles, or orgone energy, is only about 1/3000 of that around hard electrons. The direct radiation from the bions had little chance or time to absorb any hard electrons. Their effect on the electroscope, without the presence of the hard electrons, was consequently miniscule. When they absorb electrons, their field effects are much greater, although they are still much less than if the hard electrons alone were present.

The more cogent reader may have become aware of another paradox by this time. It has been stated with complete justification that it is the soft electrons accompanying light which are responsible for the chemical changes produced by it, and not the photons. Yet if a photographic film is covered, it will not be exposed even when subjected to direct sunlight, and the soft electrons accompanying the light readily penetrate the cover. This paradox reveals an important property of soft electrons in their promotion of chemical changes. However, it has not yet been satisfactorily resolved.

Chemical changes are expedited during the disintegration of soft electrons when they release great quantities of harder electrons. The normal field intensity around soft electrons alone is insufficient to promote chemical changes. When film is exposed to direct sunlight, it encounters a large quantity of very unstable soft electrons, which immediately disintegrate and release hard electrons. These hard electrons cause the film to be fogged. The more stable, soft electrons pass on through the material without interacting. The more unstable, soft electrons of light impinging on shielded film immediately disintegrate at the shield.

Reich demonstrated that bions could fog photographic film through thick shielding. In this instance, the soft electrons emitted by the bions were stable enough to penetrate the thickness of the shield without disintegrating, yet insufficiently stable to go through the remaining film thickness intact. The film was therefore fogged. The reader may see by now why it is the soft electrons and not the photons which are responsible for the chemical changes produced by light. The range and combination of hard electrons housed by light are dependent on the frequency and hence the type of soft electrons accompanying light.

The demonstration by Reich and others of the seeming spontaneous generation of life from "inert" matter is in agreement with the principles introduced in the chapter on the pyramid of life, which is to be presented in Part IV. All intelligences are potential creators in varying degrees, regardless of their position on the pyramid. This creativity manifests itself in projecting simple bodies into realms below that in which their creators exist. Reich's experiments in the creation of bions provided the ideal conditions for elemental intelligences, in a realm slightly above the physical, to start the projection of a body into the physical realm. Bions were the first step in this creation. It is expected that bions would generate high concentrations of these energies, since soft particles play a vital role in all of the life processes in this realm. This happened to be the frequency range Reich called orgone energy. These elementary intelligences are in turn created by a higher order of intelligence.

One of the characteristics of living tissues and organs is its ability to generate large quantities of orgone energy and other kinds of soft particles. This ability is considerably lessened in an impaired or unhealthy organ. Consequently, such organs have a higher positive charge than a normally functioning one. This is why orgone energy concentrates around these afflicted areas when an individual is exposed to this energy in an accumulator. This puzzled Reich, since he was unaware of the true nature of orgone energy. Soft particles in relatively high concentrations are radiated by living tissues, thereby creating the aura seen around plants, animals, and people by sensitives and psychics.

THE ORANUR EXPERIMENT

One of the most remarkable aspects of Reich's research was called the Oranur Experiment. He placed a small quantity of radium in an orgone accumulator with near disastrous results. A high concentration of what was called deadly orgone energy quickly permeated the area and spread to considerable distances beyond the accumulator. This energy produced all the symptoms of radiation sickness, and nearly killed Reich and his assistants. Reich's conclusion about the results of the Oranur Experiment is taken from his book entitled *Selected writings* on page 358:

Figure 19
REICH'S ORGONE ACCUMULATOR

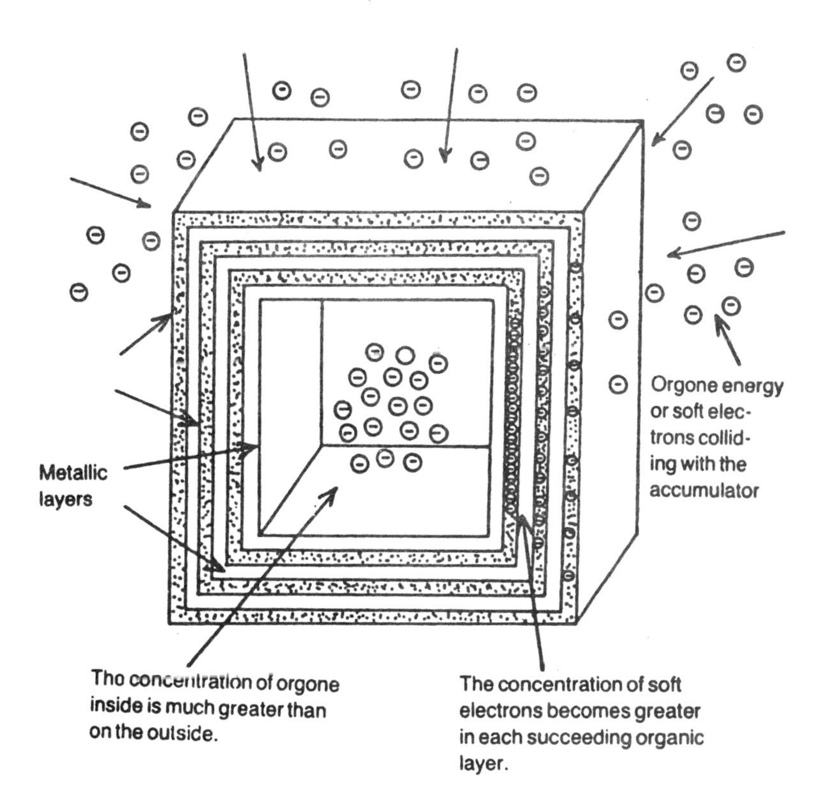

Accumulators consist of alternate layers of organic and metallic material. Many soft electrons are slowed up or completely stopped when they encounter the outside of an accumulator. As they bleed through the metallic layers, many are absorbed by the organic layers. The average velocity of soft electreons from outer space becomes progressively lower as they penetrate deeper into successive layers. This creates increasingly higher concentrations in deeper layers and a concentration inside the accumulator.

> It was found, beyond any reasonable doubt, that so-called radiation sickness is not, as heretofore assumed, a direct result of NR radiation upon living tissue; but an immediate expression of a severe reaction of organismic OR energy against the action of NR radiation.(100)

He also found that when radium was placed inside heavy lead shielding, and this in turn was placed in a heavy safe, functioning as an orgone accumulator, unexpected results occurred in the radiation count. Although a Geiger counter showed an abnormally high count in the vicinity of the safe, the radiation proved to be harmless. When the radium was removed from the shielding and safe and tested in the open, the counter gave a relatively low reading.

Once again all of the phenomena related to the Oranur Experiment are easily understood in light of concepts and principles already introduced. Radium supposedly emits alpha particles, which are helium nuclei supposedly made up of two protons and two neutrons. The deadly orgone energy consisted of abnormally high concentrations of soft electrons clustered around the positively charged alpha particles and also soft electrons that captured concentrations of protons. The harder electrons associated with gamma rays are also ejected and captured by the soft electrons. These particles are different from the hard electrons of normal electricity. They have no preferred direction of spin, and are relatively unstable and destructive. This combination results in considerable excitation and a high rate of orgone disintegration with the sudden release of these particles within the living tissues.

Alpha particles are attracted to high concentrations of orgone energy. In turn, lower concentrations move in to fill the void left when the higher concentrations cluster around the alpha particles. This explains what Reich thought was a violation of the standard law of basic physics, stating that a high potential will always move toward a lower one, instead of vice versa. The lower concentrations of orgone, in the case of the Oranur Experiment, always had a greater affinity for the higher concentrations of orgone energy.

When radium was placed in lead shielding and then put in the safe, the alpha particles were largely confined to the region inside the safe. However, the orgone energy was not restricted and reacted with the concentration of alpha particles inside the safe. This affinity of negative charges for the positive caused a large accumulation of orgone in the vicinity. The orgone, which permeated the walls of the safe and the shielding,

Figure 20
THE CLOUD-BUSTER

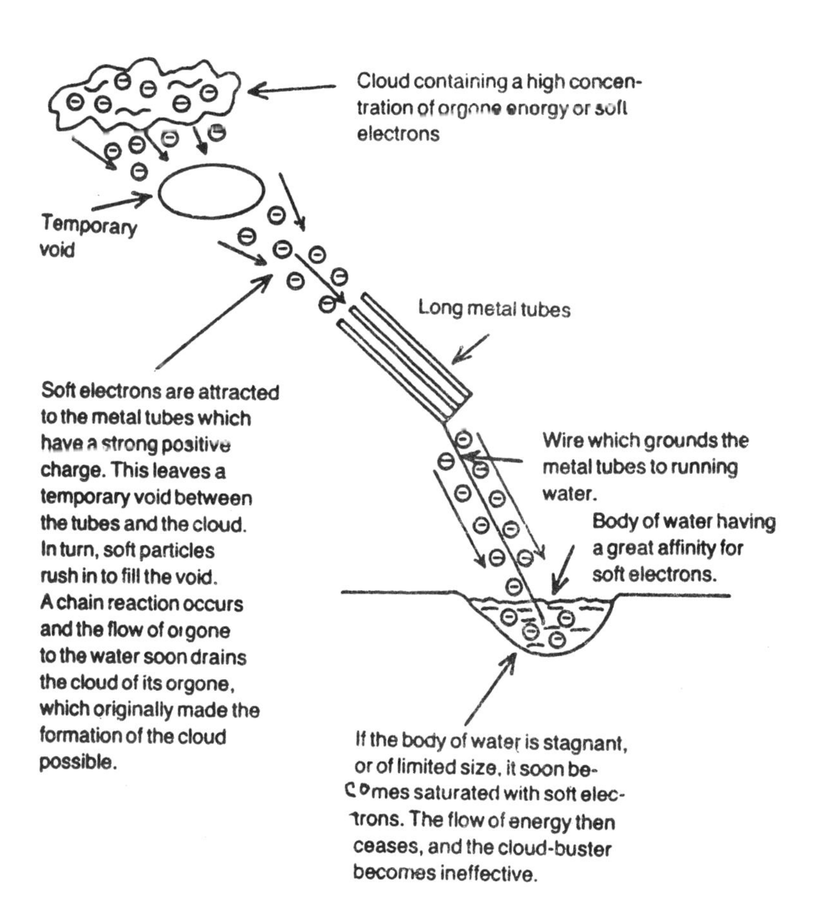

opened the door for some alpha particles to escape. In turn, some deadly orgone energy was produced outside the safe, but not in lethal concentrations. The abnormally high count outside the safe was the result of the breakup of quantities of orgone energy releasing great numbers of harder electrons, which reacted with the counter. The interactions of the orgone energy with the very high concentration of positive charges inside the safe caused an inordinate degree of disintegration of soft electrons. The undisturbed orgone allowed the hard electrons released to escape to the outside. It is now apparent that the unshielded radium did not produce a high count, because alpha particle concentration was not allowed to build up.

The radium used in the Oranur Experiment was then placed in lead shielding and buried in a place miles from the site of the experiment. It was exhumed after five years and tested. Surprisingly, it was found that the radium had lost much more than was expected. This was in direct violation of the established "laws" of nuclear physics. The continuous presence of high concentrations of orgone energy had transformed the radium atoms in a manner which will be described in the chapter on the transmutation of elements.

Another phenomenon associated with orgone, which Reich believed was a violation of the second law of thermodynamics, is that the temperature above an orgone accumulator is always higher than its surroundings. A deeper analysis shows the law is not violated. Gravity tends to repel negative charges. Since orgone energy consists of soft electrons, a higher concentration appears at the top of the accumulator. The earth's gravity then forces some of the soft electrons to escape outside the accumulator, resulting in a high concentration in this area. The increased concentration at the top, coupled with the bombardment from particles coming in, results in interactions and disintegrations. A general rise in temperature in this region is inevitable. Figure *19* shows how the orgone accumulator functions.

It has also been found the bottom of an accumulator becomes warm when suspended over running water. As mentioned before, soft electrons have a tremendous affinity for water. The orgone energy near the surface of the water is quickly absorbed. This creates a void automatically filled by orgone directly above. A chain reaction results with a rapid flow from the bottom of the accumulator to the water. The bottom vicinity of the accumulator is a focal point for this flow, and heats up in a manner similar to that of a short in an electric circuit. If the water were not flowing, it would soon become saturated; and the action would stop before much heating could occur. The flowing water provides a continuous outlet for the flow of orgone energy.

THE CLOUD-BUSTER

The orgone principle just described is also the basis for an invention of Reich's for controlling the weather, called a cloud-buster. Incidentally, the operation of the cloud-buster was known in ancient times and employed by Egyptians for weather control. This is and has been part of the teachings in mystery schools. The principle of its operation is depicted in Figure 20. It consists of a combination of parallel, hollow metal tubes. One end is grounded in water, preferably running water. The tubes are mounted so they can be pointed in any direction. When pointed at a cloud, the cloud-buster draws orgone energy out of it in the same manner that the bottom of an accumulator heats up when suspended over running water. The metal tubes have a positive charge, which attracts the orgone and starts a flow of orgone along their surface toward the water.

It should be kept in mind that the orgone, or soft electrons, by themselves do not have a strong attraction for metals, because of the ethers with which they are associated. Some have not completely camouflaged the hard electrons they contain. Therefore, they will be quickly drawn to the metal. This creates the void that will be filled by other particles. The resulting excitation causes many to disintegrate and others to lose some of their ability to camouflage the hard electrons they contain.

Not all of the soft electrons comprising the orgone completely camouflage the hard electrons they have captured. Therefore, a significant number of orgone particles coming in contact with the metal are conducted in the manner of ordinary electricity. This produces voids along the conductor and a rush of orgone toward the metal tubes. There is more than enough water vapor in the atmosphere at any time or place to produce clouds. Water molecules have a strong positive charge, and tend to collect negative charges or move toward high concentrations of them. Orgone is attracted to dust particles having positive charges; and water molecules, in turn, congregate around the combination of orgone and dust particles. If there is a high enough concentration of negative charges, water molecules will concentrate in sufficient numbers to form water droplets.

It is apparent that a cloud will quickly dissipate when the orgone energy is drawn out of it. The water molecules simply evaporate again, with nothing to hold them together. Thunderclouds contain a higher concentration of orgone energy than normal. The damaging and lethal effects of lightning are not due to the discharges of orgone energy itself as Reich thought, but to the hard electrons it releases when the orgone disintegrates. Lightning bolts consist of discharges of hard electrons, not soft ones. Reich was only partially correct when he concluded that lightning was a discharge of orgone energy. Thunderclouds are more likely to occur in the lower latitudes, because these regions receive more orgone energy directly, and indirectly, from the sun. They are more likely to build up over land masses than over large open bodies of water.

Reich's cloud-buster can also enlarge clouds, and even create them when pointed toward an open area near a cloud. This again draws orgone energy away from that region, producing a strong positive charge. This, in turn, causes a rush of orgone from all directions to the affected area, and a chain reaction occurs. More electrons are attracted or set into motion than can be drawn off by the cloud-buster. The cloudbuster must then be pointed in a new direction, or the reverse process occurs.

Reich's method of producing rain was far more effective than the popular one of seeding clouds with silver iodide crystals. Unwittingly, our present rainmakers are utilizing the same principle as Reich, but in a crude way. The tiny crystals have a positive charge. When the are dumped into a cloud, a flow of orgone energy to the area follows, slightly increasing the concentration of orgone.

The principles described above also explain how UFOs interrupt the flow of electricity in power lines and auto ignition systems. UFOs probably employ sophisticated devices for drawing off and lessening the concentration of soft electrons around electric conductors. By drawing soft electrons away from the conductors, the source of hard electricity is cut off.

It should be mentioned that there is a minimum length for the tube employed in a cloud buster if it is to be effective. There is a critical velocity or kinetic energy of the flowing orgone or soft electrons below which a general flow cannot be maintained because of frictional forces. The same principle is involved in the flow of electricity through conductors. Up to a point, the longer the tubes the higher the velocity of flow which can be achieved.

Reich allegedly employed the cloud-buster to disable hostile UFOs in the area around his laboratory. The cloud-buster disrupted the electrical systems of these ships much in the same manner UFOs have stopped the flow of electricity in power lines. Reich and others have had experiences suggesting that many UFOs do not have the best interests of this planet in mind. The principle of the cloud-buster action may underlie a wide range of phenomena to be discussed in later chapters. The ability of a cloud-buster to stop the flow of electricity in power lines is, of course, a dramatic proof of the validity of what has been discussed concerning the source of electricity. Other phenomena produced by the cloud-buster show the validity of other things presented in this treatise, and will be revealed later.

Another interesting phenomenon which is associated with orgone energy Reich investigated, is the presence of tiny particles resembling spots of light darting about in the atmosphere. Anyone with normal eyesight can see them at almost any time. They are not figments of the imagination or optical illusions, since lenses will magnify them. Reich built an instrument called the orgonoscope for studying them. In fact, they consist of dust particles combined with orgone enegy; and are not affected by gravity, since the positive charge is neutralized by the negative charges.

The cause of other atmospheric phenomena may be apparent by now. A low barometric reading indicates an excess of negative charges in the atmosphere and an impending storm. A high barometric reading means a lower concentration of orgone in the atmosphere and a small likelihood of clouds forming. The concentration of negative charges is not uniform.

This is a major factor in the changing weather. Ionized air molecules in the atmosphere will tend to rush toward concentrations of soft electrons. This sets up a chain reaction, affecting the atmosphere for great distances and generates winds.

Occasionally, and under rare conditions, a combination of large quantities of orgone, or soft electrons, and positively ionized gas molecules is formed. The highly ionized gas molecules are almost completely camouflaged by the orgone. This is known as ball lightning. It is not affected to any extent by gravity, due to the balancing effect of positive and negative charges. The conclusion that it is largely a conglomerate of soft particles is demonstrated by its ability to pass readily through any metallic or nonmetallic material and carry the gas molecules with it. It can be extremely dangerous, since it houses and camouflages large quantities of hard electrons along with the ionized molecules.

A sect skillfully organized, trained to utter one cry, combined to cover with reproach whoever may differ with themselves, to drown the free expression of opinion by denunciations of heresy, and to strike terror into the multitudes by joint and perpetual menace—such a sect is as perilous and palsying to the intellect as the inquisition.—W. E. Channing

CHAPTER 19

THE NATURE OF RADIOACTIVITY AND NUCLEAR DEVICES

POPULAR MISCONCEPTIONS OF ATOMIC AND PARTICLE PHYSICS

To switch from the research of Wilhelm Reich to academic science in the realm of particle physics is like going from the sublime to the ridiculous. Ordinarily, no space would be devoted to such vacuous endeavors, if it were not for the vast sums of money and resources being poured into the construction and operation of worthless particle accelerators. One of these giant accelerators consumes as much electricity as an entire city. The purpose of this chapter is to expose the thought processes of physicists who have spawned the building of such monstrosities, and to evaluate what takes place in them.

The host of new particles observed by experimental physicists is produced by unnatural means, and has nothing to do with the operation of the atom. Their lifespan is so fleeting no rational person would call them particles. "Phantom particles" would be a more appropriate term. Perhaps the most remarkable of these phantoms is the neutrino. It is a true figment of the imagination, since it has never shown up in cloud chambers. Physicists continually invent these particles, which possess special properties, to enable them to surmount difficulties. Such is the case with the neutrino.

A few decades back, theorists were apparently confronted with a violation of the law of conservation of mass energy, as determined by the theory of relativity. This was really because of a faulty interpretation of certain nuclear experiments and the fallacy of the relation $E = mc^2$. The discrepancy was blamed on some hypothetical and illusive particle they called a neutrino. They had to assign it impossible properties to make it conform with their other misconceptions. They assumed it must have a rest mass of zero and a charge of zero!

The next step was to design some experiment to detect this wraith. Success was finally announced to the scientific world, after many years of frustration. However, an aspect of this great achievement was soft-pedaled. It was the reluctant admission the experiment only gave indirect, and hence inconclusive, evidence of the existence of the neutrino. Such a "minor" detail, and the consideration that any number of interpretations that could have been placed on the results, would not stand in the way of progress of modern physics for long. Their enthusiasm was not to be denied after such a long period of suspense and frustration. Consequently, these annoying facts were pushed out of the way, as many others have been. The neutrino is now given the same status of reality as the electron, proton, and even the atom itself. They can now discuss the neutrino with reckless abandon, without displaying any sign of remorse or guilt.

Physicists picked out the most illogical of all the various interpretations that could have explained the experiments, allegedly confirming the existence of the neutrino. Ironically, the neutrino was invented to salvage conservation, but it was assigned properties which violated the law! How could a particle with a rest mass of zero and a zero charge ever acquire any momentum or produce any energy effects without creating something out of nothing?

This is an example of the quality of thinking in which academic physicists indulge. Is there any reason to expect anything better in their present lines of research, which cost billions of dollars? The comedy centering around particle physics and its participants is too preposterous to have been conjured up by any dramatists prior to the advent of atomic physics. Instead of comedy, perhaps burlesque would be a more fitting description.

A theorist will dream of some weird drama which should take place with certain particles. This, in turn, necessitates the involvement of a previously unknown particle with peculiar and unique properties. It is then decided what type of path it should produce in a cloud chamber. A long series of experiments follows with high-speed particles produced by acelerators. Thousands of photographs are examined to see if such paths can be found. Almost invariably, such diligent efforts are finally rewarded with success; and another grotesque theory has been "confirmed". What usually follows is great rejoicing and a celebration among the brotherhood. They have come a step closer to understanding the universe. There is an enigma usually connected with these events. It is indeed strange that right after the discovery nearly everyone starts finding them, although, prior to this, multitudes had been engaged in the search for weeks or months without success.

Their greatest ally in such endeavors is the law of averages. One can usually find any kind of path one wishes to find when a sufficient number of interactions is recorded. The conclusion that the illusion of increase of mass with velocity is only a cluster held together by magnetic fields has been demonstrated in some of these experiments. High-speed protons meeting head on seem to produce a large number of new particles, which scatter in various directions. In reality, this is what happens when clusters of protons collide. The collision causes the clusters to break up into many of the protons, which were captured by the magnetic fields of the aggregate. The end of a path in a cloud chamber is frequently interpreted as the destruction of a particle. In many cases, it only indicates the particle lost its kinetic energy, or was captured by an atom or molecule or by soft electrons. The names assigned to the fantasy particles are congruent with the odd thinking of the physicists working on these projects. Examples of these are quarks and charms. The real tragedy is the wasted time, effort, material, and astronomical sums of money poured into these worthless projects, which only test out intellectual excursions into dream worlds, which are far removed from reality.

A typical article, supposedly justifying all of this nonsense, appeared in the February, 1978, issue of *Scientific American* entitled "Supergravity and the Unification of the Laws of Physics." This article brings one up to date on the work being done in theoretical physics and paints a rosy picture for the future. The following passage is taken from this article on page 131:

> The present understanding of the fundamental laws of nature arose from three principles: special relativity, general relativity, and quantum mechanics. Each of them resolved an experimental or theoretical conflict, and each went on to predict new phenomena subsequently verified by experiment. Today there can be little doubt about their validity.(50)

A NEW LOOK AT THE PHENOMENON OF RADIOACTIVITY

The conventional picture of the atom is that of electrons moving around a tightly packed nucleus of protons and neutrons in certain prescribed orbits. This nucleus is supposedly held together by some mysterious binding force. This is not the case. There are only two forces to consider: electrostatic and magnetic. This is in accordance with the Hermetic Axiom. It is the neutralizing effects of electrons intermingling with protons, and the pinch effect of magnetic fields, which hold the atom together. The activity region of the protons is small compared to the electrons, since electrons are more active. The interaction of electrons with protons is the origin of neutrons, and in the larger atoms they constitute the majority of the particles in the nucleus.

Neutrons play an important role in keeping protons confined within certain boundaries, by moving between repelling protons. Zonal effects, as described previously, have actually been detected around neutrons, which of course was baffling to physicists. This is an excellent confirmation of the principles discussed earlier.

The chances for an electron to collide head-on with protons and neutrons in an atom will increase as the number of particles comprising the atom increases. If the electron and nucleus are moving in opposite directions, the collision can result in the disintegration of one or more of the particles, and the release of gamma rays. Sometimes, a combination of protons and neutrons can be ejected completely from the atom in the form of alpha particles, as well as neutrons.

The hard electrons associated with gamma rays have no preferred direction of spin, as is the case with softer electrons. Consequently, many of them can follow the right hand rule and be mistaken for positive charges and be called positrons. The alleged annihilation of a positron and an electron, when they collide with each other, is no doubt the collision of an unstable hard electron of a gamma ray following the right-hand rule colliding with an unstable gamma ray electron following the left hand rule. Such events have given rise to bizarre speculations about antimatter.

Antimatter has become such a widely discussd subject that even science fiction writers have gotten into the act. The theory of antimatter considers the possibility of matter existing in the universe which consists of atoms with positive charges orbiting a negative nucleus. Such an arrangement is impossible. It is the nature of negative charges to be far more active than positive charges comprised of the same frequency photons. Therefore, a nucleus will always be positive, surrounded with negative charges.

It is the occasional collision of electrons with a particle, or particles, of the nucleus that produces the type of radiation which is known as radioactivity. For a given radioactive atom, the probability of such an event is infinitesimal. However, when great numbers of atoms are combined, the probability of this occurring in any given time interval increases in direct proportion to the number of atoms present. When the number becomes great enough, the concern is not about the probability of one such event, but how many during a certain time interval. The half life of a given radioactive substance is not difficult to understand.

After a definite period of time, one-half of the atoms will have experienced this event and have thus been transformed. This leaves one-half of the atoms, which means that such events take place with half the frequency. Therefore, in the same amount of time, one-half of the remaining atoms will have transformed, and so on. This idea of half-lives has been used to determine the age of various rocks and minerals, but it is extremely unreliable. The presence of high concentrations of soft electrons can greatly alter the half-life of radioactive materials, as demonstrated by the late Wilhelm Reich.

THE SOURCE OF THE ENERGY RELEASED IN NUCLEAR EXPLOSIONS

Despite the fact that our illustrious physicists have managed to develop as highly a destructive device as a nuclear bomb, they still have no concept of the nature and source of the energy released after a detonation. As with all other well known phenomena, they try to create the illusion that they comprehend and have explained. As a matter of fact, academic science has not yet supplied satisfactory explanations for any of the simplest and most common everyday phenomena. The energy released by nuclear devices is explained away by stating that it is a conversion of matter into energy in accordance with the false Einstein relation $E = mc^2$. Many readers, especially those steeped in orthodoxy, may be shocked to learn there is no conversion of mass into energy during such a process, nor by any process in which energy is released! The tremendous heat produced in a nuclear blast means that an abnormal quantity of hard electrons were suddenly released by the complete disintegration of all the soft electrons within the area of the explosion. The intense light that accompanies the blast is the result of the photons set free by the disintegration of those soft electrons.

The key to the triggering of the reaction is the neutron. As indicated earlier, a neutron is equivalent to a collapsed hydrogen atom, and yet it is more than this. A hydrogen atom has a strong net positive charge, while the neutron has no net charge. This means that a neutron has collected more hard electrons than a hydrogen atom. Since a neutron has no charge, it cannot add to the weight of an atom, as is commonly believed.

The concepts introduced in this treatise render all of the old beliefs concerning atomic structure invalid. The weight of an atom is dependent almost entirely on the number of orbital electrons and the number of protons in its nucleus. This will be discussed in more detail later. There is an exception or two to the above rule in the case of certain radioactive elements where the presence of neutrons can actually reduce the weight of an atom. An interchange of excess electrons between protons and neutrons within the nucleus, and thus transformations of protons into neutrons and vice versa, can occur. The neutrons greatly outnumber the protons in the heavier atoms, especially those that are radioactive. During the interchanges between neutrons and protons, excess neutrons disintegrate into protons and hard electrons are ejected from some of the atoms. This results in a transformation of such atoms. Simultaneously, the tremendous interactions between electrons released in this manner as well as from the disintegration of soft electrons in the vicinity cause the higher ethers to be disturbed, ultimately resulting in the production of gamma rays.

The isotope of the more common uranium 238 atom known as U235 is lighter yet it is fissionable and more radioactive than the uranium 238. It is lighter because it supposedly has fewer neutrons than the ordinary uranium atom. The opposite is actually the case. The U235 having more neutrons is more radioactive. The greater interactions within the nucleus result in more hard electrons being released, which reduces the overall positive charge of its nucleus. There is a continuous interchange of ejected protons transforming back into neutrons and vice versa among the U235 atoms. A similar but less violent interchange takes place among the atoms of uranium 238. A low percentage of the U238 atoms receive more than their share of these interchanges and thus transform into U235 atoms. Most of the hard electrons released which contribute to such interchanges and transformations is the result of the disintegration of soft electrons which permeate the atoms. It follows that the main contributing factor of radioactivity is the presence of soft electrons which house the hard electrons! Therefore, if the soft electron concentration throughout the vicinity of a radioactive substance is reduced, it will lose much of its radioactivity. By now it has no doubt occurred to the reader that a Reich cloud-buster pointed at a radioactive material would cause it to lose its radioactivity! This has been proven to be the case. For example, a glowing piece of radium stops radiating when it is placed in front of a cloud-buster.

The source of the energy released during a nuclear blast is now becoming clear. When a fissionable material like U235 or plutonium is bombarded with additional neutrons, the increased activity in the nuclei causes even the most stable soft electrons in the vicinity to disintegrate. A chain reaction of soft electron disintegration in areas well beyond the confines of the fissionable material results. All of the hard electrons and protons originally camouflaged by the soft particles are suddenly released. A tremendous gamma ray production also occurs. Adequate quantities of fissionable materials suddenly brought together can result in a sufficient increase of neutron bombardment of the interior atoms to produce such a result. It is known as the critical mass. The proper fusion of hydrogen atoms can also cause enough soft electron disintegration to produce a similar result. It is now apparent there is no conversion of mass into energy during the process. All of the fundamental particles of the atoms involved remain intact. In fact, there is even more mass following a blast than there was previously, as a result of the additional hard electrons and protons released. Once again it is obvious that the theory of relativity is in no way concerned.

The monstrous hoax fostered on the public by the defense department of the Government now becomes more than obvious. A Reich cloudbuster can completely deactivate nuclear devices for great distances by drawing away the soft electron concentration from the vicinity of such a device. In fact, a cloudbuster can be used for downing fleets of planes carrying nuclear weapons. Combustion is also dependent on soft electron concentrations which of course includes jet engines. Therefore jet engines or missiles cannot function in an area affected by a cloudbuster. For a mere several thousand dollar investment any country can be rendered invulnerable to any missile and nuclear weapon attack! The fact that a simple cloudbuster can deactivate a nuclear reactor from a great distance has been proven on numerous occasions. This means that hundreds of billions of tax dollars are being funneled each year to support a multibillion dollar nuclear industry and other related industries which are rendered obsolete by the device used by Reich.

It is evident that the proper use of the cloudbuster could throw modern warfare back to the stone age. Combatants would be reduced to the use of clubs, rock throwing, bows and arrows and the catapult. Invasion fleets would consist of sailboats, canoes, rafts and balloons. The cloudbuster could even nullify this kind of hostilities. Obviously the drawing of soft particles away from any group would completely enervate each individual and even turn him into a block of frozen flesh. Although a cloudbuster could not completely deactivate a particle beam weapon it could bring down any craft carrying such a device before it could get into position. Since officialdom in Washington, D.C., including the defense department, is fully aware of the potential of the cloudbuster, one can only speculate as to what kind of moral degenerates have been dictating the policies of this country and the enormity of the crimes they have inflicted upon humanity. A discussion on the nature of radioactive contamination and the remedy has been reserved for Chapter 34 for reasons that will become apparent later.

The potential of the cloudbuster is perhaps greater than even Reich himself realized. Since heat is transferred from one body to another by soft electrons which release harder electrons, the cloudbuster can be used as a highly efficient refrigeration system by drawing soft electrons away from a body. It has been made apparent that this simple device can render present fire fighting techniques obsolete. By use of the cloud-buster in the proper manner, the loss of life and property from fire and storms could become a thing of the past. It also provides dramatic proof of the validity of many of the new concepts introduced in this treatise.

Radioactivity was the subject of a ridiculous, if not amusing, fiasco more than two decades ago when two physicists, Lee and Yang, received the Nobel Prize in 1957.(36) The incident, which was given wide publicity, concerned an error in the parity principle. The parity principle has been defined as "a mathematical concept impossible to define in physical terms." How such a concept could have any bearing on physical reality is not made clear. Generally, anything relating to reality can be defined in terms of reality, which is in conformity with the law of cause and effect.

Incredibly, an experiment was devised to test the validity of this great revelation. It was based on the idea that a radioactive substance should eject more particles in one preferred direction, than in any other. Radioactive cobalt was chosen. It was cooled down to near absolute zero and exposed to a powerful magnetic field produced by a solenoid, in order to align the nuclei. Another physicist, a Dr. Wu, had devoted six months of hard work setting up the experiment. Indeed, it was found that more particles were ejected out of one pole of the solenoid than the other. Which pole was it? Of course, it was the pole out of which the magnetic lines flowed. Naturally, the experiment merely demonstrated that particles tend to travel down magnetic lines of force. The excess of particles that came out of the pole were those barely ejected from the atom. They had such a low initial velocity that, regardless of what direction they happened to be traveling initially, the magnetic field would dictate their final direction of travel. Lee and Yang were accorded every scientific honor, including the Nobel Prize, as a result of this experiment.

Instead of giving them the Nobel Prize, the awarding of an Oscar would have been more appropriate. Accompanying the extensive publicity given this comedy act was a photo appearing in a prominent magazine showing one of the recipients pointing to a grotesque mathematical equation containing over 100 terms! He was allegedly explaining the reasoning behind their great revelation. Outside of the mathematical equation, the most amazing aspect of this performance was that he was able to keep a straight face throughout the demonstration. If the true significance of her experiment should ever dawn on Dr. Wu, a likely reaction could conceivably be (excuse the pun) "Wu is me!" This event is another indication of how much so-called theoretical physicists lean on mathematics in their attempts to discover the secrets of the universe.

In view of the new concepts introduced in this treatise such as: the nature of gravity; that neutrons are virtually weightless and can even have a negative weight and therefore do not add to the atomic weight; that charge varies with velocity; there are thousands of electrons to every proton in an atom; etc., it becomes evident that the conventional picture of the atom is completely false. Our venerated scientists have had no way of determining the number of neutrons and protons in any given atom. The number of orbital electrons in a given atom can vary considerably while the atom remains perfectly stable. The only differences will be in the physical properties of the materials comprised of these atoms. The chemical properties, however, will be unchanged. This presents an interesting paradox. The actual weights of the individual atoms will vary, but the determined atomic weights will be the same, which becomes evident from the fact that alotropic forms of a given element, including the isotopes, have the same chemical properties. It should be kept in mind that an alotropic form is produced by changing the number of orbital electrons. A question which arises at this point is: What is the difference between an isotope and an alotropic form of an element, since the conventional explanation is false?

The logical picture of the atom which emerges from these new concepts is as follows: The orbital electrons consist of concentric shells surrounding the nucleus. Each shell is comprised of electrons moving at the same velocity but in different orbital planes and in the same direction clockwise or counterclockwise, depending on the point of view. The electrons in each of these shells have the same general orbital direction. The velocity is such that the mutual electrostatic repulsion is offset by magnetic attraction. This is why all orbital motions must be in the same general direction. It also tends to prevent collisions between electrons. All orbital velocities must be well below light velocity, since it is electrostatic attraction which keeps the electrons in orbit. The outer electrons, of course, travel at lower velocities. They can be easily stripped off an atom because mutual electrostatic repulsion is greater. It is only the outside pinch effect of magnetic fields that tends to hold them in orbit.

An alotropic form of an element is one whose atoms contain more or fewer orbital electrons than the common form. The chemical properties of an element is dependent almost entirely on the nucleus of the atoms comprising it. Consider what happens when an alotropic atom with more than the normal quantity of orbital electrons combines with another atom to form a molecule. During the process, soft electrons which are vital to all chemical processes absorb the excess outer orbital electrons which are more easily captured. The compound formed from the combination has all the physical properties of that produced by the combination with the common form of the element. There is, however, one subtle difference between the two compounds. The one produced with the alotropic form will contain soft electrons locked into it which are overloaded with the captured hard electrons and are thus relatively unstable. Most processes which reduce the compound to isolate the original element will also cause the captured orbital electrons to be released, and they will tend to resume their original orbits. The result is usually the original alotropic form. The author once witnessed a demonstration of this principle with an alotropic form of gold. Incidentally, there are many alotropic forms of elements which conventional science has never recognized or even suspected had an existence. This particular type of gold was in the form of a clay with about one sixth the specific gravity of saleable gold. The gold chloride produced from this clay had all the properties of normal gold chloride which formed an extremely heavy yellow precipitate. When heat was applied to the precipitate to reduce it, the result, instead of being gold as we know it, was the original clay!

Compounds produced from alotropic forms with fewer than the normal orbital electrons will have the same properties. In such cases, soft electrons involved in the process supply the additional electrons to make up the shortage. This form of the element has a higher net positive charge which draws more soft electrons to the area. The question as to the difference between an isotope of an element and its alotropic form now becomes clear. Essentially there is none. A heavy so-called isotope is a form that has fewer orbital electrons. A lighter isotope has more orbital electrons. Those which are known as isotopes tend to revert back to the original form after the reduction process following a combination. A radioactive isotope has additional neutrons but the net positive charge effect of the nucleus remains virtually unchanged. It now becomes apparent that it is the overall positive charge effect of the nucleus that determines chemical properties. Chemists have mistakenly attributed the increased weight of a "heavy" isotope to additional neutrons in the nuclei instead of fewer orbital electrons. The previously unknown fact that there are thousands of electrons to every proton in an atom readily explains facts concerning the atom that cannot be resolved by using conventional beliefs.

The structure of the nucleus has not as yet been properly analyzed. A group of protons by themselves would obviously fly apart in all directions. It follows that only the presence of particles with opposite charges could offset this. The neutron is the key. As mentioned earlier the neutron is equivalent to a collapsed hydrogen atom with far more than the usual number of orbital electrons. When a group of neutrons is clustered around each other the number of orbital electrons attached to any given neutron can fluctuate considerably. Outer electrons of a neutron can be stripped off by interactions with adjacent neutrons and then recapture electrons from another neutron with an excess of electrons. Soft electrons which permeate all matter can be disturbed sufficiently by these interplays to disintegrate and release additional electrons among the aggregate. Some electrons will escape the combination continuously but are replaced by disintegrating soft electrons, discharging new ones. The overall effect produced by this combination is a strong negative charge. Since the aggregate is relatively immobile, the protons will tend to orbit this combination. The mutual repulsion of the protons tends to be offset by magnetic attraction resulting from their motion. This in conjunction with the pinch effect produced by the surrounding ethers and the attraction of the protons to the negative charge holds the nucleus together.

Large fluctuations in the negative charge effects produced by the aggregate of neutrons result in corresponding changes in the velocity of the protons. This in turn affects the motion of the orbital electrons. The overall result is the creation of photons covering a complex range of frequencies. The greater the number of particles in the nucleus, the more complex the frequency pattern or the spectra.

It is exceedingly difficult to secure an honest hearing for any criticism of authority. Established beliefs are well nigh invulnerable because they are accorded infallibility by the masses who are educated to believe they will be damned for thinking, and because of this, few will tolerate opposition of any nature to anything they have been educated to believe. People who have their thinking done for them are always intolerant.—J. H. Tilden

CHAPTER 20

ATMOSPHERIC PHENOMENA

There are several factors which have not been considered in the academic explanations for winds and other atmospheric phenomena. It is significant that the moon has a substantial atmosphere, and receives about the same intensity of radiation from the sun as the earth, yet relatively minor winds occur. Unlike the earth, the moon has a feeble magnetic field. This is one of the keys for interpreting atmospheric currents. Other factors include the hollow condition of a planet, the thickness of its shell in relation to its diameter, and the Coriolis effect. Winds, tornados, and cyclones can only be adequately explained by taking into consideration the nature of orgone energy, or soft electrons, and their interactions with air molecules. These explanations for atmospheric phenomena will be followed by suggested methods of weather control, based in part on the research of Reich and others.

Air currents seem to be generated from electrostatic forces caused by the presence of concentrations of hard and soft electrons in the atmosphere. The rush of these charges toward lower potential areas creates a charged particle stream. This stream generates wind, because the ionized air molecules tend to be drawn along with it. Since soft electrons are continually disintegrating and releasing camouflaged hard electrons contained inside, the electrostatic forces will primarily be the result of hard electrons.

It has been demonstrated that a bar magnet which is long in proportion to its width has a number of nodes distributed along its length. These nodes result from the magnetic lines which tend to follow oval or circular paths. The magnetic lines flow out of one pole and back into the side, instead of flowing into the opposite pole. This point of entry generates a node, which becomes the starting point for another flow out of the side and back into the magnet at a second node.

Geomagnetism was explained in a previous chapter as the result of charges in the atmosphere moving with the earth in its rotation. In addition, the shell of the earth should act then as a bar magnet. It was shown that particles bombarding the earth tend to slow down as they penetrate the shell. A cross section of the earth would look like two curved bar magnets 800 miles thick and 12,000 miles long. This configuration should result in multiple nodes, since it fits the pattern of a long, narrow bar magnet. At each nodal point or line, there should be a magnetic flow into and out of the outer surface of the shell, which carries a high concentration of soft electrons. The earth's gravity would then tend to repel the ejected negative soft electrons out beyond the confines of the magnetic flow, so that they would tend to move north and south of the nodal line by mutual repulsion.

Magnetometers may not show great deviations in the earth's field in these regions, because they only measure the fields produced by hard electrons. The majority of the particles ejected at these nodes will probably be the more stable soft electrons, which do not readily disintegrate to release the hard electrons contained inside. Sufficient groundwork has now been laid to explain the prevailing atmospheric winds, which are broken into six discrete bands from the north to the south pole.

Since the earth has polar egresses, there should be a rapid flow of electrons of all kinds from both poles, in addition to those particles ejected from the nodal areas. Although the magnetic flow is into the north polar magnetic region, particles ejected out of the northern egress tend to spread out and flow in a southerly direction. The Coriolis effect then comes into play as particles move toward the south. This causes an additional accelerating force on the particles relative to the earth's surface because the rotational velocity of the earth increases as one moves toward the equator. The flow of the particles will be in a southwesterly direction since the earth's rotation is toward the east. This produces a tendency for the earth to move away from the particles, thus giving them a motion relative to the surface and toward the west. The flow will tend to carry ionized air molecules with it, creating the belt of westerly winds in the higher northern latitudes.

The six prevailing wind belts suggest the existence of two magnetic nodal lines between the north and south magnetic poles. Ejected particles at the first nodal line below the north pole will tend to move both north and south from the belt, as explained previously. Those that flow north will tend to move in a northeasterly direction because of the Coriolis effect. They will be given an acceleration relative to the earth's surface in an easterly direction because they are going where the earth's rotational velocity is lower. A cancellation effect is produced between the first nodal line and the north pole because the air masses moving in a northeasterly direction encounter the air masses moving in a southwest direction, nearly at the midpoint.

The particles that move south from the first nodal line produce the westerlies in the lower latitudes. The Coriolis effect weakens rapidly as one moves from the higher to the lower latitudes. As a result, the accelerating effect is less able to offset frictional forces as they approach the equator. Consequently, prevailing winds become weaker in the lower latitudes and vanish near the equator. This produces the doldrums or zones of calm along the equator. The same explanation that was mentioned above applies to prevailing winds in the southern hemisphere.

The pattern presented above will also be affected by land masses and the angle of inclination of the earth in the plane of its orbit about the sun. If the earth were spinning in a plane perpendicular to the orbital plane and were completely covered with water, these wind belts might completely surround the earth without any changes. However, the existing situation tends to disrupt this pattern and, as a result, produce a very complex weather picture.

The parallel belts on Jupiter may also be explained using these arguments. Recent space probes have indicated that the Jovian belts consist of high-velocity winds, which move in alternating directions similar to those on the earth. Since Jupiter has a very strong magnetic field, its lines and belts are quite pronounced and relatively stable.

Since the earth's shell seems to act like a bar magnet, due to the high concentration of rotating soft electrons in that shell, it is probable that the previously mentioned terralines running along the earth's surface are the result of this magnetic field. In addition, pyramids of the past may have been constructed over areas ejecting large numbers of soft particles in order to take advantage of these natural concentrations and their various properties.

During an eclipse, there seems to be a significant flow of soft electrons from the lighted portion of the earth to the shadow. It has been noted that animals are noticeably affected during a total eclipse in the same way they behave prior to an earthquake. This has been attributed to a psychological effect produced by the darkness. The author personally experienced a definite physiological effect, which was exceedingly pronounced, during the February 26, 1979, eclipse. The effect was the same as produced by a magnet, an orgone accumulator, the Oregon vortex, or a pyramid. The author does not believe he is particularly more sensitive than many other individuals, but was likely more observant and attentive to these effects. Due to the short duration of a total eclipse, and the excitement it causes, it appears most people might ignore the physiological effect the author experienced. What actually happens seems to be that the moon momentarily blocks out the flow of soft electrons to the eclipsed area. This creates a void, which creates a subsequent flow of soft electrons to the area from all sides. This quickly results in a higher concentration of soft electrons in the eclipsed area than existed before the eclipse. Apparently, the duration of an eclipse is not long enough for large masses of air to be set into motion and generate winds.

A number of factors are required for a cyclone to develop. One of these factors is an abnormal concentration of soft electrons in an area. When this occurs, a rapid flow of soft electrons to the surface of the earth takes place. This effect is enhanced over a large body of water, such as the ocean. A condition analogous to pulling the plug out of a drain is the result. Winds accompanying this effect produce a gigantic vortex. Once started, it increases and can continue to increase for a long period. The vortex creates a low potential in that area, and therefore causes a continuous flow of soft electrons to rush in from surrounding areas. It is extremely significant that most cyclones originate over oceans.

Tornadoes are more widespread and frequent than cyclones, and can be either clockwise or counterclockwise. The major cause, as with cyclones, is an extremely rapid discharge of soft electrons to ground. A cloud with an abnormal accumulation of relatively stable soft electrons will seek out a channel of least resistance to ground. The flow of soft electrons through this channel produces a vortex consisting of a combination of highly ionized air molecules and soft electrons. This is accompanied by the rapid disintegration of soft electrons, which results in electrical discharges and lightning. A number of witnesses have seen the inside of a twister and attest to the continuous lightning discharges. Tornadoes occasionally lift off the ground when they encounter an area with a strong negative charge. This repels the concentration of negative charges in the vortex. Once a tornado starts, the cloud that feeds it receives an increased flow of orgone energy from all directions, which perpetuates it. The tornado will burn itself out when it cannot draw in enough soft electrons to maintain the flow to ground.

Scientists are constantly seeking methods for stopping or preventing cyclones and tornados. Wilhelm Reich provided them with the fundamental means of weather control through his cloudbuster. Areas prone to cyclones could be monitored for abnormal concentrations of orgone, and these concentrations would be dissipated with giant cloudbusters on ships before they could attain destructive size. If a cyclone develops, these same cloudbusters could be placed around it and might be effective in eliminating it before it reached a land mass. On land, tornados could be stopped or prevented with cloudbusters, if a substantial quantity of running water were available to act as an orgone sink. If running water is not available, a device known as the Searl generator could be used to disrupt the abnormal concentration of soft electrons. The Searl generator can produce the low potential necessary to drain orgone from the cloud which feeds the tornado. The Searl generator will be discussed in detail in Chapter 22. Such devices could be set up in every area that is likely to experience a tornado.

This chapter has presented some of the basic rules governing atmospheric phenomena. At times, the weather pattern may be affected by nature spirits which are projections of the planetary logos. These intelligences help to render a planet habitable and will be discussed in Part IV.

Figure 21

CROSS SECTION OF EARTH BETWEEN OPENINGS
SHOWING CONFIGURATION OF EARTH'S MAGNETIC FIELD
AND HOW SIX ZONES OF PREVAILING WINDS ARE PRODUCED

Cancellation of air currents occur between magnetic modal lines as a result of air masses moving in opposite directions and converging at such points.

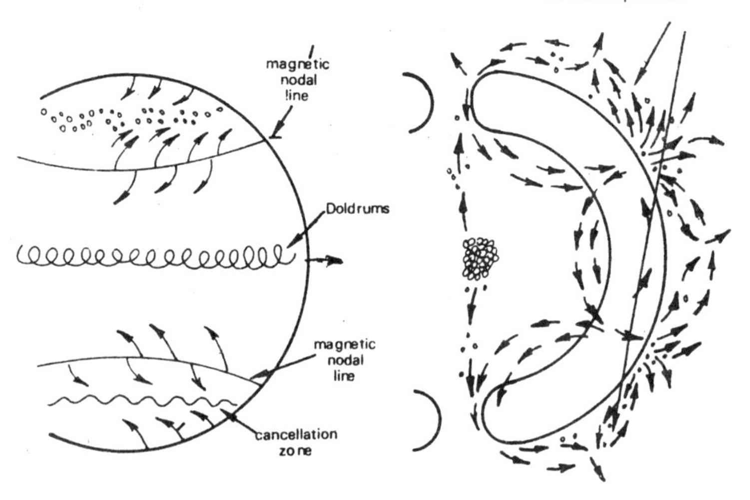

Coriolis Effect weakens rapidly as one moves from north or south to equator. Consequently, the accelerating force is not enough to compensate for frictional forces as equator is approached. As a result, prevailing winds become weaker in lower latitudes and vanish near equator.

Particles moving with magnetic flow coming out of earth will have a higher velocity than those in the magnetic flow going into the earth since they have added velocity due to gravitational repulsion. Consequently, they will tend to escape the earth's magnetic field. Because of mutual repulsions some of them will be pushed south and some north.

CHAPTER 21

PRACTICAL "FREE ENERGY" DEVICES WHICH COULD REVOLUTIONIZE OUR WAY OF LIVING

A free energy device can be defined as a machine that extracts or puts out more energy than it draws from its surroundings, or is put into it, to obtain this energy. The world of academic science has always considered this to be an impossibility, since it supposedly violates to law of conservation of energy. Despite continual and undeniable proof to the contrary, the vast majority of orthodox scientists still refuse to recognize such realities. In view of the type of minds possessed by these men as has been revealed throughout this treatise, it would be completely out of character for them to behave in any other manner.

Many such discoveries have been made in this century. They have passed every test designed to prove them fraudulent. In each instance, the invention was suppressed and lost to the world by the underhanded tactics of such vested interests governed by unscrupulous men, whose only interests are the acquiring of money and power. Their success in preventing the widespread use of these devices was facilitated by afflictions which all but a few of the inventors seemed to have in common. These included acute cases of laryngitis and writer's cramp, at least where the details of their inventions were concerned.

In the pages to follow, three devices of this nature will be described and analyzed in detail. Two of them are self-sustaining electric generators, and one is a magnetic motor or a device that is powered only by permanent magnets. One of these, a self-sustaining electric generator, is a design of this author.

With the exception of magnetic motors, all of these various devices, including Tesla's famous wireless transmission of electrical energy, are based on a principle and a fact that has been discussed repeatedly in this treatise. The principle is that all known space is permeated with soft electrons which, in turn, harbor enormous quantities of hard electrons. Essentially, all of such inventions consist of various methods of exciting these soft electrons to the extent that they give up the hard electrons they contain. Less energy is required to disintegrate a soft electron than the energy that is released in the flow of hard electrons as a result of the disintegration. This is not a violation of the energy conservation law, since the total kinetic energy of the ethers involved remains constant.

THE SELF-SUSTAINING ELECTRIC GENERATOR

With one possible exception to be discussed later, perhaps the most practical and useful free energy device is the self sustaining electric generator. Many have probably been developed by different individuals at different times. The most famous and spectacular of these was demonstrated publicly at Seattle, Washington, in 1919, by an inventor named Hubbard. His invention was featured in Seattle newspapers at that time. One of Hubbard's generators was supposedly 14 inches long and 11 inches in diameter, and powered a 40 horsepower electric motor, which pushed a boat continuously around the bay for several hours. This demonstration was witnessed by thousands. A former associate of the author was one of those who claimed to have seen it. He stated that the most interesting part of the spectacle was the tendency for the boat to levitate. The reason isn't difficult to discern. The generation of the electricity created such a high negative charge in the vicinity that the boat was impregnated with an inordinate quantity of soft electrons. Hubbard soon afterwards abandoned his experiments and became silent with regard to his invention. It is not difficult to surmise what happened.

During the time of his demonstrations, Hubbard made a sketch of one of his smaller generators used for ordinary electrical appliances. It was approximately six inches long and about five inches in diameter. It consisted of eight coils in series, wound on iron cores which, in turn, surrounded a slightly larger central coil. The central coil was wound on a hollow tube which contained many small rods. They were, undoubtedly, comprised of soft iron. Four terminals extended from the unit. Two of them represented the outer coils, while the other two came from the central coil.

It is highly significant that both wires used in the generator appeared to be of heavy gauge like those used in telephone or power lines, with the same kind of insulation. Each core had only one layer of this wire. This means that only a moderate number of turns were used in the entire generator, or a total of about 250-300 turns on the outer coils and about 35 turns on the central coil.

It is known that the generator produced a fluctuating current of an undisclosed frequency and had no moving parts. The basic principle on which the generator operated is apparent. A small initial fluctuating current (more than likely DC) was introduced in either the central or outer coils. The fluctuating magnetic field surrounding the primary coil or coils resulting from the primary current introduced an EMF in the secondary coil or coils. There is another important factor to consider when a fluctuating current passes through a coil wound on an iron core.

A small current passed through such a coil with a moderate number of turns per unit length will magnetize this core to a surprising degree. This principle is utilized to great advantage in electromagnets. What apparently hasn't been realized is that during the brief interval in which the current builds up after it is turned on, an induced EMF is produced in the coil by the changing magnetic flux, which is in the same direction as the current. This induced EMF is the result of the magnetic field produced by the magnetization of the iron core. If this induced EMF were in the opposite direction of the current, a sizeable current could never be produced in the coil. The EMF opposing the current would automatically cancel it before it could increase.

Figure 22 shows a graph of the magnetization of an iron core plotted against ampere turns per unit length. The term "ampere turns" is the number of turns of the coil per unit length times the number of amperes of current flowing through the coil. For example, a current of one ampere flowing through a coil of 100 turns will produce the same effect as two amperes flowing through a coil of the same length, which has only 50 turns. There is a section on the curve where a slight increase in ampere turns will produce a tremendous increase in the magnetization of the iron core.

The cause of this phenomenon should be analyzed. It seems paradoxical that a modest number of ampere turns can produce extensive and significant magnetization of the iron core. Yet the observable magnetic field produced by the current without the magnetic core is miniscule in comparison. A similar field, produced by a permanent magnet, would be unable to induce a noticeable magnetization of iron. This is something conventional science has found convenient to ignore. The solution to the dilemma becomes apparent in view of concepts already introduced. The

Figure 22
THE CURVE OF MAGNETIZATION OF AN IRON CORE VERSUS AMPERE TURNS PER UNIT LENGTH

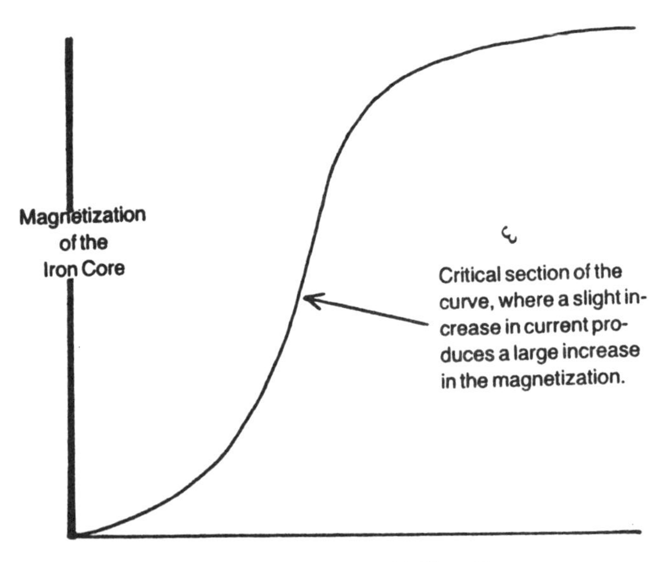

normal flow of current in a wire is accompanied by an extensive flow of soft electrons in the same direction. This flow of soft electrons also permeates the iron core. As this flow of soft electrons passes through the iron, many of them tend to disintegrate, which tends to create a hard electron flow in the iron. This induces magnetism in the iron a considerable distance from the coil. The magnetic field produced by a permanent magnet does not produce a flow of soft electrons to the extent of that produced by an electric current flowing in a conductor. When the ampere turns exceed a critical value, the soft electron flow in the iron reaches an intensity that results in a sudden and inordinate degree of disintegration of the soft electrons. The great increase in the hard electron flow in the iron creates a sudden increase in the magnetization of the iron.

If an alternating current is passed through an electromagnet and the ampere turns exceed this critical point, a chain reaction will take place in the coil, which will result in a tremendous increase of current in the coil. This principle is responsible for transformers which occasionally burn out during current surges. The sudden increase in current is sufficient in some cases to put the ampere turn value over into this critical range. Strangely, such effects have baffled electrical engineers. The chain reaction results from an increase in the magnetization of the iron, which produces an increase in the current, which in turn produces an additional large increase in magnetization, and so on. This ends when the iron reaches its maximum degree of magnetization.

The above process occurs during the first half of the cycle. The EMF is flowing in the direction opposite to that of the current after it reaches its maximum value, and the second part of the cycle begins. This EMF, which is of the same magnitude as that which brought the current to its maximum value during the first part of the cycle, now acts as a brake and stops the current. The applied alternating EMF then starts the current in the opposite direction, and the same identical process described above occurs with this current flowing in a new direction.

The normal operation of tranformers involves ampere turns well below this critical point. The additional EMF induced in the coils by the magnetization of the iron offsets the natural inductive impedence of the coils. This is why tranformers have such a high degree of efficiency. If any material other than iron or special steel were used for the core, the efficiency would drop significantly.

The author tested this principle of current or voltage increase during a cycle. A pulsed DC current from a battery source could be passed through an electromagnet. The voltage from the battery source should be considerably increased after passing through the coil. This is equivalent to stepping up the voltage of the battery when the portion of the circuit coming from the coil is used in conjunction with the opposite pole of the battery. The author tested this theory by placing about 2,000 turns on a steel bolt one-half inch in diameter and joining the ends of the wire to the opposite poles of a six-volt battery. A severe shock was felt when the circuit at the negative pole of the battery was opened and closed. It required about 70 volts for an individual, other than a sensitive, to get anything resembling a shock from an electric current under normal conditions. This means that, during the interval the circuit was opened or closed, the voltage increased from six volts to at least 70 volts and possibly well beyond 100 volts!

The author and an associate then tried the experiment with a pulsed current operated by an electric motor to pulse the current from a 12-volt battery. This produced several hundred pulses per second in the manner of the distributor on a car. The voltage increase from the single coil was sufficient to produce severe shocks if one touched the wire and the negative pole of the battery. Paradoxically, the voltage and amperage increase would not register on a voltmeter or ammeter. The reason is clear. The current pulse was in the form of a square wave. The opening and closing of the circuit was instantaneous. The current during these infinitesimal intervals of time was increased tremendously in both voltage and amperage. However, the current produced consisted only of large bunches of electrons of high voltage, separated by relatively great time intervals with no current flow, except for residual electrons which would register only a small current on the instruments. This means the total amount of current, during a significant interval of time, was small. Consequently, the instruments could not record these sudden increases. They didn't have sufficient time. However, the needles did vibrate, showing these sudden increases.

It is now clear that a normally pulsed DC current cannot be used in such a device. The experiments mentioned above only demonstrated the validity of the principle. This means that a pulsed current in the form of a sine wave must be employed. Since the induced EMF in a coil is directly proportional to the rate of change of magnetic flux, the higher the frequency of this pulsed current, the better. A sine wave pattern means that the changes will not be so abrupt, as was the case with the square wave. Therefore, the rate of change of flux to which the coil is subjected will be much less for the same number of turns, than with a square wave.

It is highly significant that only small-gauge wire was employed in the above experiments. At the time, it was the only kind of wire the author had at his disposal. When the diameter of the wire exceeds a certain critical value, there is a sudden and tremendous increase in the flow of hard electrons for a given applied EMF. There are several factors involved. Soft electrons tend to congregate around a conductor. This has been proven by the Reich cloudbuster effect. Also, soft electrons which permeate all occupied space permeate the conductor in high concentrations. The number is proportional to the cross sectional area of the wire. When an EMF is applied to the wire, a hard-electron flow begins along the outside of the wire. The electrical resistance of the wire is approximately, within certain current limits, inversely proportional to its diameter. As the wire increases in size, the current flow increases, and a greater magnetization of the iron core is the result. This means an increase in EMF with a subsequent increase in hard-electron velocity and interactions. The hard electron activity in the wire produces disintegration of soft electrons in the wire and also along the outer surface. The hard electrons released increase the electron flow or amperage. The shortage, or deficiency, of soft electrons in the region results in a flow of soft electrons to the wire, as in the cloudbuster effect.

There is another, and no doubt most important,factor which contributed to the success of the Hubbard device of which even Hubbard himself could not have been aware. At that time the only insulated wire available was that with the thick and heavy insulation similar to that used in power lines. This means that adjacent segments of the wire in the coils were separated by a distance equal to twice the thickness of the insulation. This consequently resulted in a cancellation of magnetic effects produced by electrons flowing in the wire. Since inertia is dependent on the ability to generate a magnetic field the inertial properties of the electrons would be almost nullified. There is an optimum distance between the wires which would produce the maximum effect. Evidently the insulation provided this optimum distance. Most of the resultant magnetic field was that which encircled both wires and would be the weakest part of the field. This means that a relatively low EMF could accelerate a large number of electrons to a high velocity during a very short period of time. As the electrons leave the coil inertia returns. This would result in a backup of a high concentration of electrons in the coil. Since electrostatic repulsion is not affected, electrons would be ejected from the coil at a high velocity despite their increased inertia. This would result in a high voltage and amperage output.

As mentioned previously in this treatise, magnetization of an iron core is largely the result of magnetic fields produced by the flow of soft electrons, which are far more extensive than that produced by hard electrons. The soft particles captured by such fields permeate the iron and disintegrate, releasing the hard electrons which magnetize the iron. Therefore, despite the extremely weak magnetic field produced by the near inertialess hard electrons, the iron core will still be magnetized.

The above effect also accounts for the strange properties of caduceus coils which have long baffled researchers. The caduceus coil wound in the manner shown in the diagram shows no tendency to heat up with high amperages and has virtually no impedence. At high frequency AC it has a tendency to levitate. As the reader will notice, adjacent segments of the wire are separate except at the nodal points where they cross along the length of the core on which they are wound. There is a tremendous concentration of hard and soft electrons at these nodal points where the inertia momentarily returns, causing a backup in the flow. A high frequency AC produces sufficient agitation of electrons, both hard and soft, to result in the release of hard electrons inside the core. This produces levitation. Since the hard electrons flowing in the wire have little or no inertia, they are unable to produce thermal agitation in the wire. Since impedence is due to inertia, it follows that impedence will all but vanish.

The only remaining mystery of the Hubbard device is how he obtained his primary alternating current and the nature of the initial current source. The means of producing the current was very likely built into the unit. This seems apparent since the device could be carried to any site and hooked up with any available appliance such as an electric motor. A photograph of the smaller unit showed a small box-like structure below the point at which the appliances would be attached. This probably contained the source of the primary current, and was very likely only a dry cell battery which produced a DC current, which was then transformed into a pulsed sinosoidal DC or AC. The pulsing device could very well have been a small oscillator. Under the conditions just described only a small initial current and EMF would have been required.

In all probability the central coil was the secondary. A stronger magnetic field can be produced along the periphery of the hollow tube if it contained a myriad of individual soft iron rods, than would occur if the coil were wound on a solid iron core. It would require a large number of ampere turns to completely magnetize a large core uniformly. However, in the case of individual rods, this is not necessary. The outer layers can be magnetized before the inner portions. Therefore, it is logical to assume that the hollow tube was also of soft iron.

During Hubbard's demonstrations, he claimed that his invention took the energy out of the air. Many years later, he contradicted himself and claimed that radium was the source of the current produced. This was an insult to the intelligence of the more discerning members of the population. He was an employee of the Radium Company of America at the time of his later disclosures. Evidently, his later claims had a tendency to discourage experimentation with generators of the configuration shown in his sketch.

It has been claimed that Hubbard had radio antennas strung up around the area where his device was tested. This could have been the source of his initial current. A radio transmitter radiates unstable low frequency photons and very soft unstable soft electrons. These can interact with the right type or combination of conductors to release a flow of hard electrons in the form of a very high frequency pulsed DC current. Perhaps Hubbard used something akin to a crystal radio receiver to produce the input current. The employment of the proper wire separator or caduceus coil principle would obviate the need of a large input current.

Thomas Henry Moray, of Salt Lake City, developed a self-sustaining electrical generator which could produce a kilowatt of electricity for every pound of weight. This was about the same output as the Hubbard device.(84,85,86) Apparently, he did not use the principle of changing magnetic flux to generate his current. Nearly one million dollars was spent in developing the device. A government agent accidently, or perhaps on purpose, destroyed his device one day when he came into Moray's shop to examine it. Before Moray could stop him, he did things entirely contrary to the safety rules laid down by Moray for its safe operation. Lack of funds prevented him from ever rebuilding it. This was the story Moray told a former classmate of the author. As with all the others, it seems that the complete secret of Moray's device died with him.

The Moray free energy device was quite complex, and operated by ultrahigh frequency charging and discharging of condensers in resonance with transformers. The key to the successful operation of the device was the use of special tubes he called ionic, cold cathode tubes. Interestingly, the wires carrying the high amperage never heated up. Undoubtedly he applied the principle described above involving the Caduceus coil and the original version of the Hubbard device. Two or more wires running parallel to each other with the right separation and carrying currents moving in the same direction would offer no resistance to a heavy flow of inertialess electrons. When they entered an electrical appliance the immediate back up of electrons in the wires would produce sufficient repulsive forces to force the electrons into the circuit with adequate voltages. The major drawback to Moray's generator was its complexity and delicate balance, which also made it susceptible to damage if improperly handled. Because of this it was definitely inferior to Hubbard's generator.

Moray had a remarkable intellect. He developed sound detection devices and radio receivers, which were vastly superior to any in operation today and completely static free. All parts of his devices remained cool during their operation. He was also able to transmute elements. He had no peers in the field of metallurgy. He produced metals with abnormal melting points. One of his alloys had a melting point of 12,000 degrees Farenheit! Unfortunately, it seems that none of his discoveries is being utilized today.

Wilhelm Reich also developed a free energy device. He was supposedly able to draw enough electricity from concentrations of orgone energy to operate a 25 volt electric motor. In the book, *The Cosmic Pulse of Life*, on page 325, Trevor James Constable specifies some of the parameters involved in this discovery.(25) Even Reich kept the details of his methods to himself and one other assistant, for reasons as yet undisclosed. The assistant disappeared, and sadly, as has always been the case, Reich's secret died with him. Reich utilized the concept that orgone energy houses vast quantities of hard electrons. A high concentration of orgone could be maintained in an accumulator. The orgone could then be made to disintegrate periodically in a manner similar to that of a lightning bolt. This was the source of the hard electrons. This ability of orgone to release hard electrons must have led Reich to the erroneous conclusion that orgone is the source of all matter.

A design for a self-sustaining electric generator will now be presented, which could be the most efficient of any yet developed. At the same time, its simplicity is incredible. It involves the principle already described and experimentally proven, with a pulsed DC current passing through a coil wound on an iron core. One layer of a heavy gauge wire is wound on a small and relatively long iron core. The core consists of a thin walled tube filled with soft iron rods. This layer is then covered with a layer of nonmagnetic, and preferably nonmetallic, material which functions as a separator. It should be not less than one quarter of an inch thick. A soft iron sheet is placed over this material on which the winding continues. One layer of this second series of winding is then covered with another layer of nonmagnetic spacing. Over this, another sheet of soft iron is then placed. This process continues until the desired number of turns is made. If the nonmagnetic spacing were not employed, cancellation of magnetic effects in the iron sheets would occur. The windings on one side of the sheet tend to magnetize the iron in the opposite direction to the direction of magnetization produced by the winding on the other side of the sheet. The nonmagnetic spacing minimizes this effect.

The air spaces between the various portions of the coil should be filled with iron filings or iron dust. As a result, every part of the wire is in intimate contact with soft iron. Consequently, the wire is exposed to a more intense magnetic field, as the iron is magnetized.

A high-frequency pulsed DC current in the form of a sine wave is then introduced into the coil. A battery can supply the current, and a portion of the amplified current is fed back into the battery to maintain its charge. A small DC electric motor can be used to mechanically pulse the current in the desired manner. Most of the current built up in the coil must bypass the battery and the pulsing unit, or damage to both can result.

The device can undoubtedly become more efficient by utilizing, in part, the Hubbard principle. The above coil can be surrounded by smaller coils arranged in series and each wound in an identical manner with heavy gauge wire and using copious amounts of iron powder, as with the central coil. The input current is introduced into these coils, as with the Hubbard generator. The larger central coil remains the output coil, but is no longer both the input and output coil. The advantage of this modified version of the Hubbard device is that a higher initial EMF and current can be induced in the large coil. In addition, the magnetized iron cores of the input coils tend to induce additional magnetism in the iron of the central core, and vice versa. Since the induced EMF is directly proportional to the frequency, it is obviously advantageous to employ as high a frequency as possible. That is, within certain limits. Iron will not properly respond to frequencies much above 500 cycles. This generator should be more efficient than the original Hubbard device, because it has a superior output coil. It seems that this has been recently verified. The author has been informed that someone in California has built such a generator, based on the design just described. The large coil was eight inches in diameter and 13 inches long. The input coils were about 1½ inches in diameter. The frequency and amperage of the input current was not revealed. In any event, the output far exceeded all expectations. It burned out the coil! The author has heard that this particular individual died soon after this monumental experiment. It would be somewhat naive to assume that this was coincidental. From what has been discussed earlier successful experimenters who are a potential threat to the vested interests have always been efficiently dealt with. More than likely the biggest factor in the success of the above design is that non metallic spacers were used in the central coil. This would make it similar to an orgone accumulator and result in an inordinate concentration of soft electrons around the inner coils. The orgone accumulator effect may also have been an important factor in the success of the Hubbard device. A diagram Hubbard made of one of his smaller generators showed that it was enclosed in a four layer cannister! Perhaps later experiments showed that it worked much better if it were covered with many alternate layers of sheet metal and non-metallic sheets and may have employed it in his larger and more successful model. Perhaps the wire separation in his coils were not of the optimum distance. In the case of the caduceus coil the nodal points play an important role in its performance.

In the final analysis the use of the right type of orgone accumulator could be by far the greatest factor in the building of a practical self sustaining electric generator. It should be kept in mind that during intense auroral discharges from the egress in northern Canada into the hollow interior of the earth, transformers in Canada have been known to literally explode. If a similar orgone concentration is simulated in an accumulator with a sufficient number of layers even an ordinary transformer could be converted into a highly effective self-sustaining generator! The author suggests not just a few layers, but as many as 30 or 40 layers. Aluminum foil and paper should be very effective. It follows that covering the gas tank and gas line with multi-layers of such material would greatly increase the mileage and performance of any car. Gasoline has a great affinity for soft electrons. A high soft electron concentration in gasoline would give it a much higher heat potential. If a sufficient number of layers are used around the tank it is entirely possible that water could be used instead of gasoline! The greater the number of layers, the greater the soft electron concentration becomes. This in turn results in a greater excitation and a greater instability of soft electrons.

Motors powered by permanent magnets are another source of free energy. Several inventors have found a way of building such devices during this century. Apparently, only one of them has been willing to share his secrets with the world. His name is Howard Johnson. An amazing article concerning his discovery appeared in the spring, 1980 issue of "Science and Mechanics" magazine. The author of this article, Jarma

Hyypia, personally tested working models of this invention and found that they worked very well. Johnson has managed to patent his idea. The patent number is 4,151,431. He deserves the admiration and respect of all those interested in promoting truth.

As to be expected, the scientific community has tried to discredit him, and claim that his ideas are a violation of the law of conservation of energy. To a rational mind, the Johnson motor obviously does not violate this law. All it is doing is harnessing a minuscule portion of the kinetic energy of the orbital electrons of the atom, which are partially manifested in the magnetic fields of the magnets.

Johnson's magnetic motor consists of armature magnets and stator magnets. The stator magnets cause the armature magnets, which are attached to the rotating part of the motor, to move. The stator magnets consist of U-shaped magnets magnetized through the length, which are pointed at each end. The armature magnets are wafers, which are magnetized through the thickness. They are arranged so that the same pole is directly exposed to the stator magnets with air gaps between them as shown in the diagram.

It can be shown that the sides of the north and south poles of the armature closest to the armature magnets will experience a net force in one direction at any position, as indicated in the diagram. The opposite side of the stator magnets, or that further removed from the armature, will tend to be forced in the opposite direction. Since this side is further from the stators then the side facing the stator, the net opposite force will be weaker. Consequently, there will be a resultant force in one direction only.

The author has also designed a magnetic motor, which he feels would be still more efficient than the one just described. Tests have proven that the principle involved is valid. It makes use of unipole magnets, so that a net force is exerted at all times on armature magnets in one direction only. The unipole magnets consist of wafer magnets, magnetized through the thickness, and arranged and beveled in such a way that a unipole is the result.

The accompanying cross section diagram shows the direction of the force exerted on the armature magnets by the unipole stator magnets which consist of wafer magnets magnetized through the thickness. In all positions the force exerted on the stator is in only one direction. However, it has been found that if stator and armature magnets are arranged in a complete circle the force disappears. The reasons for this will not be given here. The optimum portion of a circle for which this force is effective is about 30 degrees. The difficulty can be surmounted by arranging a series of stators and armatures along a shaft which are each 30 degrees out of phase with each other. The armatures are all attached to a long shaft which is free to rotate. Each combination of stator and motor comprising a 30 degree of a circle is magnetically shielded from all the others. In each section the rotor magnets are far enough removed from the shields to prevent magnetic drag. This arrangement will produce a constant torque throughout the entire 360 degrees. There are any number of ways such a device can be controlled. Despite this, the author feels that DC electric motors used in conjunction with self-sustaining electric motors would be more practical than magnetic motors.

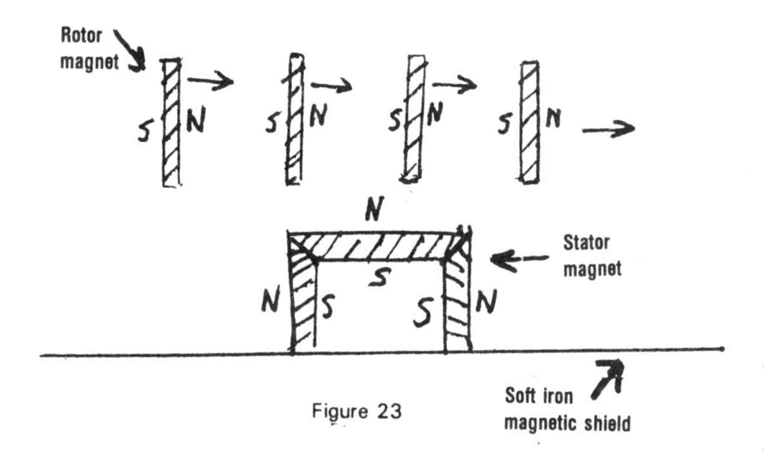

Figure 23

THE GREAT POTENTIAL OF CRYSTALS IN THE OBTAINING OF FREE ENERGY

Crystals may have played an important role in the technology

The approximate energy capacity of a one cubic foot crystal will now be calculated on the basis that the dielectric constant between the layers is unity. The presence of soft electrons produces a dielectric effect of mammoth proportions. The distance between the layers is on the order of 10^{-8} cm. This means that there are about 2.5×10^9 layers in a cubic crystal one foot long. The total area of these layers is on the order of about $.09 \times 2.5 \times 10^9$ square meters or 2.25×10^8 square meters. The formula for the capacity, C, of a parallel plate condenser is

$$C = \frac{Ake}{d}$$

where C is the capacity in farads, A is the area in square meters, k is the dielectric constant between the plates, $e = 8.85 \times 10^{-12}$ coul²/newton-meter², and d is the distance between the plates in meters. Since $A = 2.25 \times 10^8$, $k = 1$, $e = 8.85 \times 10^{-12}$, and $d = 10^{-10}$,

$$C = \frac{(2.25 \times 10^8)\ (8.85 \times 10^{-12})}{10^{-10}}\ 2 - 4 \times 10^7 \text{ farads}$$

If the dielectric effects of the soft electrons are taken into consideration, it could conceivably be $4^8 \times 10^{10}$ farads! A farad is defined as the capacitance of one coulomb of electricity contained in a capacitor, with only one volt of potential between the plates. The voltage between successive layers of molecules is beyond normal comprehension. Two plates of one square CM separated by one centimeter with a charge of one ESU have a potential of one volt. This potential varies inversely as the distance between them. The amount of charge on a layer of molecules in a crystal and the potential between the layers is astronomical. The mind of the reader will not be boggled any further by bringing these considerations into the calculations. If only one volt exists between the layers of molecules in such a crystal described above, it would contain enough free electricity at any instant to supply a 100-amp current continuously for about 10 years!

It follows from the above consideration that crystals contain practically an unlimited quantity of electricity, which is not locked up in the atoms. Civilizations of the past and builders of UFOs have found a practical way of drawing off some of the electricity from these crystals, whose store of electricity is replenished as quickly as it is tapped. It has been shown that the physical universe is impregnated with a vast ocean of conglomerates of particles comprised of photons, which cover the entire frequency range. The density of particles is virutally uniform throughout the part of space occupied by the universe, except where it is concentrat-

Figure 24

Soft protons are captured at the negative end of a crystal and soft electrons at the positive end

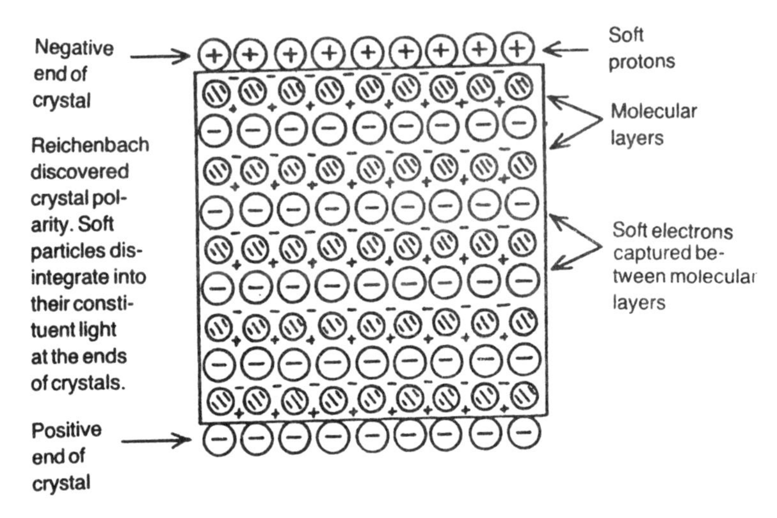

The repulsion and attraction of the fundamental particles in atoms and molecules in adjacent layers of a crystal make it equivalent to a charged condenser.

Hard electrons are camouflaged by soft electrons, which are captured between the molecular layers of a crystal. These hard electrons are drawn toward the positive side of the molecular layer due to the crystal's polarity. This makes them susceptible to escape from the soft particles.

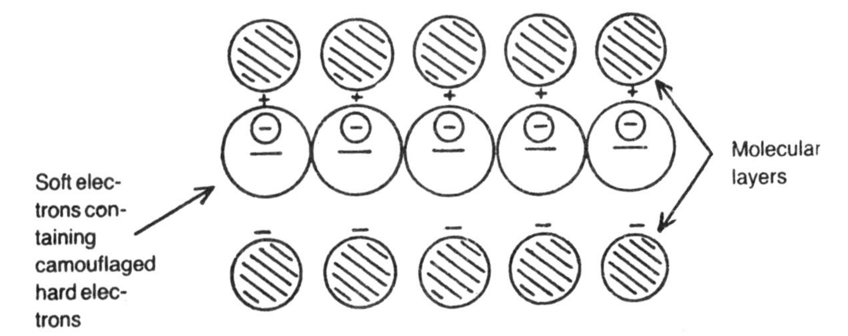

ed by bodies such as crystals.

The fundamental reason for the electrical properties of the crystal will now be given. Consider two adjacent layers of molecules. The electrons in one layer tend to repel those in the adjacent layer. This produces a partial displacement of the electrons in these layers from their normal isolated positions. The protons are likewise displaced toward the electrons in the adjacent layers, with no chance for any of the particles within the atoms to jump across. These great fields are mitigated by the soft particles permeating the crystal. An interesting effect results from this. The hard electrons contained within the soft particles tend to concentrate along the positive side of the layers. This produces a stress on one side of the soft particles, with a tendency for the hard electrons to escape from them. This renders the soft electrons more susceptible to disintegration with the consequent release of hard electrons. This suggests a method for discharging large quantities of hard electrons from crystals.

If crystals were caused to resonate by sound of the right frequencies, great numbers of the soft electrons within the crystal would disintegrate. This would release great quantities of hard electrons. The flow could be regulated by the intensity of the sound and also by periodically chopping off the sound. This is one possible source of power utilized by UFOs. The crystal could also be employed as a lethal weapon by altering the sound so that the crystal would project beams of particles of any desired intensity, both hard and soft. The origin of the expression "the terrible crystal" may have been from this application.

Perhaps the best way of tapping the energy concentrated within a crystal is by utilizing the principle described earlier, involving repeated reflections of a light beam from a combination of mirrors. A light ray, after many reflections, is converted into a beam consisting of a high concentration of soft electrons. If light traveling inside a transparent medium, such as glass or a crystal, hits the outer surface at the correct angle, it will be reflected back inside the material. This principle is employed in prism binoculars to make them more compact.

Assume the outer surface of a crystal is cut into a myriad of smooth facets at the proper angle to each other, so a light beam introduced at one of the facets will be reflected back and forth many times within the crystal before it escapes from a certain facet. If this beam experiences a sufficient number of reflections inside the crystal before it escapes, it will emerge as a potent laser. The concentration of soft electrons near the point of exit will be so intense that soft electrons housed by the crystal which are in the path of this ray will disintegrate, releasing a flow of hard

Figure 25

DIAGRAM SHOWING HOW MAGNETIC AND CONSEQUENTLY INERTIAL EFFECTS OF FLOWING ELECTRONS ARE CANCELLED IN ADJACENT SEPARATED SEGMENTS OF COIL IN HUBBARD GENERATOR.

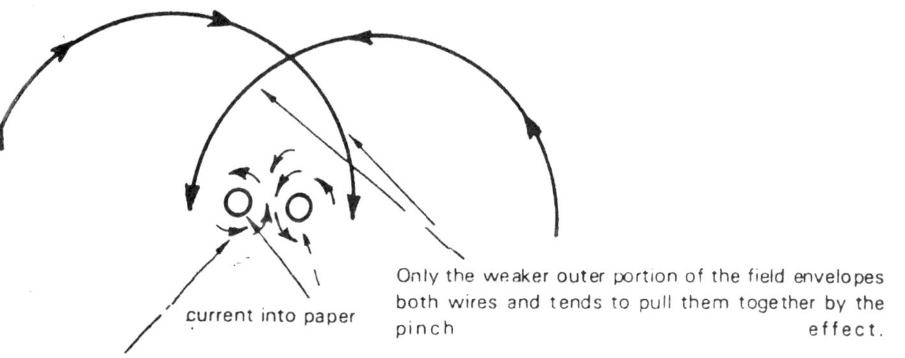

TOP VIEW OF HUBBARD GENERATOR

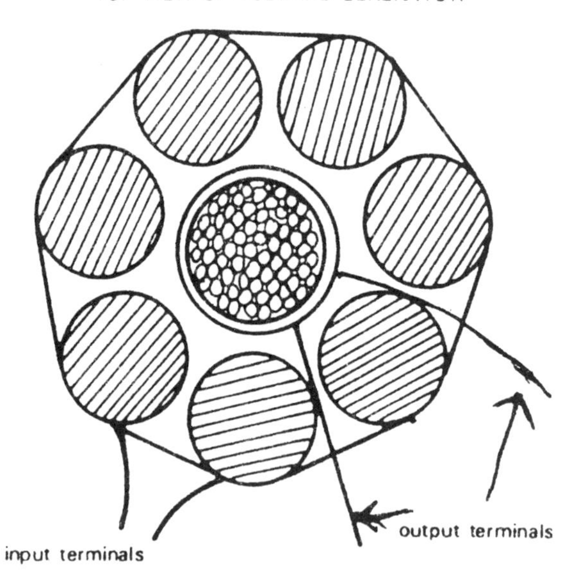

electrons from the crystal. The disintegration of soft electrons and the subsequent flow will create a void, which will tend to be filled in by surrounding concentrations. A constant flow of high voltage electricity accompanying the laser will be the result.

Crystals seem to have more of the characteristics of what is considered a life form than that of "inanimate" objects. Electron microscopes show a cellular-like structure. The size of the crystal also appears to be predetermined. A crystal grows by the orderly arrangement of atoms and molecules. There are three-dimensional constructions which cannot assume their final shape until the building process is complete. For example, one cannot start out with a replica of the complete structure in miniature, and by building on this miniature replica, end up with an enlarged version of it. The size must be predetermined and the building process must proceed with this in mind.

The conclusion that the size of a crystal is predetermined seems to be inescapable. This means an external intelligence builds the crystal in a manner analogous to an embodiment. A parallel case is the creation of bions from inert matter, as mentioned in Chapter 18, which covered Wilhelm Reich's experiments. There is one essential difference between the embodiment of an intelligence with inorganic matter and that with organic matter. There is no periodic removal and replacement of molecules and cells in the inorganic case. The molecules are permanently fixed in the body. The opposite situation exists with organic life. This makes it possible to start out with a miniature replica of the final body and steadily increase its size while maintaining the original proportions.

Pure iron crystals are the strongest substance known to science. Whiskers of iron crystals have a tensile strength of over 500,000 pounds per square inch. Scientists have failed to explain why these crystals possess such strength. Once again, the explanation is practically self-evident. Since these crystals consist of pure iron, the individual iron atoms are in closer contact with each other. This results in a more complete, magnetic orientation of the atoms. The normal cohesion added to the powerful magnetic attraction is a far greater factor than the cohesive forces alone. No comments were made public in regard to the magnetic properties of the crystals. Evidently, the whiskers were so fine that this aspect was not observed. Impurities normally found in iron prevent close mutual contact of the iron atoms, reducing the magnetic attraction of the atoms.

THE WORK OF TESLA WITH FREE ENERGY

This chapter would scarcely be complete without some mention of the work of Nikola Tesla. Of all his many inventions and ideas, it seems only one of them was oriented toward what is termed "free energy". It is his much talked about wireless transmission of electrical energy. The idea incorporates the earth as part of a resonating circuit. The earth is treated as a terrestrial conductor, which is thrown into resonance with electrical oscillations impressed upon it by a resonant circuit, which was grounded. Tesla assumed the earth would behave like a perfectly smooth or polished conductor of inappreciable resistance, with capacity and inductance uniformly distributed along the axis of wave propagation, and transmit low frequency electrical oscillations, with scarcely any distortion or attenuation. Any given conductor would have a certain natural frequency to which it would respond and produce resonance.

A receiving device could be set up any place on earth, and draw off any desired quantity of electrical energy (that is, within certain limits). The system would amount to so-called standing electrical waves of very low frequency being set up in the earth. The degree of success Tesla had with this system in his experiments at Colorado Springs during 1899-1900 is questionable. His principle is feasible in the light of concepts already introduced in this treatise.

The electrically oscillating earth generated ultra-low frequency photons, which were bounced back and forth from the earth's surface to the ionosphere. This, in turn, set the ionosphere to oscillating at a similar frequency with the subsequent generation of new photons of the same frequency. This offsets the attenuation of the original radiations by the law of redistribution and the inverse square law. As a result, a transmitter can radiate these ultra-low frequencies, and the strength of the signal scarcely diminishes as the distance from the transmitter increases. The ionosphere consists of a conglomerate of soft electrons associated with a wide range of ethers, especially the lower ethers. The majority of the soft particles is comprised of ultra-low frequency photons. Consequently, the lower the frequency of photons radiated from the earth's surface, the more likely they are to be reflected back to the earth.

A number of factors are involved in the ionosphere's maintaining its position above the earth. The earth is continuously bombarded by photons and soft electrons of all kinds from outer space. Many of them have lost most of their original velocity by the time they reach the earth, for reasons elaborated upon earlier. The earth's gravitational field repelling effects bring many of them to a halt some distance above the earth, while others continue and concentrate in the earth's shell. Those affected most by the earth's field indirectly impede others that are not affected to as great an extent by the earth's field. The slowest particles are the softest ones, which have traveled the greatest distance and have had more time to be brought down to the lower frequency by the redistribution law. Thus, the greatest concentration is of the softest particles. They concentrate in both the ionosphere and the earth's crust. This is why the ionosphere and the earth can resonate at the same frequency, and are responsible for the feasibility of the Tesla system.

Because of the range of ultra-soft electrons and photons concentrated in the ionosphere and the earth, there will be more than one resonant frequency. Experiments with ELF radiations (extremely low frequency) have indicated that the earth resonates at 8, 14 and 20 cycles per second. Tesla predicted that these frequencies would be 6, 18 and 30 cycles per second.

The photons and soft electrons associated with ELF radiations are gigantic when compared to those associated with visible light. The ELF photons are of the order of 5×10^{13} times the diameter of the photons of visible light. Consequently, ELF photons and electrons house gigantic quantities of hard electrons. The disintegration of an ELF photon or electron starts a chain reaction. The harder particles they contain disintegrate with the release and progressive disintegration of still harder particles, until the subsequent release of the hard electrons themselves. By repeated reflections the ELF radiations, which are unstable to begin with, become excited to the extent that they can easily be made to cough up the hard electrons they camouflage.

Tesla's idea was that resonance and transmission of such energies, without attenuation, could only be accomplished by using high voltage and great quantities of electrical energy. He was right in only one respect. The high energy transmission was necessary in order to tap large quantities of electricity at any place on the globe, because of the intensity of photons and soft electrons being radiated throughout the earth. However, a resonance can be achieved with low voltage energy, but the photon intensity would be low at any point. Therefore, the amount of energy that could be obtained at any point from the source would be relatively low.

It was shown earlier during the discussion on the properties of light that it is difficult, if not impossible, to obtain 100 percent monochromatic light. Any light ray of a given alleged frequency consists of a conglomerate of photons of different frequencies. They tend to be bound together by mutual magnetic attraction. The famous Land experiments demonstrated this fact. This same pattern applies to all electromagnetic frequencies down to, and including, the ELF radiations. The frequencies assigned to any radiation generated by an oscillator are the average frequencies of the photons comprising the radiations. The majority cluster around this average. Some of them are a higher frequency and some are lower. This makes the tuning of a radio receiver easier. If the incoming signal consisted entirely of monochromatic radiations or of only one kind of photons, extreme precision in tuning would be required. In fact, such precision might be beyond the capabilities of most radios.

Certain types of shielding can strip off some of the photons and soft electrons furthest removed from the average frequency of a radio signal or an ELF radiation. Physicists and technicians interpret this effect as stripping off the magnetic or electrostatic component of an electromagnetic wave. As stated earlier, the Maxwell electromagnetic theory erroneously states that a so-called electromagnetic wave consists of magnetic and electrostatic components, each at right angles to each other. This, of course, is contrary to the relationship between electrostatic and magnetic fields.

The main drawback to Tesla's idea is that everyone would be dependent upon a central power source. In case something went wrong with it, everyone would be out of power. In any event, the populace would be at the mercy of a utility company as they are today. Ironically, Tesla is the father of the present system of electric transmission, which is controlled by huge vested interests. As indicated earlier, these same interests have prevented the utilization of free energy devices. Had it not been for Tesla's contributions in this field, devices like that of Hubbard or Moray would likely have been in widespread use long before now. Consequently, the public would be independent of corporations for all their energy needs. The petroleum industry would not have the power and influence it has today, as well as many other corporations which are controlled by the same unconscionable people.

The Tesla patent on wireless transmission of electrical energy involves the use of pancake coils. A primary coil of a few turns surrounds the secondary pancake, one end of which is grounded and the other end attached to an antenna. An AC or pulsed DC put through the primary induces a tremendous flow of soft photons and electrons throughout the secondary, which are radiated outward by the antenna. Tesla claimed a great amplification of current in the secondary by this process. From the standpoint of hard electricity, he was wrong. The production of hard electricity in the secondary was marginal. However, the production of soft particles by this process is startling. This is a highly effective method of disturbing the lower ethers in order to create soft photons by the implosion process. An associate of the author duplicated this experiment with the hope of producing a high output of hard electricity from the secondary pancake coil. The results were impressive. The "electricity" produced could not be contained by the coil. It was highly penetrating and its effects were evident at considerable distances from the device. The electricity would not produce a significant shock, yet it would create the illusion of high voltage. The hard electricity induced in the secondary was minimal. The associate was both puzzled and disturbed over the result. What he did not understand was that the soft particles produced were virgin particles created directly out of the lower ethers, which had had insufficient time to captures significant numbers of harder particles.

Since Tesla did not comprehend the principles of soft particle physics, he misinterpreted the results of many of his experiments. He was not producing voltages even approximating the magnitude he and others believed he was producing, even though the soft particles created by his experiments gave the illusion of high voltage. Many of the soft particles would travel considerable distances before disintegrating and releasing harder particles. The misconceptions are identical in principle to the fallacies involving cosmic rays. The low frequency photons and soft electrons produced by Tesla experiments are relatively enormous and are capable of absorbing hard electrons.

There can be little doubt that a practical, self-sustaining electric generator, such as those already described, would be vastly superior to the Tesla system. Tesla was a great electrical engineer and inventor. His ability was tremendously enhanced by a photographic memory and strong psychic and mediumistic abilities. By his own admission, etheric images, or thought forms of something he was trying to invent would appear in front of him, showing all the working parts. All he needed to do was reconstruct it, as it was shown to him. His invention of the AC electric motor came about in this manner. Exterior intelligences no doubt projected these images that could not be seen by anyone other than a psychic with clairvoyance.

Despite these special abilities, Tesla was neither a theorist nor a profound abstract thinker. He was at odds with Einstein in regard to the relativity theory, but for the wrong reasons. He didn't believe matter could be converted into energy or vice versa, until the splitting of the Uranium 235 atom in 1939, with its consequent release of energy. He then changed his mind. It is ironic that Tesla was unwittingly correct in his original assertion concerning relativity, but was unable to see that the experiment with U235 did not demonstrate the conversion of matter into energy. He was also taken in by the false and highly illogical theories and teachings of Walter Russell, as many others were. He thought Russell's ideas were too advanced for the time, and that the world would not be ready for them for at least 100 years. (The evaluation of Russell's scientific ideas will be given in Part IV.) Tesla's life style and the manner in which he handled personal problems were not what one would expect of a great intellect.

Figure 26
THE CADUCEUS COIL

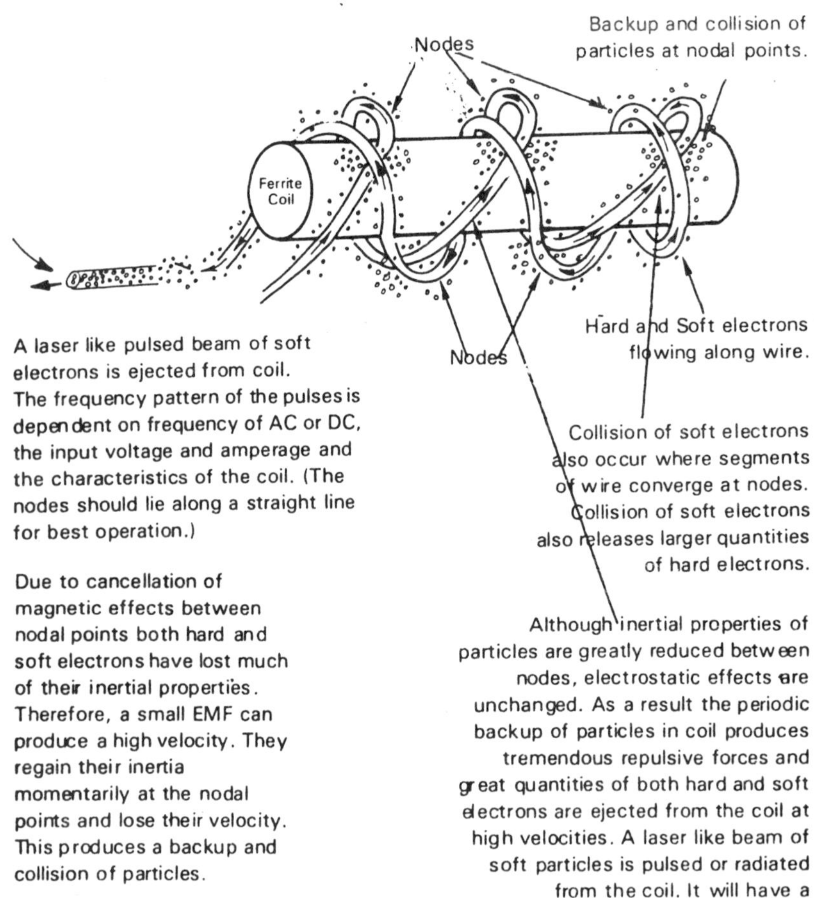

CHAPTER 22

THE SEARL EFFECT AND RELATED UFO PHENOMENA

The Searl effect was discovered by an English electronic technician named John Searl in 1949.(109) He noticed a small EMF or voltage was induced in rotating metal objects. The negative charge was on the outside, and the positive charge was around the center of rotation. He reasoned that free electrons were thrown outward by centrifugal force, leaving a positive charge in the central portion. It followed that an electrical generator might be built utilizing this principle.

He constructed his first generator in 1952, and tested it outdoors. Its performance and behavior far exceeded his expectations. The armature was rotated by a small engine. It produced a powerful electrostatic effect on nearby objects, accompanied by crackling sounds and the smell of ozone. Beyond a critical rotational speed, the armature continued to accelerate without the aid of the engine. The generator finally lifted off the ground, while still accelerating, and rose about 50 feet, breaking the connection between it and the engine. It remained at this height for a brief period, while still increasing its rotational velocity. At this time, a pink halo surrounded it, indicating ionization of the surrounding atmosphere at an extremely low pressure. It also caused local radio receivers to go on of their own accord. While still accelerating, it apparently reached another critical rotational velocity, at which stage it rapidly gained altitude and disappeared.

Since 1952, Searl and others have constructed numerous generators of varying sizes from 3 to 30 feet in diameter. Some of them have been lost in a similar manner. They claim to have developed a means of controlling them in the process.

Explanations for the phenomena just described are easily determined from the new concepts presented. When the armature rotated, soft particles impregnating the material were thrown outward, leaving a low concentration around the center. Although Searl's reasoning was partially correct, he was wrong in assuming that free, hard electrons were affected by the centrifugal force. A similar effect is demonstrated by drag racers. It enables them to accelerate an average of about two G's over the quarter-mile course. The coefficient of friction between rubber and pavement is somewhat less than one, yet the performance of drag racers seems to indicate that this coefficient is much greater than two! Soft electrons are forced outward by the centrifugal force and readily penetrate the tire, producing a strong negative charge around the tire. This results in a bond between the tire and the road surface of sufficient strength to prevent slippage. It is interesting to note that there is considerable wheel spin before the dragster takes off. The wheels need to attain a sufficient rotational velocity before the bond between tire and road surface is enough to compensate for the power surge applied to the wheels.

The low concentration of soft electrons at the center of the Searl generator, due to the centrifugal force of the rotating armature, produced a rush of soft electrons from surrounding areas toward the center. This was expedited by the metallic construction of the armature. The principle is similar to that involved in Reich's cloudbuster. Since the armature was not a solid disk, but consisted of spokes like a wheel, a vortex motion of soft electrons above and below it was generated. Ionized air molecules tended to be carried along with this motion of soft particles by electrostatic forces. The vortex motion was in the same direction as that of the armature. The abnormal activity of soft electrons permeating the armature released a high concentration of harder electrons throughout the material of the armature. This in turn lessened the inertial properties.

The combination of the reduced inertia and the torque induced by the vortex soon enabled the armature to turn without the aid of the engine. The overall charge of the armature became slightly negative because of the presence of the additional electrons released in the material. As a result, it was repelled upward by the earth's gravitational field. The highest concentration of soft electrons is close to the ground. When the generator rose above this concentration, there was a temporary reduction or loss of its negative charge, causing it to stop rising temporarily. Since the rotational velocity was steadily increasing, the negative charge finally increased again to the extent that it continued its ascent.

The concentration of soft particles ejected laterally from the generator was so great that many disintegrated, thereby releasing enormous quantities of hard electrons. This drove most of the air molecules away from the periphery of the generator. This produced a heavily ionized section of rarified air. The pink halo around the generator was evidence of this. It was also noticed that the generator carried some of the ground with it as it rose. This was a result of the powerful electrostatic forces produced in the generator by the hard electrons released from disintegrating soft electrons.

The automatic turning on of local radio receivers was caused by the flow of hard and soft electrons in all directions. Many of the soft particles were rendered partially unstable by collisions with air molecules and other soft particles. When they entered the circuits of radio receivers, they released hard electrons having a wide range of voltages. The concentration in the circuits was sufficient to produce the necessary amperage and voltage to operate the receivers.

Many researchers believe the Biefeld-Brown effect mentioned earlier is a major factor in the behavior of the Searl generator. From the analysis just presented, it is apparent that this is not the case. The Biefeld-Brown effect has also been erroneously termed the electrogravitational effect. This is a misnomer, since the Biefeld-Brown effect is the result of the greater affinity electrons have for protons than do protons for electrons. This effect has no more relationship to gravity than does the rocket principle. However, it can be utilized as a highly sophisticated means of space propulsion in conjunction with the Searl generator. This might be superior to the method suggested earlier, using gravity-inducing radiations for space travel! When the inertial properties of a spaceship and its contents have been nullified by the Searl effect, only a slight force exerted on its exterior could give it unlimited acceleration. Condensers attached to the outside of a ship could be used to exert a force in any desired direction, utilizing the Biefeld-Brown effect.

Interestingly enough, the phenomena associated with the Searl effect are similar to those observed around many UFOs. It is more than likely that most UFOs employ this principle. According to information received by the author about 30 years ago, which supposedly came from the Air Force, UFOs have been clocked by Doppler radar accelerating as much as 1500 Gs. This might be difficult to achieve with gravity-inducing radiations alone. UFOs may also use crystals to generate the concentration of charges needed for the above mentioned purposes. Perhaps they can be utilized even more effectively than the Searl effect for this.

Several other well-known types of phenomena associated with UFOs need to be explained. UFOs have been known to freeze large ponds of water or ground over which they have been hovering. They have also accomplished the opposite, and burned or dehydrated areas of ground and vegetation. An analysis of heat transfer and generation is mandatory in order to understand such phenomena.

The temperature of a body increases when it receives more soft particles than it is radiating. The temperature increase is the result of the soft particles, which disintegrate inside the body and release the hard particles they contain. The sudden presence of hard particles and especially electrons, which are not a part of the molecules, then agitate them. This generates an increase in temperature. Incidentally, it is the disintegrating soft particles releasing hard electrons that are responsible for thermionic emission.

If a body of moderate size receives no soft particles from outside sources, it will soon reach a state in which all of its molecules are in equilibrium with each other, and all relative motion ceases. This is a condition known as absolute zero or zero degrees kelvin. Practically all the soft particles generated by the body pass through it, and are radiated outward without disintegrating. If a body is of sufficient size, most of the soft particles it generates disintegrate before they can reach the surface, and a radiating body like the sun or the larger planets is the result.

The reason for the burning and freezing effects of UFOs is now apparent. A UFO employing the Searl effect can quickly draw all of the soft particles away from a given area or body, and a rapid drop in temperature occurs.

The same principle is unwittingly applied by physicists and technicians in achieving extremely low temperature. A magnetic field is employed. When the correct polarity is used, it draws soft particles away from the material being cooled. UFOs produce the burning effect by discharging great concentrations of soft particles at high velocities into a given area. It has also been noticed that UFOs passing over bodies of water cause water directly below them to move upward in a series of wavelets. The same principle was involved when Searl's generators carried chunks of ground with them as they moved upward.

The Searl effect is deeply involved with the behavior of everything that spins on an axis. Consider the spinning top or gyro. Conventional science has never come up with anything even remotely resembling an explanation concerning its behavior. Physicists try to create the illusion that they understand it and camouflage their ignorance with nebulous descriptions of its action accompanied by meaningless equations. A precessing gyro actually confutes the basic foundations of conventional physics. For example, as it precesses, its center of mass extends well beyond its point of contact with the surface. It should tip over according to all the rules of academic physics. What force prevents it? Also the moment of inertia increases with the RPM, a property which is utilized for stabilizers. Also according to the "laws" of orthodox physics, the moment of inertia is a constant.

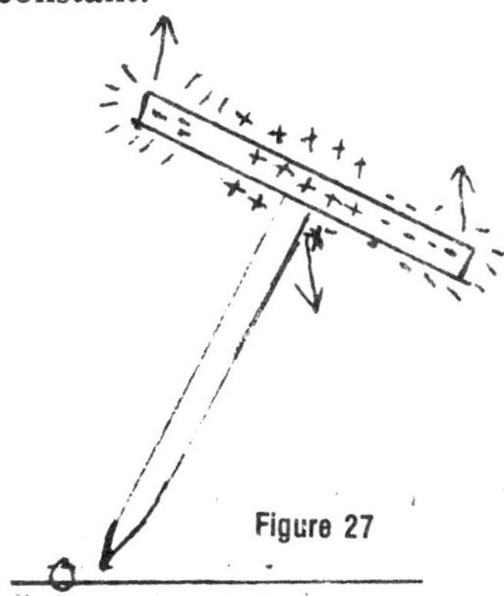

Figure 27

The explanation becomes almost self-evident in the light of principles already expounded upon. At a critical RPM, the outer rim becomes heavily charged negatively while the portion closer to the center of mass begins to take on a positive charge. The rim tends to be repelled upward by the earth's gravity. The total effect is a counterclockwise moment about the point of contact, O, which counter-balances the clockwise torque tending to tip it over.

The greater tendency for a rotating body to maintain its plane of rotation which produces a stabilizing effect is the result of the increase in the moment of inertia. The outer portion is given a total negative charge which is greater than that of its original positive when it was at rest. This means that the mass comprising the outer portion has a greater overall inertia than it had before. This portion of greatly increased inertia is also further removed from the center of mass than the rest of the body which accentuates the moment of inertia and also the portion closer to the center of mass or rotation has a higher net positive charge than it had before. This means that its inertial properties have also increased which also adds to the moment of inertia.

The opposite effect is produced by the more advanced stages of the Searle effect, especially when the disc is metallic and spoked. The rapid flow of negative charges through the disc prevents the build-up of high negative charges throughout the disc. At the same time the net positive charge nearer the center is nullified.

The precession of a gyro is another property in which explanations by "scientists" consist only of descriptions. The moment of the momentum of a precessing top about the point of contact, 0, is the key. The moment of the portion of the disc further removed from 0 in a horizontal direction is in the direction of rotation. The moment of the portion on the opposite side of the disc is closer to 0 in a horizontal direction and is also in the opposite direction to the other half of the disc. The result is a net

Figure 28
PRINCIPLE OF SEARLE GENERATOR

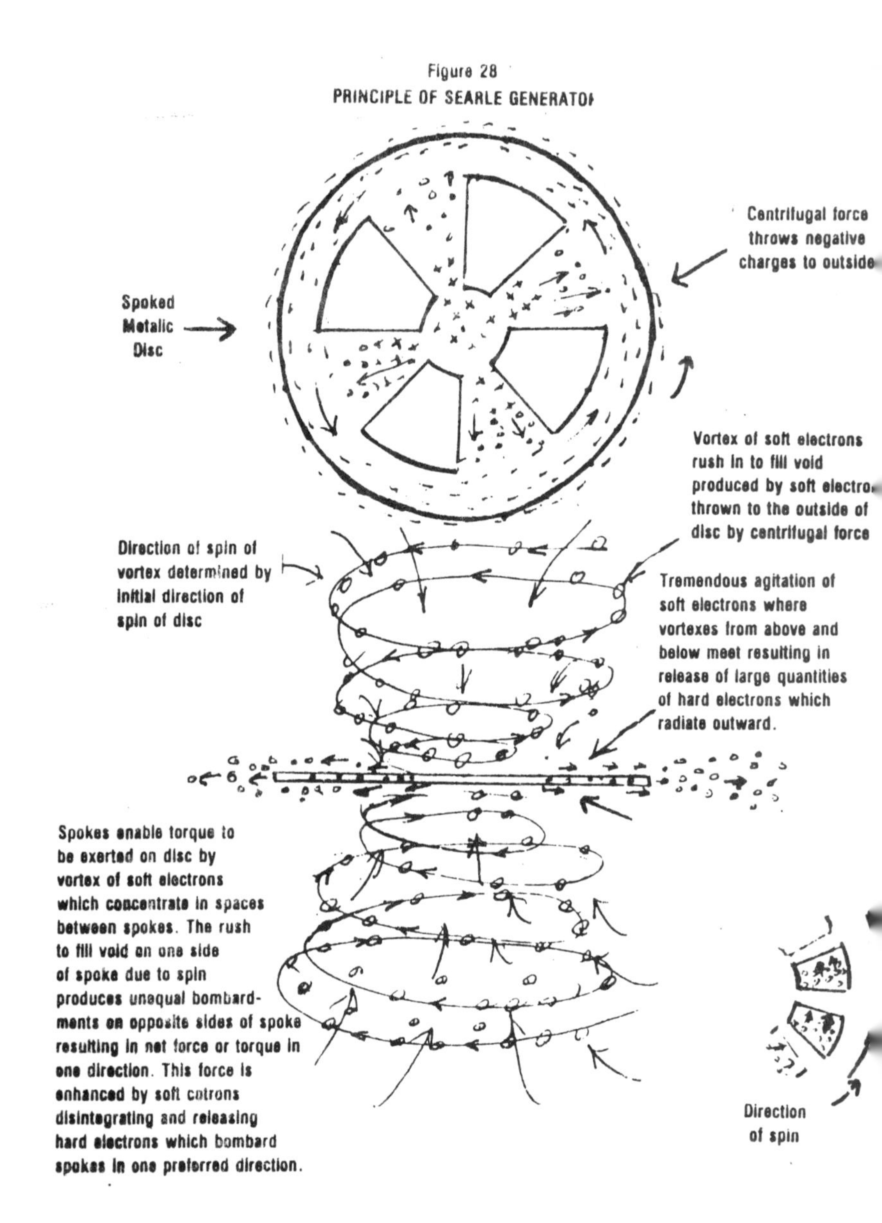

torque about 0, in the direction of spin. As the RPM increases, the greater the repelling force on the rim of the gyro. This results in a greater tendency of the gyro to assume a vertical position. The difference in the clockwise and counter-clockwise moments of momentum becomes less and thus the rate of precession decreases.

The British scientist Eric Laithwaite demonstrated in 1974 the validity of what has just been presented. He had two electronically driven gyroscopes, each of which was placed on a hinged metal arm fixed to a central pivot. He made the gyroscopes rotate at high speed and they rose in the air on the arms until they reached a curved rail that pushed them down again. The process then repeated. When the gyros were motionless, the entire assembly weighed 20 pounds. With the gyros spinning, the contraption weighed 15 pounds. The gyros rose on the hinged arm because of mutual electrostatic repulsion, produced by the strong negative charge caused by the Searle effect. The strong mutual repulsion would also impregnate the gyros to their center with negative charges. When they reached the curved rails they lost much of their rotational velocity and consequently dropped back to their original positions. Despite the fact that this demonstration was made at the Royal Institute at London in front of distinguished "scientists", it received little publicity because it was too damaging to accepted theories.

It is interesting to note that the principle of the Searle generator as shown in the above diagram also provides proof that soft electrons have no preferred direction of spin. If they did the forces involved in the spin of the disc would tend to cancel out and the Searle generator would not perform as it does.

The principles elaborated upon in this chapter are demonstrated by an enigmatic toy known as the trippe top. Its behavior has completely baffled everyone, including the prominent physicists although they are reluctant to admit it. They try to cover up their ignorance with an assortment of vacuous explanations, none of which are in agreement. This top consists of an hemispherical mass attached to a stem as shown in the accompanying diagrams. When it is spun with the hemisphere resting on the surface it quickly flips over and starts spinning with the stem as a base. More surprisingly, the direction of rotation of the mass is now reversed. This means that from a top view the direction of rotation has not changed. This violates all of the conventional rules of academic physics including the energy conservation law since the center of mass in the second stage is higher that it was initially.

The following explanation may perhaps be the least odious of all the inane explanations offered by physicists. Jearl Walker, in *Scientific American*, claims the simplest explanation ("simple minded" would be a more apt terminology) is that the flip over "arises from friction between the top and the surface on which it spins." That is, whenever the spin axis tilts away from the vertical the top slides on part of its spherical surface. The friction creates a torque that precesses the top to an inversion.

This is in keeping with the standard explanation of why a spinning top precesses. "Precession results from the torque due to gravity." It has not been made clear how a given force can directly produce another force in a direction perpendicular to that of the original force. Such explanations as above are an affront to the intelligence of even a semi-rational person.

Diagrams C and D clearly show how the Searle effect in conjunction with gravity produces the flip-over. The hemispherical base has a strong negative charge around its outermost periphery. The resultant levitation effect reduces the weight of the top. The centrifugal force around the stem is much weaker than that around the hemisphere. Consequently there is little change in gravity effects in this region. This results in a net torque about the center of mass in the direction of the flip. This torque increases as the angle of tilt increases.

The change in direction of rotation remains to be explained. The reason is evident from diagram E which shows an end view of the hemisphere in conjunction to the surface. The side moving toward the surface experiences a greater braking effect than the opposite side moving away from the surface. It is analogous to an object moving against the wind and one moving with the wind. There is always a concentration of soft electrons at a surface. The negative charges at the periphery will encounter greater repulsive forces at the side moving toward the surface than that moving away from it. There tends to be a greater compression of soft electrons on one side than on the opposite one. It should also be kept in mind that as the rotation slows down and stops, a residual negative charge remains around the outside long enough for it to be given an impetus in the opposite direction. A greater number of hard electrons have been released on the one side at the surface than on the opposite side because the soft electrons at the former location have experienced greater agitation. Thus F_1 in the diagram is greater than F_2. The effect is similar in principle to a compressed spring being released or a ball thrown against a wall bouncing back.

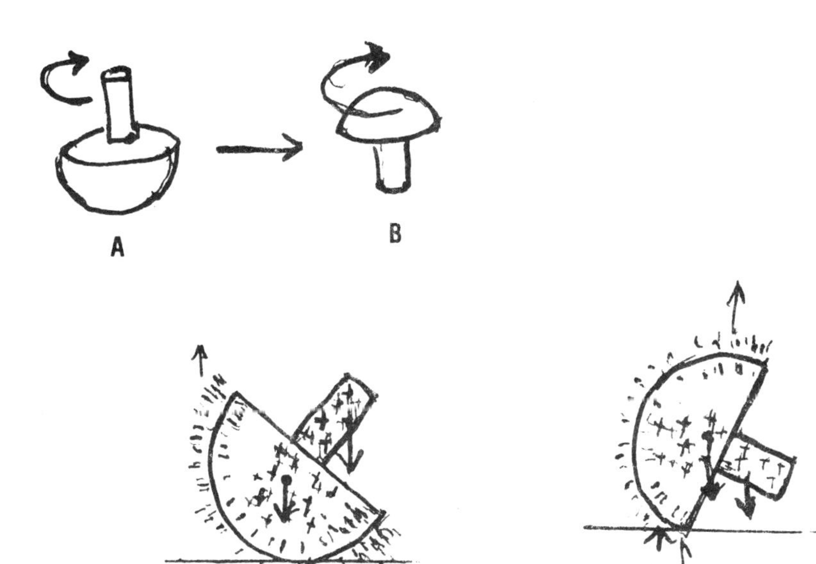
A
B
C
D

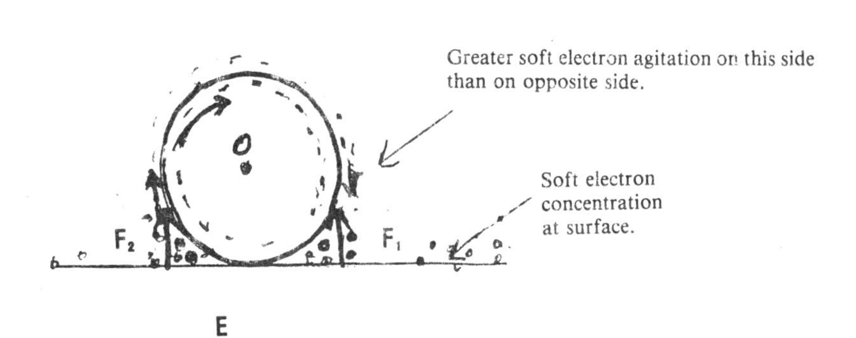
Greater soft electron agitation on this side than on opposite side.
Soft electron concentration at surface.
F_2
F_1
O
E

SUMMARY OF PART III

Part III developed new ideas introduced in Parts I and Part II to a higher degree. It presented revolutionary concepts which will enable the more astute reader to comprehend some of the most baffling, borderland phenomena known to man, which will be presented in Part IV. Fundamental weaknesses and limitations of present mathematical techniques were outlined. The nature of the ethers, light, soft particles, gravitation, electrostatic and magnetic fields, and the structure of the fundamental particles were explained and integrated by the unifying principle, for the first time in the entire history of this civilization.

These new insights made simple explanations possible for well-known anomalies which had never before been explained. These included the properties of helium at low temperatures, the Oregon vortex, certain gravitational paradoxes, and others. Some of the great research work of Wilhelm Reich was explained for the first time. It was shown that the Reich cloudbuster can be used to deactivate all modern weaponry yet hundreds of billions are extorted from the American public each year to support a multibillion dollar nuclear and armament industry and also a parasitic military organization for our alleged "protection". The effects of a cloudbuster are a wonderful confirmation of principles elaborated upon which show that soft electrons are vital to all the chemical and life processes. By drawing soft electrons away from a given region no chemical changes can take place in that area. The technology for the complete prevention of loss of life and property from fire and storm has been known for a long time but miscreants in positions of authority have managed to suppress it until now. Finally, a number of free energy devices were explained and descriptions given for practical inventions which can be built by the more enterprising researcher.

PART IV

THE UNIFYING PRINCIPLE APPLIED TO BORDERLAND PHENOMENA

INTRODUCTION TO PART IV

Part IV deals with the most perplexing phenomena known to man. The anomalies to be analyzed here are so far beyond present understanding that entirely new concepts had to be devised in order to cope with them. The previous three major sections have laid the necessary groundwork and supplied the tools for probing into these aspects of natural phenomena. The explanations to be presented are, again, with reference to the hermetic axioms.

Phenomena to be analyzed for the first time include teleportation, spirit manifestation, the science of psionics, apparent discrepancies and anomalies of time, and other related topics. The forces and causes which have shaped the destiny of this planet and have brought it to its present state of being, will also be touched upon. Some of the more important research of great pioneers in fields outside the domain of academic science will be included. This will cover the work of such scientists as Von Reichenbach, De La Warr, Lakhovsky, and Brunler.

The summary given thus far by no means outlines the entire scope of Part IV. Other surprises and revelations await the reader. It is impossible for a book of this size to cover all of the strange types of recorded phenomena. Consequently, the author has selected what he considers to be the most unique and baffling to be included in this part, with the assurance that others not discussed here can be dealt with in like manner and with an equal degree of efficiency.

CHAPTER 23

THE EXTRAORDINARY RESEARCH OF BARON CARL VON REICHENBACH

It is fitting to begin this part of the treatise with an introduction to some of the more significant findings of Baron Carl Von Reichenbach, since much of his research confirms many of the concepts elaborated upon in the first three parts. Von Reichenbach was undoubtedly the greatest experimental scientist of the nineteenth century, even though he received little recognition for his work. Much of his work was outside the domain of what is considered material science, which is the primary reason he has generally been ignored. His experimental and theoretical work in the occult and physical fields far surpassed that of those who have slighted him.

Von Reichenbach experimented with orgone energy, as did Wilhelm Reich, but each used different terminologies. Sensitives were employed in many of Von Reichenbach's experiments, which enabled him to gain insights he would not otherwise have obtained. "Sensitives" are defined as individuals whose senses are more highly developed than those of normal people. Hence, they perceive stimuli which are too tenuous to be recorded by the normal senses. Such procedures are frowned upon, even today, by the narrow and inflexible thinking of orthodox scientists and are denounced as unscientific. These scientists do not possess the mental prowess necessary to realize how the proper use of sensitives in the hands of a genius can be as objective as any laboratory procedure. There is a great deal that present day researchers can still learn by studying the research work of Von Reichenbach.

Carl Von Reichenbach was born at Stuttgart, Germany, February 12, 1788, and died in Liepsic, January 22, 1869. He built an industrial empire during his youth consisting of iron, steel and metallurgical establishments. He is perhaps the only industrialist in history who achieved true eminence in any scientific or intellectual pursuit. He made a number of important chemical discoveries during the building of his empire, including creosote and paraffin. After amassing considerable wealth, he retired from the business world in 1839 to devote all his time to scientific research. He was unique among all the big industrialists in mental capacity, and he used his wealth as a stepping stone to higher attainments.

Most of his experiments dealt with the properties of magnetic fields, light, and the energies which are termed soft particles. Some of these energies were known in his day as "animal magnetism" and the "vital force". Von Reichenbach grouped them into one category which he called "od". Because of the vast extent of his research, only a few of the highlights can be presented here.

The sensitives employed by Von Reichenbach consistently observed a luminosity at the poles of magnets when in a dark room. The rays of light were not at rest. They continuously fluctuated in length and exhibited a scintillating effect displaying all the colors of the rainbow, including white. In general, the luminosity resembled the light of the sun. Some of them saw this more clearly than others. Von Reichenbach concluded that the Aurora Borealis is the same kind of phenomenon. The Aurora Borealis is primarily caused by the disintegration of soft particles into their consitutent light photons as they accumulate in the upper atmosphere at the high latitudes. The light patterns and colors seen around magnets were identical to those of the northern lights. There is a higher concentration in the atmosphere, in the higher latitudes, due to the magnetic radiations through the large egress from the inner earth near the north pole, as explained earlier. A similar principle produces the light effects at the poles of magnets, since the concentration of soft particles captured by the magnetic field is much greater at the poles. Figure 22 depicts this effect.

An electromagnet produces the same results as a permanent magnet. It is interesting to note that the light at the poles of the electromagnet persisted after the current was turned off, when the iron bar was no longer a magnet. The concentration of particles produced by the original magnetic field remained for a brief period, with a continued disintegration of the more unstable particles. When the poles of the electromagnet were placed close to those of a permanent horseshoe magnet, an interesting thing was observed. Von Reichenbach describes it on page 32 of *The Dynamics of Magnetism, Electricity, Heat, Light, Crystallization and Chemism* as follows: "The flame of the steel magnet was completely turned aside by that of the electromagnet, and as distinctly as the current of a blow pipe directs the flame of a candle."(101) Von Reichenbach did not mention whether or not like poles were adjacent to each other. Regardless of whether like or unlike poles were in juxtaposition, the light around the electromagnetic was little affected by the permanent magnet. This is to be expected, as the electromagnet is much stronger than the permanent magnet, and will concentrate a much higher charge with a consequently far greater mass, than that captured by the weaker magnet. Being of like charge, the heavier concentration will push the lighter one away, without itself being moved to any great extent.

A photographic plate was placed in front of a magnet and sealed in a box. This was done to find out if it was real light which was seen around the magnets. After 64 hours, it was found that the plate exposed to the magnet had indeed shown the effect of the light, whereas the control plate which wasn't exposed to a magnet had in no way been affected. This also verifies another principle mentioned in the chapter on Wilhem Reich. It is the disintegrating soft particles releasing hard electrons which affect a photographic plate and promote chemical changes.

Other Von Reichenbach experiments with magnets also gave conclusive evidence that the energies seen around a magnet are soft particles of varying degrees of stability. Some of them are always disintegrating into light of various frequencies. Von Reichenbach concluded that the emanations had a dual nature, which he called the magnetic or odic flame and the magnetic light. The light seemed to possess all the characteristics of a flame. It would curve around objects placed inside it and would flare divergently to the side when blown upon like any other flame. From this flame issued scintillating lights, which he called the magnetic light.

As further evidence that this magnetic "flame" is really a concentration of soft electrons, another passage from page 240 of his treatise is given:

> . . . The odic flames, even when they blaze forth side by side from the poles of a horseshoe magnet, display no attraction; nay, even when the unlike polar flames are directed immediately toward one another, not only are they not attracted when brought close, but are even mutually repelled at the places where they are forced to meet. This is directly contradictory to all we know of magnetism.(101)

This effect is depicted in Figure 22. Since the outline of soft electron concentrations was being observed, it is to be expected that they would tend

Figure 29
REICHENBACH'S EXPERIMENTS WITH MAGNETS IN A DARK ROOM

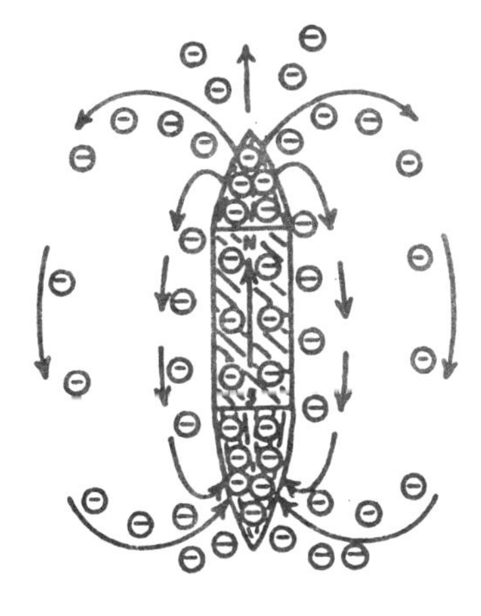

The odic flame is seen at the ends of a magnet

Odic light is produced by the increased interaction of soft particles which disintegrate into their constituent light.

The flow is out of the N pole and into the S pole. By the time the flow reaches the S pole, the field has captured additional soft electrons. This is why the odic flame is largest at the S pole.

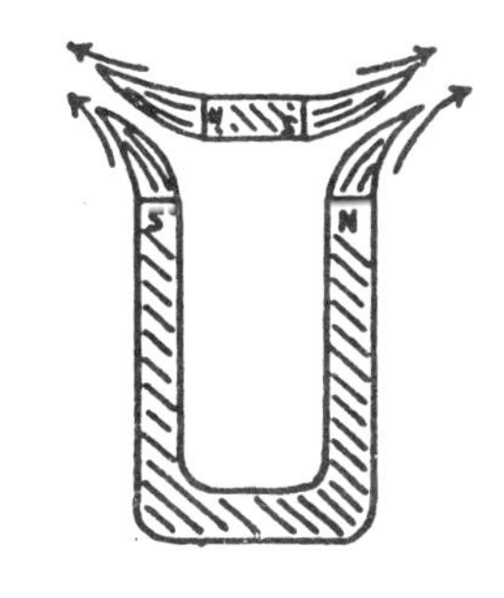

Odic flames repel each other when magnets are placed in the configuration as shown. This demonstrates that the energies around the poles of magnets consist of like charges or soft electrons.

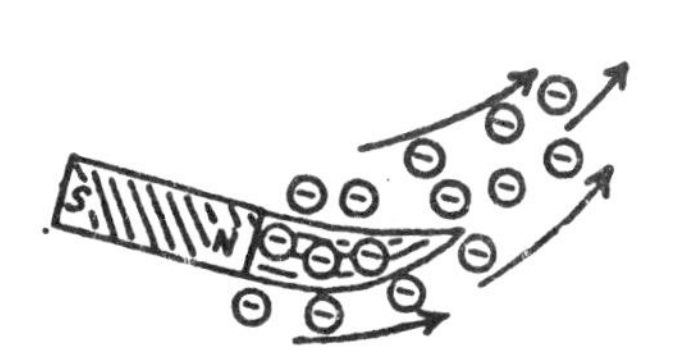

As considerable distances beyond the pole of a powerful horizontally placed bar magnet, the flame rises in opposition to earth gravity. Particles ejected from the pole at high velocity are carried beyond the magnetic field. Consequently, they come under the influence of the earth's gravitational field which repels them. This is another confirmation that negative charges are repelled by a gravitational field and that the particles consist of negative soft electrons.

to repel each other.

Sensitives also noticed the end of the magnet from which the lines flowed produced the sensation of heat, while the opposite pole felt cool. This is in conformity with the normal pattern of objects, which produce the sensation of heat or coolness. It has been shown that one pole of a magnet forces soft particles into a substance, while the opposite pole draws them out. A warm body forces heat into a substance, while the cold body draws heat away from it.

Von Reichenbach also found that the odic flame at the pole of the magnet into which the lines flowed, or the drawing end, was about twice the size of the flame at the opposite pole. Since the magnetic flow follows a closed curve which passes through the magnet itself, many of the soft particles producing the odic flame are dispersed during their passage through the dense material of the magnet. As a result, only about half of them emerge at the other end of the magnet from which the magnetic current flows. By the time the flow curves around and enters the other pole again, it has picked up new particles.

It is significant that the larger flame produces more of the blue and bluish gray light corresponding to orgone energy. At the other end of the magnet, the colors tend to be red, reddish yellow, and reddish gray. The particles comprised of higher frequency photons are not as penetrating as particles consisting of lower frequency photons. Therefore, the particles comprised of the higher frequency photons are more readily dispersed. Although blue was the predominant color seen at one pole and red at the other, all the colors of the rainbow were seen at both poles. This is not surprising, since soft electrons of all kinds are captured by the magnetic field. The pole of the magnet with a predominantly red light also harbors a higher percentage of the infrared, which produces the sensation of heat. The light around the opposite pole in the higher frequencies contains a lower percentage of the infrared. This, combined with the tendency for the pole to draw energy out of a body, produced the sensation of coolness.

Another significant discovery of Von Reichenbach was that crystals produced identically the same effects on sensitives as magnets did. They created similar light effects in a dark room, and one end produced a cooling effect while the other end generated a warming sensation. This tends to confirm the analysis of crystals given in Part III. Since crystals are great capacitors, one end possesses a negative electrostatic effect. As explained previously, they concentrate a large quantity of soft electrons, which contain harder electrons inside. The negative end of a crystal tends to give up electrons to an organism with a lower potential. Since soft electrons congregate around a crystal, there is the usual disintegration of the more unstable particles due to collisions.

Von Reichenbach found that the human body displays polarities similar to those of a crystal or battery. The right-hand side is negatively charged and the left-hand side is positively charged. Another passage from page 115 of Von Reichenbach's great treatise is in order:

> . . . The same force really resides in the human hands as manifests itself in crystals; thus the crystallic force and the so-called animal magnetism are thoroughly identical, and therefore the same laws which rule the former are also fully applicable to the latter . . .(101)

These same energies are applied by a healer during the traditional "laying on of hands". By placing both hands on the subject, the circuit is completed and a flow of soft electrons moves from the right hand toward the left, permeating the patient with healing energies during the process. Some healers don't require direct contact. They are able to project energies out of the hands and into the subject.

Von Reichenbach performed an experiment in which a metal plate was exposed to sunlight. A wire was connected to the plate and extended into a darkened room. The end of the wire inside the closed room always felt cool to the subjects he used. This was a result of the photoelectric effect. The sunlight had a tendency to drive electrons from the surface of the metal, giving it a positive charge. This caused a drawing of electrons from the end of the wire held by the sensitives. Reichenbach also performed the same experiment with moonlight. This time sensitives holding the end of the wire experienced a sensation of warmth. The reflected light from the moon consists mainly of lower frequency radiation. This is another application of the law of redistribution of energy. In addition to its interaction with the moon, reflected light also has to pass through the moon's atmosphere twice. The lower frequency radiation doesn't produce as strong a photoelectric effect. This caused the plate to retain more of its conglomeration of negative charges at the surface. This and the greater ability of the plate to repel and slow down soft electrons reflected from the moon gave the plate a higher concentration of soft electrons, which would flow along the wire to the sensitives. These energies contain a higher percentage of infrared, which contributed to the heat sensation.

Von Reichenbach also found, as others have, that terrestrial magnetism is always lower during a full moon than during a new moon. Large bodies of planetary dimensions have a strong positive charge for the reasons given in Part III. This is why negative charges have a strong tendency to flow to the ground. When the moon receives radiation from the sun, many of the positive charges in this radiation are repelled back into space by the positive field of the planet. This repelling force is much stronger within a very small zone, close to the surface, than is the gravitational attraction. It is enough to give the positive charges, which always travel much more slowly than negative charges, a high enough velocity to escape from the moon and reach the earth's atmosphere. The subsequent increase in the number of positive charges in the atmosphere produces cancellation effects in the magnetic field. Positive charges are inimical to living organisms. This explains why people are strongly affected by a full moon, and the origin of the term "lunacy".

Other experiments which Von Reichenbach performed with magnets provide additional evidence that the particles captured by a magnetic field are predominantly soft electrons of various kinds. On pages 289-290 of his treatise, Von Reichenbach explained what happened when the end of the magnet with the blue odic flame was pointed toward a large body with a positive charge:

> . . . The intensity of the light was exalted, the blue became brighter. When I turned the magnet round and directed the southward, positive, red, lighted side, to the positive conductor, not only did all the red quickly disappear, but it shortly turned into blue. The odic polarities were reversed; the Od-positive turned toward E-positive, was converted into Od-negative and in correspondence with this the blue Od-negative of the distant side of the magnet was changed into red-glowing od.
>
> I reversed the experiments by electrifying the conductor negatively. It now acted in the reverse way upon the odic poles of the magnets. It changed the Od-negative, blue-glowing pole, turned towards it, into a red-glowing; the Od-positive pole, at that time turned away from it, into a blue-glowing, Od-negative, all at the distance of forty inches . . .(101)

When the opposite pole was turned toward the negatively charged body, the original colors were enhanced. When the body was no longer electrified, the poles on both ends became pale and then returned to their original colors in a matter of seconds.

These different experiments can now be analyzed and it will be shown that each is in harmony with principles previously presented in this treatise. When the large body is charged positively, soft electrons comprised of higher frequency or blue photons are more strongly attracted to it, than soft electrons of the lower frequency red photons. This is because the body is charged with hard particles. This tendency will be directly proportional to the frequency of the photons of which the attracted particles are comprised. This produces higher than normal concentrations of higher frequency soft electrons in the vicinity of the charged body. When the blue-glowing end of the magnet was turned toward this positively charged body, the magnetic field captured more soft electrons of the higher frequency photons. This means more disintegrations of such soft electrons occured. This produced a more intense blue light. This blue effect is enhanced by the magnetic field having a greater tendency to capture soft particles made up of higher frequency photons.

When the blue end was in the presence of this positive electrostatic field, the red end of the magnet became brighter. The higher percentage of the particles, which manage to get through the magnet and concentrate at the opposite end, are the softer particles which contain more of the red. This results in the brighter red seen at that pole. The soft electrons of higher frequency photons have a more difficult time getting through the magnet. Two factors are involved. First, the material of the magnet and the energies concentrated within offer greater resistance to the passage of particles comprised of higher frequency photons. Second, the positive electrostatic field has a greater pull on those particles than on the softer electrons. This attractive force is in the opposite direction to the magnetic flow.

When the positive or red-glowing end of the magnet was turned toward the positive charge, the conditions for the capture of soft electrons of higher frequency photons were greatly improved. The concentration of such particles near the conductor was greater. The soft electrons responsible for the blue glow at the end which was turned away from the conductor were drawn toward the conductor, leaving behind the softer particles, which produced a red glow.

The explanation for the phenomena which resulted when the conductor was negatively charged is now almost self-evident, and practically identical to that given for the first two experiments. When the red-glowing end was pointed toward the negative conductor, the soft electrons of higher frequency photons were driven away from this pole and toward the opposite one, leaving the colors at both poles virtually unchanged except that they became brighter. Naturally, when the ends were reversed and the blue end faced the conductor, the higher-frequency soft particles responsible for the blue glow were driven away and such particles were forced to the opposite pole and captured. As a result, the normally blue-glowing pole turned to red; and the opposite pole turned from red to blue.

Some of Von Reichenbach's experiments also demonstrated that negative charges are repelled by a gravitational field. In these experiments, the poles of very strong magnets with long flames were situated in a horizontal direction. The following passage, from pages 303-304 of his treatise, explains what happened:

> . . . It first shot out some distance horizontally in the direction of the limb of the magnet, then rose in a curve upwards and formed a quadrant, so that it at length flowed vertically upward at its point. . . . Thus the odic flame is sent out from the poles of the magnet with a certain force, an impetus is communicated to it, which drives it forth from the poles; but, on the other hand, a tendency is implanted in it to ascend in the air . . .(101)

The influence of the magnetic field close to the poles was too great for the earth's gravity to have any effect on the concentrations of soft electrons. Strong magnets give many of the particles momentum, which takes them beyond the influence of the field. Such particles then come under the influence of the earth's gravity and are repelled upward. It should be noted that the odic flame represents only the disintegrating particles. The bulk of the particles captured by the magnet are invisible.

Another phenomenon always accompanied Von Reichenbach's experiments with magnets. It was termed "odic smoke". It had the appearance of a luminous vapor or smoke, which rose from the magnet. It followed a pattern similar to that of smoke ascending from an ordinary fire. Bright sparks were also seen in these clouds. The following is an interesting passage which appears on page 374 of Von Reichenbach's treatise on this phenomenon:

> The odic smoke is thrown out by magnets with a certain force, which gives it the first direction, but after that it exhibits a constant tendency to ascend, to flow upwards. When it reaches the roof of a room it spreads out, flowing away over it, illuminates the painting on it, and displays a certain, though short, permanence. Whatever material substratum

> may form the basis of its manifestations, it is in any case either lighter than atmospheric air, or it suffers some kind of repulsion from the earth's surface, driving it away; that is, upwards. . . .
>
> . . . The relation between odic flame and odic smoke is a question we now approach; but is one very difficult to answer at present . . .(101)

The odic smoke was the result of negative charges attaching themselves to dust particles. Water vapor, in turn, was attracted to this combination. This resulted in minute water droplets forming in the concentration of negative charges. The conglomerate, having a net negative charge, was repelled by the earth's gravity after it escaped from the magnetic field. Magnetic fields are affected by magnetic fields; and a small charge is unable to generate a magnetic field of any consequence. Therefore, after the soft electrons captured by the magnetic field attached themselves to dust particles and combined with water molecules, the magnetic field was unable to contain them. Sparks seen in the odic flame and smoke were the result of sudden disintegrations of soft particles.

The great affinity which water has for soft particles was demonstrated when magnets were submerged in water. When this occured, the odic flame and smoke vanished. When the magnet was removed, the odic flame and smoke immediately reappeared. The soft particles captured by the magnet were quickly dispersed throughout the water.

Von Reichenbach demonstrated that water vapor was responsible for odic smoke by experimenting with a magnet under varied atmospheric pressures. The magnet was placed under a glass bell and the air was slowly drawn off. At first, the odic flame and smoke increased with the drop in air pressure. With fewer collisions of air and water molecules, more of the soft electrons were able to combine with water and dust particles without being dislodged. This tendency continued up to a certain point of rarefaction, beyond which it decreased again, and vanished by the time the glass bell was almost evacuated.

During the increase of the odic flame and smoke, while the air was being drawn off, the glass bell itself became "charged" with the essence of the odic flame, so that it was rendered odically incandescent. The odic flame did not penetrate the glass. The glass absorbed and held the soft electrons. This accounts for the absence of odic smoke on the outside. The odic flame manifests itself around a magnet, because collisions of soft electrons with air and water molecules cause disintegrations of the more unstable particles, resulting in the formation of light. There are fewer collisions in a near vacuum and less light to mark the presence of soft particles; consequently, the odic flame is diminished. It must also be kept in mind that air and water molecules around a magnet at normal pressures greatly outnumber the soft particles. This makes possible more collisions. Magnets remain incandescent when placed under water because some of the soft particles following the magnetic lines through the magnet disintegrate from collisions with the magnetic material.

Von Reichenbach's experiments showed that all materials readily absorb this so-called "odic essence" and thereby become luminous. Apparently, the odic flame was not absorbed, but instead had a tendency to move around objects, instead of through them. Since blowing would displace the odic essence, this shows that the odic flame was actually illuminated air, which was created by the intimate contact of disintegrating soft particles captured by the magnetic field. When this illuminated air was displaced, it had a tendency to carry some of the concentrated soft electrons with it. The magnetic field limited the extent to which the particles would be displaced. The air marked the location of the higher concentrations of soft particles.

It was found that the position of a magnet in relation to the earth's magnetic field had a profound effect on the color of the odic flame. It is the flow of particles down the magnetic lines of the earth's magnetic field which affected the odic flame. The principle involved in the changing colors has already been discussed. Prior to Von Reichenbach's experiments, it was found that geomagnetism was lessened during the northern light display. Once again, the reason is not difficult to discern. The Aurora Borealis results from mass disintegrations of soft electrons in the earth's atmosphere, mostly from the upper portion. This produces a temporary void or shortage of such particles in surrounding areas to compensate for it. This lowers the concentration of electrons in these vicinities with a subsequent drop in the intensity of the magnetic field. This is in accordance with the explanation previously given for this phenomenon, which fits all of the facts in regard to geomagnetism.

Von Reichenbach was aware of the dual nature of light more than 100 years before researchers like Oscar Brunler. He found that light consisted of two parts, the part normally visible and an invisible portion he called Od. This is in harmony with the description of light as a conglomerate of photons and soft particles. Von Reichenbach found that even sunlight could no longer expose the photographic plates used in his day after passing through glass about six inches thick, even though its visibility was only slightly impaired.

It has already been shown that it is the disintegration of soft particles and the subsequent release of harder electrons which promotes chemical changes and exposes photographic plates. Light loses most of its unstable soft particles after passing through considerable thicknesses of glass. Most of those which get through are of the more stable variety, and pass through a photographic plate without affecting it. The ability of glass to absorb od or soft particles was demonstrated in Von Reichenbach's experiments. This particular property of glass is also responsible for the greenhouse effect. Since most soft particles, after passing through the glass, have little tendency to get back through the glass intact, large numbers continually disintegrate with the release of much energy. This causes the heat in the enclosure to increase more rapidly than it can be dissipated.

Von Reichenbach's experiments with pendulum movements and table-turning laid the groundwork for a clear understanding of the mechanics of dowsing with pendulums and other tools. He built a pendulum which was free to move under a glass shade, thus cutting off the influence of air currents. There was a small aperture at the top through which a finger could be laid on a string wound on an axle. The other end of the string was attached to a lead ball, which was free to oscillate. It was found that ordinary people could not make the pendulum move. When a finger on the right hand of a sensitive was placed on the fixed end of the string, the pendulum began to swing. When the right hand of another sensitive was also placed on it at the same time, the rate of oscillation increased, yet the left hand of the sensitive produced no motion.

It is extremely significant that if the operator had any metal objects in his or her pockets, or if there were iron nails in the shoes being worn, the pendulum would not move. As soon as they were removed, the pendulum would respond. The explanation is simple and, once again, is another confirmation of the principles previously discussed. As mentioned before, Von Reichenbach showed that the right hand could project od or soft electrons, while the left hand, which was positively charged, could draw od out of an object. Some of the channels to the higher bodies are less obstructed in the case of sensitives than with ordinary people. This is what makes sensitives more perceptive. It also enables many of them to project a high concentration of soft electrons from their right hands. In other words, their right and left sides can generate a higher potential difference, like the opposite poles of a battery.

When a sufficient quantity of soft electrons flows down the string to be absorbed by the lead ball, the ball attains a high negative charge near its surface. As a result, it is attracted to the nearest glass wall of the enclosure. At its nearest approach, the bob loses some of its charge to the wall and then swings back in the opposite direction. It becomes charged again during the interval and gives up some of its regained charge to the opposite wall. A new cycle then begins. The additional energy added to the ball by another sensitive increases the force, and consequently the velocity of swing. A certain minimum flow of soft electrons is required in order for the pendulum to move, since they constantly escape from the string and ball to the surrounding air. The charge on the ball must build up faster than it can escape to the outside.

When the operator has metal objects on his or her body, a situation similar in principle to Reich's cloudbuster occurs. Negative charges are strongly attracted to metals. Therefore, if the operator of a pendulum is wearing any metal, much of the flow from the right hand will be diverted toward the metal. The domino effect, or chain reaction principle, is involved in the flow of charges.

Not all the sensitives Von Reichenbach employed were necessarily good dowsers. A skilled dowser can offset the tendencies of the energy flows just described. In the case of a good dowser, there is a similar flow of energies from the dowser to the dowsing instrument to the mineral or water source which is being dowsed. For example, consider a dowser with a bent twig who is over a body of underground water. If the dowser is sensitive to the radiations emanating from the water which penetrates the surface, he automatically projects a stream of soft electrons which flow from the twig to the source of emanations. The water has a powerful affinity for soft electrons and, therefore, creates a condition similar to that involved with Reich's cloudbuster. In some instances, the flow of soft electrons becomes so great that the twig breaks as a result of the powerful electrostatic forces generated.

It naturally follows that if these radiations are diverted from the dowser his dowsing instrument will be unable to respond. This has been confirmed on numerous occasions. An article entitled "Radiethesia: Science of Tomorrow" appeared in the December, 1965 issue of *Fate* magazine on pages 80-89, and gives a full account of experiments which confirm this. It was written by someone using the pen name of Rho Sigma. The article is extremely well written. Perhaps Rho Sigma is a member of the scientific community in good standing and wants to avoid being ostracized by his colleagues. According to this article, properly positioned magnetic fields can render a dowsing instrument useless. The following passage is taken from pages 84-85 of this article:

> . . . Of utmost importance is the fact that artificial magnetic fields in a predetermined arrangement can block the magnetoid radiation completely, meaning that the dowser will not get a reaction under these conditions! This very important fact, discovered by Dr. Wust, has meanwhile been confirmed by
>
> 1. Prof. Ives Rocard of the Faculte des Sciences, Paris, France. He describes in his book, *Le Signal du Sourcier* his own experimental investigations of dowsing and states that his dowsers were made insensitive by properly placed magnets!
> 2. Mr. Verne L. Cameron of Elsinore, California, probably the best known dowser on the West Coast of America, an open-minded researcher in his own right.
> 3. A group of engineers and technicians in the Southeastern part of the U.S.
>
> These outstanding important facts should cause the scientific community to think and listen . . .(110)

The reason for this phenomenon is clear. The magnetic fields captured the soft particles radiated from the object to be dowsed and diverted them from the dowser.

Dowsers can also make pendulums swing outside a glass cage. Motion occurs only where unbalanced forces exist. This also holds true for a pendulum. This means a dowser automatically charges one side of the plumb bob more than the opposite side. This is accomplished by directing the flow to only one side. The attraction of this side to the surrounding air produces a swing in that direction. The flow of the particles is then directed to the opposite side to produce a pull in the opposite direction. The periodic flow from one side to the other produces the steady swing of the pendulum. The dowser is not consciously aware of this process.

The same principles described above are also involved with the experiments Von Reichenbach conducted in table-turning. A group of sensitives seated around a table, with their hands placed on top of it, caused the table to move in a variety of directions after a period of time. Sometimes it would rotate with such a force that an individual would be unable to hold it back by grabbing it along the edge.

Other vitally important aspects of Von Reichenbach's research were concerned with friction and sound. Rubbing one body against another produced luminous effects in a dark room. Shaking water and other liquids in a container caused similar effects. Instruments or objects producing sound emanated colors and color combinations characteristic of the sounds being produced. For example, a given note always produced the same colors. They were produced by the disintegration of a very small percentage of the soft particles projected by the vibrations resulting from the sound. It follows that sound produces energy effects which can be either beneficial or detrimental, and it can be seen why some people, consciously or unconsciously, associate sound with color.

Von Reichenbach found that all substances produce the odic glow and that metals produce brighter colors than nonmetals. It was also found that each substance radiates its own configuration of colors. This is in conformity with the concept discussed earlier, that all substances have a characteristic or unique radiation. It was mentioned in Part III that there is less proton activity in the atoms of metals. This means the soft electrons radiated by metals are more the result of orbital electron fluctuations than those of nonmetals. This would produce light in more sharply defined frequency ranges. This accounts for the brighter colors emanated by metals.

Von Reichenbach has never been given the recognition and serious study he deserves by the world of science. The major objection to the validity of his work was that he used the so-called subjective approach instead of the objective approach. As a matter of fact, he was just as objective, if not more so, than any of the more famous scientists. He used many different sensitives in his experiments, and the experiments were so ingeniously planned and executed that any chance of fraud, guesswork or hallucination was ruled out of the recorded results.

It was Von Reichenbach's misfortune to encounter the same incredible degree of stupidity among his colleagues that is universal in the world of science today. This condition seems to be more apparent now than in the past, but only because there are many more individuals who aspire to be scientists than ever before in recorded history.

The following is a quotation from Von Reichenbach, in answer to one of his "illustrious" scientific detractors, taken from pages xxvi-xxvii of the introduction to the book *Von Reichenbach's Letters on Od and Magnetism*:

> . . . Is not Dr. Fechner ashamed to credit me on the one hand with all sorts of brilliant mental qualities, and on the other to treat me like a simple-minded youth? . . . Does he quite forget

the fact that at least a hundred of my two hundred sensitives are men of scientific education, and among these there are something like fifty who are physicians, or physicists, or chemists, or mathematicians, or philosophers, men, in short, who in many cases are just on the same high level of scientific attainment as Mr. Fechner himself? . . .
. . . I have examined at least 100 others without taking written notes; the basic experiments consequently were carried out with nearly 300 subjects, with inexhaustible patience and in uninterrupted sequence, and yet it is not enough for Mr. Fechner that all these three hundred have unanimously — in a sort of unprecedented delirium, I suppose — experienced, seen, deposed, and confirmed one and the same thing for the space of 10 years! If the maintenance of such an opinion, under such circumstances, is not reductio ad absurdum and self-destructive, then there is no such thing as logic, and no such thing as a sound human understanding any longer in existence . . .(102)

Even today the work of Von Reichenbach is frowned upon because his approach was allegedly subjective. If one wishes to be technical, the subjective approach is employed in all scientific investigations. Regardless of the type of observations or instrument employed, the scientist's own senses and mental processes are required in observing, recording, and interpreting phenomena. In each case, intelligence is required in order to arrive at a correct interpretation of the results; and most scientists seem to be severely handicapped in this respect. How often have completely erroneous conclusions been derived from information obtained from highly sophisticated instruments and supposedly objective approaches?

There is much more which could be said about the research of Von Reichenbach and others, than can be presented in this treatise. Due to the unprecedented scope of the material to be analyzed and limited space available, the treatment accorded these men will have to suffice. A careful examination of the facts has led the author to conclude that Von Reichenbach and Reich, along with the Indian scientist, Sir Jagodis Chandra Bose, have had no peers in the realm of experimental and natural science since the time of Roger Bacon. Ironically, it is largely because of their greatness that they have received little recognition. Their ideas were too far advanced over those of their contemporaries, and too much in opposition to accepted theories to be tolerated.

I think we're property.—Charles Fort

CHAPTER 24

THE PYRAMID OF LIFE AND THE UNIFYING PRINCIPLE

By now it should be apparent to any intelligent reader that all things are interrelated. In order to gain an adequate understanding of any broad subject, it must be examined from all sides. Since all things are interrelated, there must be a few basic principles which underlie all phenomena. These basic principles make the use of analogies possible, since the pattern is repeatable. The repeated pattern of the universe has given rise to the most important principles of all, the old hermetic axioms, which have been applied many times in this treatise. This axiom is generally stated, "as above, so below". It is just another way of expressing the interrelationship of all things.

As the reader has already witnessed, the proper application of this axiom has been a powerful tool in unraveling many previously unexplained phenomena. By its application, physical phenomena can be used to better understand metaphysics and the occult and vice versa. It follows that the true metaphysician must have a thorough understanding of the causes underlying so-called physical phenomena, as well as the laws directly associated with his own area of specialization. The true scientist must also be a consummate metaphysician. How many scientists of the past or present have lived up to this definition? In the real sense of the word, the terms "scientist" and "metaphysician" are practically interchangeable, since they both have a broad view of the universe.

Metaphysics is a word originally coined by Aristotle which means beyond physics, as the physical scientist sees it. It not only embraces physics, but goes far beyond it and considers the origin, meaning, and function of all life as well. Since many kinds of phenomena are encountered in this broader field which are completely beyond the scope of academic science, it is natural for the scientific community to deride anyone who takes metaphysics seriously. The narrow, ossified mind typically denounces anything that doesn't fit into its miniscule comprehension of the universe. This was dramatically illustrated recently when 18 former Nobel Prize winners, in addition to 170 distinguished colleages, spearheaded an all out attack on astrology.

Astrology is a study that has attracted the best minds down through history, including the most advanced students of metaphysics. Because of this alone, one must logically conclude that astrology has substance and a solid foundation, or at least something which gives this impression. For the pseudoscience this eminent group claims it is, astrology has shown and continues to show an uncanny degree of accuracy when properly used. On the basis of performance, it seems that their own science of astronomy is more deserving of the label pseudoscience. There are certain underlying metaphysical laws concerned with astrology still not understood by students and teachers of the art. Such laws will be clarified in this treatise.

This recent and much publicized attack on astrology by the elite of the scientific world has done little to improve their public image, since millions have learned that astrology does have merit. This and similar incidents involving the supercilious attitude of scientists has produced a steadily deteriorating attitude of disrespect. Many scientists have shown an amazing degree of inconsistency. In some situations they are as dogmatic as anyone, and in other instances they carry skepticism to ridiculous extremes. For example, what they consider to be hard scientific evidence in some areas seems to be that, and only that, which can be perceived by all of the five senses simultaneously!

Chaotic conditions and misconceptions rivaling those existing in the physical sciences are also prevalent in the field of the occult and metaphysics. The different schools of thought have been stumbling around on the fringes and have never been able to get to the core of the problem. The physical sciences and metaphysics have been largely divorced from each other because of a lack of understanding of the basic unifying principle. Each has its own subdivisions detached from one another. Confusion creates unnecessary complexities. This results in a myriad of books which have been written on the subjects, and which tend to cloud one's thinking even more. As indicated previously, the occult and physical phenomena are merely special effects of the same general laws. This is basically the thought behind the hermetic axiom.

The proper use of hermetic principles, in conjunction with the clues available, makes it possible to arrive at the central core of the cosmic scheme, and thereby gain a still better understanding of our own planet. It has been shown that growth and progression proceed from the simple to the complex, and energy can only flow downhill or from a higher potential to a lower one. In a broader sense, this means that a high can give up to a low, but a low cannot give up to a high. As an analogy, it is pointed out that a wise man is far more likely to impart wisdom to an ignorant person than vice versa.

In the discussion to follow, it should be kept in mind that all activities follow a cyclical pattern. This is in accordance with the fifth hermetic principle, known as the Principle of Rhythm. There are major cycles and minor cycles, and of course cycles within cycles. The creation of the first planetary system in our present universe was evidently the beginning of a major cycle. According to the academic viewpoint, the universe started with one great explosion. Everything that followed either happened by chance or took place according to impossible theories. There was supposedly no intelligent planning behind the chain of events. Intelligence somehow emerged from the nonintelligent, and therefore, the effects transcended the cause.

Intelligence clearly exists on this planet, even if to a limited degree. It could not have evolved out of the supposed inert matter as suggested by material science. It is a product of superior intelligence in accordance with the first hermetic axiom. Nothing comes into existence in the material world, as we know it, with an orderly arrangement and a useful purpose, that did not require intelligent planning. When the universe is looked at objectively, order and purpose are apparent.

All advanced students of the occult are aware that there are realms of higher frequency matter far above that of the physical realm. The ethers associated with each realm are much higher than those of the realm below it.

It has been said that every planet in the physical realm has twelve major realms of higher frequency matter associated with it, called astral realms. The same laws of physics apply in each realm. For example, each has its own range of gravity radiations which affect only the matter of that realm. The inhabitants experience their own visible spectrum of light, the ultraviolet, infrared, and so on. All of this conforms with the hermetic statement, "as above, so below". There are significant differences in each realm which will be explained later.

The creation of the physical universe with its twelve astral realms was the start of a major cycle. Since there are realms far above even the highest astral realms, it is apparent this cycle is still only one part of a greater cycle. It follows that there is at least one cycle that encompasses all of them. However, it seems impossible to go back to an ultimate beginning. It is possible to go back to the beginning of the greatest kind of cycle involved in any creative process. The present physical universe is the product of previous cycles, all contained within the greatest kind of cycle just mentioned.

Everything has a comparatively modest beginning, and the beginning of the greatest cycle was no exception. The fundamental building block, or the very highest ether particle of which the present universe is comprised, was the end result of the greatest cycle that preceded the present one. This ether particle is of infinite complexity, a universe in its own right, since it is the product of countless previous cycles. It is motivated by and contains the essence of the great creative intelligence, since it is through such particles or universes that this intelligence created the present universe and all contained within it. This source of all things, or the life giver, has an unlimited ability to duplicate. This is an application of the hermetic axiom. In a more crude sense, the universe follows the pattern of a manufacturing plant. Years of planning and engineering may be applied in developing and perfecting a single product or working model. When this has been accomplished, the factory can tool up and produce myriads of them in a very short time.

After the infinite intelligence duplicated the perfected universe, with an infinitude of such universes or particles, the highest realm of this present cycle came into existence. The ether particles of this realm were not isolated from each other. If they were, how could they be controlled? They are all interconnected by subtle lines or channels of communication through which messages and energies can be transmitted as described in Part III. Such channels are of unlimited flexibility and can never be broken. In a like manner, the infinitude of integral parts of these fundamental units are connected. This can be likened to the electrical circuit of any electrical device. It is these channels which make possible all known phenomena, including telepathy, psychometry, psionic devices, and all related phenomena. This concept has not been a part of the teachings of science and metaphysics in the past. It is being introduced for the first time. It is summed up by the well known phrase, "all is one".

It follows that everything in the universe is interconnected, and thus the life giver is in complete control of all that happens. Nothing ever occurs, not even the interactions of the most remote ether particles, that is not planned. It will be shown in Part IV that the seemingly unexplainable phenomena associated with the science of psionics confirm the concepts just presented.

An account of the hierarchical pyramidal structure of the universe, beginning with the first integrated intelligence and subordinate Elders on down to individual humans, is given in a book entitled *The Book of Truth* by H. C. Randall-Stevens.(95) It was supposedly a treatise channelled by a discarnate Elder to a subordinate, incarnate Elder. Although written in a strange style, it contains many profound metaphysical concepts including a brief overall history of the earth. The material in this book and the logical implications of the hermetic axiom were used in developing the detailed relationships of the pyramid of life.

After the new realm was created out of the ethers, the supreme intelligence started the present cycle by projecting the first integrated intelligence of the new cycle into this realm. This intelligence was fully developed at the start. The duties of this intelligence were to supervise the development of the new cycle to its completion. The building blocks of this realm were used to create the soul body this intelligence would need in order to function. By application of the hermetic axiom, there is an identical pattern in the physical realm when an incarnating intelligence takes up a physical body in order to operate in this realm.

This first intelligence was and is, of course, more powerful, more versatile and more complex than any that came later. It is the primary guiding force behind the entire universe, and as such is actually an embodiment of the life-giver. This first being then brought the Elders into existence, the oldest and most advanced beings in the universe. They were the first solar and planetary logos, but in a realm far removed from the physical realm, which came later. The logos of any major cycle are the creators of the planetary systems of that cycle, and they use the ethers of the realms in which they are operating to form the planetary and solar bodies. The planetary systems are actually the embodiments of the logos.

The Elders created the first planetary system out of the highest ethers. Each system had its higher and lower realms. Each structure follows identically the same pattern as exists with the physical and the twelve higher major realms above it. Between the physical plane and the first astral realm are several intermediate planes of higher frequency matter. A discussion of their purpose in the plan will be given shortly.

The question some readers may ask at this stage is: Why do creation and progression follow the pattern of the high to the low instead of the reverse? Many schools of thought speak of progression to the higher realms and the earth going into a "higher vibration". This is due to a lack of understanding of the nature of creation, and of the principle that energy can only flow from a high potential to a lower one. Some of the experiments performed with orgone energy by the late Wilhelm Reich seemed to violate this law, but a deeper look into the phenomenon shows that this doesn't happen.

It was stated previously that any dynamic creation is less active than its component parts. Ether particles combine to form larger and greater ether particles much in the same manner that atoms combine to form molecules. This is another example of the hermetic axiom. The larger ether particles are consequently less active than the ether units of which they are made. They form the lower ethers, from which the lower realms of lower frequency matter are created.

Along with the first planetary systems existing only in the highest realms, the original logos created a myriad of souls to inhabit these systems. Each soul was created according to a certain plan or blueprint. These new souls were created as completely integrated beings, as with the first intelligence. Bodies were projected from these intelligences into realms below that from which they themselves originated. It is apparent from this picture that the term "soul development" is a misnomer. The soul or original intelligence that motivates the bodies it projects into the lower realms is already made complete and fully developed according to the role it is supposed to play in the cosmic scheme. What is thought to be the evolutionary process is actually the projection of a body or bodies into successively lower realms, until all of them are in perfect rapport with the source that is sustaining them. In most cases, this is a slow and painful process, as is the situation with any major development.

The above creative process follows a cyclic pattern which, again, is the situation with all evolvements. A projected body goes through a series of tests and experiences during each cycle. The reactions of this embodiment to these experiences enables the projecting intelligence to make the proper adjustments and plans for the next cycle, when a new body will be created in that same realm. This embodiment will hopefully accomplish its planned tasks. The principle involved can be likened to the building of a robot to be operated by a remote control device. In fact, the creation of this device also has to be accomplished by the manipulation of tools by remote control. It is not difficult to visualize what kinds of problems such an operation entails, and how many models one might have to create before getting one which will respond perfectly. Some readers may see a powerful argument for the reincarnation principle at this stage.

Since energy flows from a high potential to a lower one, it follows that

Figure 30
THE PYRAMID OF LIFE

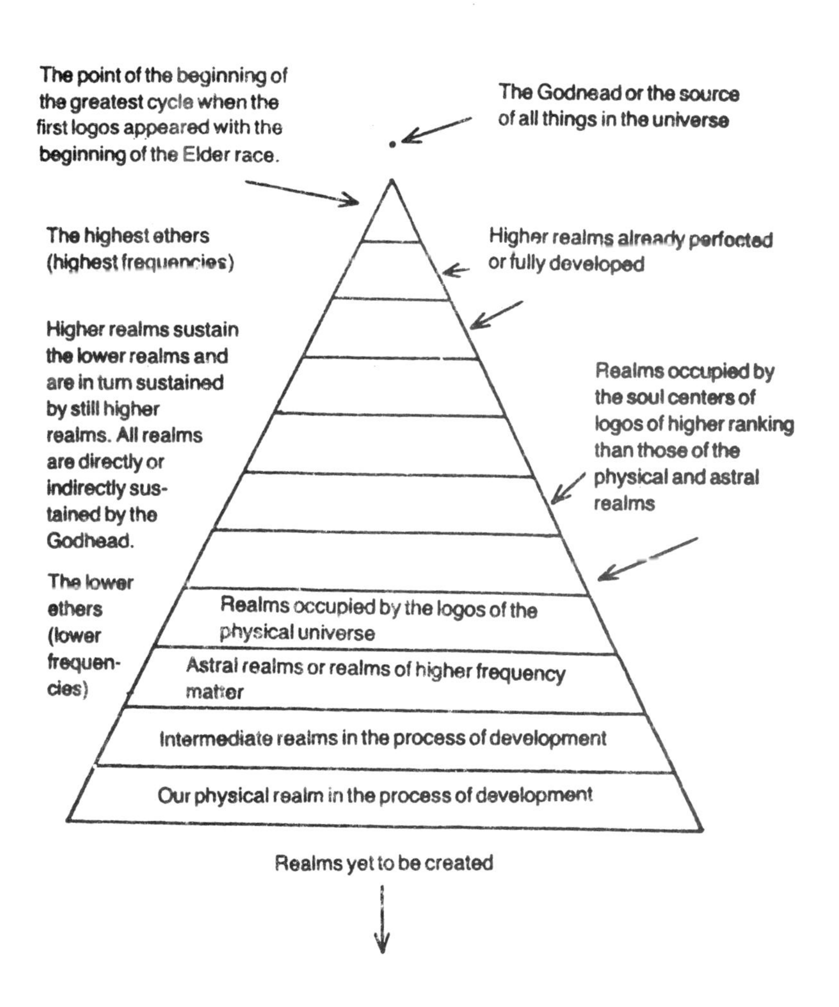

the higher realms will sustain the lower ones. One can see from the pattern that the higher bodies of a projecting intelligence sustain and motivate the lower ones, and in successive order. It should be apparent that the activities of these projected bodies can no more alter their source than energy can flow uphill. The absurdities in Darwin's theory now become evident. The more intelligent members of the scientific community are beginning to seriously question it, although this theory is still accepted by the academic world. Practically all academic concepts ignore the possibility of an exterior intelligence motivating a body. According to these materialistic viewpoints, the body is the essence and contains all that is that being.

A given embodiment has freedom of choice or free will during each life span, since he or she is not intended to be a programmed robot. This illustrates the omniscience of the primary guiding intelligence, since the finished product of such a method will be more versatile and creative than any robot. When a soul center is able to project into the lower realm and the body is in perfect rapport with the soul center, it is then qualified to become a logos or a logos' helper depending on its role in the cosmic scheme. As a logos or logos' helper, the soul entity then begins the creation of a planetary system, in realms yet to be created, below the realms in which they have been operating.

According to *The Book of Truth* on page 32, a significant percentage of these souls never reach this stage.(95) Many prove themselves unworthy to use this free will and are obliterated from the cosmic plan. This may seem to be a flaw in the creative process, but only when looking at it from a very superficial viewpoint. They have provided, by their failures and negative life styles, the tests and resistance which expedites the development of those who make the grade. It is analogous to the dead plants, manure, etc., providing fertilizer for the growth of other plants, or the temporary scaffolding erected during the construction of a building, which must be torn down later.

The above presentation lays the foundation for the concept of reincarnation, which has been a controversial subject for a long time. According to some historians and Bible researchers, many books were taken out of the Bible during the time of Constantine, especially those referring directly to reincarnation. This was done by church elders and other individuals who wanted to keep their charges completely under their wing. A belief in reincarnation would have made this more difficult. Careful deletions from any document can change its meaning. This is being done all the time. Even the latest editions of the Bible are worded differently in some areas from earlier editions. If this is so, then what kind of changes have taken place over the past 1500 years?

The consensus of the Eastern world is that reincarnation is a reality. The Western world is supposedly more advanced and less addicted to superstition; therefore, the concept of reincarnation must be false and all of the major western religions reject it. Eastern religions do not use a Bible which has been changed drastically throughout the centuries. Both cultures tend to be grossly lopsided in their orientation. One is the direction of the tangible with the exclusion of the intangibles, while the other operates in the opposite direction. As a result, both seem to have lost touch with reality.

Reincarnation has been the central theme of the most advanced metaphysical teachings of mystery schools for thousands of years. The author must state categorically that those who reject this truth have at best only a miniscule comprehension of metaphysics and the laws of the universe. One does not need to look any further into the individual's background. How can those who reject that concept be so certain that what has already happened cannot happen again? Are they not aware that what they have experienced and learned in this life is only a very minute part of what there is to acquire in this realm? There are many misconceptions about reincarnation and related subjects which are a part of popular teachings in this vein. There will be further discussion of these later in this book.

Newly created logos eventually produce planetary systems in realms below those from which they originated. The creative pattern of the universe pyramids in descending order from the higher realms to the lower ones. In other words, the number of planetary systems increases astronomically, since each logos has produced millions of offspring. A major realm, which is the domain of a logos, is a composite of many subrealms. This realm includes the physical and astral realms of a solar system.

The universe functions in a manner similar to any well run organization, in accordance with the hermetic axiom. Those who originated in the highest realms are the "executives". The chief executive is at the peak, and then follow the subordinates who originated in the lower realms, who in turn are directly responsible for the activities of those who function in still lower major realms. This continues on down to the lower major realm in which man exists. Man can be certain of this position since it is such a long way from a desired state of development. Figure 23 depicts the Pyramid of Life.

As implied in *The Book of Truth*, beings on the highest part of the pyramid may incarnate in the lowest realms to facilitate the development of these realms by functioning as teachers and guides.(95) It does seem paradoxical that there are personalities mingling with humanity on various planets, whose higher selves are beyond the logos responsible for the humanity they came down to help, and to whom said logos are subordinate. Each of these beings, who are the Elders already mentioned, may incarnate in quite a number of bodies simultaneously. Usually one body isn't sufficient for an Elder to accomplish all he wishes to accomplish during a certain period.

If it were not for the embodiments of these Elders, or others high on the pyramid, progress in the lower realms would nearly come to a halt. This is the origin of our greatest thinkers, artists, composers, avatars, leaders, etc. All of the greatest contributions to world culture and knowledge down through history can be traced to a very small number of Elders. The channels or lines of communication of the Elders to their embodiment in the lowest realms are often far from perfect, since the lower realms are still in the process of development.

The universe, as a whole, is not infallible. However, the universal plan is without flaws. Rectitude exists only in the highest realms, as far as the universe in its present stage of development is concerned. The universe will function as one integrated perfected being when the required number of logos is created, and every unit is working in perfect harmony with every other part. The end of the greatest cycle is reached when this is accomplished. The universe then becomes the fundamental building block of a new universe with new properties, and occupying a near infinitely greater volume of space than the previous one. Surrounding it is the great black void of infinite space yet to be occupied.

CHAPTER 25

RESOLVING THE MYSTERY OF TELEPORTATION

The word "teleportation" needs no definition for the student of the occult. For the benefit of the uninitiated, it is the sudden disappearance of a material object in one place and its sudden appearance in another area. This can be any distance away and even through solid matter. As mind scrambling as it may seem to be, it is far from being a rare occurrence.

This phenomenon and the realization that many different realms of matter simultaneously occupy the same three dimensional space, contribute to a deeper insight into the nature of matter.

The approximate diameter of the atom, as well as the spacing of atoms and molecules in solid matter, have been established. This size and spacing are such that it seems impossible for two bodies of matter to interpenetrate without collisions of molecules and fundamental particles taking place. Yet this interpenetration occurs during the teleportation process. The object to be teleported is impregnated with certain energies, which temporarily render it invisible and intangible. The dematerialized atoms and molecules are unable to interact with any other matter. This means the molecules of the dematerialized object interpenetrate the molecules of the other matter, with each group being virtually oblivious to the presence of the other. There should be collisions of fundamental particles by all the rules of probability. A similar enigma exists when two beams of light of any intensity intersect at or near right angles. There seems to be no collision of photons and soft particles, as one would expect. Similarly, an infinitude of particles are involved in cloud chamber experiments with high speed accelerators, yet only very few collisions occur and are recorded.

A much closer look at the nature of matter than has previously been given is required because of such considerations. The typical reaction of an orthodox scientist to paradoxes of this nature is to either pretend they don't exist or fall back on such worn-out standbys as fourth dimensions, space warps, and time warps. These crutches are getting somewhat rickety from overwork. It is known that an atom consists of particles which are very minute when compared to the size of the atom. Such particles are concentrations of energy with outlines which are not sharply defined, since true continuity in the case of particles does not exist. The so-called diameter of such particles is perhaps much less than is commonly believed. As shown previously, fundamental particles can be further subdivided into other particles separated by relatively greater distances, because of their still higher energy concentrations. This process seems to continue on down the ladder to an infinite regression.

From the concepts and principles discussed so far, it is known that the following things happen to matter which has been dematerialized. First, its inertial properties have either vanished or all but vanished, since it can be transferred practically any distance in an infinitesimal length of time. Second, the atoms of the material or the fundamental particles thereof can no longer generate a magnetic field when given velocity. Third, the electrostatic effects of the fundamental particles have vanished since, as mentioned before, it is the electrostatic field effects of the hard electrons and protons which make matter tangible. All this means the particles must have been rendered motionless, since it is through electrostatic forces that the particles of the atom move.

From the above considerations and the following analysis, it becomes apparent why collisions of particles of dematerialized matter never occur with those of normal materialized matter. Actual collisions of stable particles are difficult to promote to the extent of producing disintegrations of particles or even strong interactions. This has been demonstrated by cloud chamber experiments. The powerful fields existing between them produce deflections before actual collisions occur. This even occurs with unlike charges. These considerations, combined with the tremendous separation of fundamental particles in proportion to their diameter, pushes the probability of direct collisions to near the vanishing point. This is even the case with experiments designed to produce collisions. This probability becomes even less when dematerialized matter interpenetrates solid matter.

A moving charge produces a magnetic vortex ahead of it, which is part of the magnetic field generated by the kinetic energy of the particle. The particles of dematerialized matter have no inertia and are automatically pushed out of the path of the charges. Therefore, there is no chance for collisions.

If the conditions mentioned above were the only factors involved in teleportation, the correct spatial relationships of the atoms of the teleported object would be difficult, if not impossible, to maintain. This would usually result in a badly distorted aport. The logos who created matter no doubt foresaw this difficulty, hence every atom and molecule, and consequently every physical object, has what is known as an "etheric double." This etheric double consists of higher frequency matter associated with ethers above those associated with hard electrons and protons. They are permanently attached to their physical counterparts by a process which will be referred to as the step down principle.

The step down process involves the interlocking of high frequency matter with matter associated with ethers slightly lower than the higher frequency matter. The difference is not great enough to prevent a bond from existing between the two levels. This lower frequency matter is in turn bonded with still lower frequency matter. This process continues until a bond is made with physical matter. The higher frequency matter is connected with matter of the physical realm by this process. This same principle is involved in spirit communication with higher realms, discussed in more detail later.

The etheric double is attached to physical matter by this method and cannot generate a magnetic field during the teleportation process. The elimination of the inertial properties of physical matter automatically nullifies the inertia of its etheric double. Since the normal motion of the particles of the etheric double and bonding matter has been, in effect, "frozen", this matter has also been dematerialized. It can therefore pass through matter of its own realm without interference. The particles of the matter of these various realms bonded together have a much better chance of maintaining their proper relationships, than would particles of matter in only one realm being dematerialized. Even this does not insure the atoms of a teleported object will hold together under all conditions of teleportation. The improper or insufficient use of energies during the teleportation process can result in a badly distorted aport. A case of this kind was described in Max Freedom Long's book entitled *The Secret Science Behind Miracles.*(79)

Although the conditions necessary for teleportation have been analyzed and explained, the process by which dematerialization occurs has yet to be fully explained. Dematerialization takes place when matter is impregnated with the right combination of soft electrons. As explained in Part III, electrostatic field effects result when the random movement of ether particles is disrupted in the presence of other particles. This causes differential pressures on the surface of these particles. When dematerializing energies are present, this randomness of the ethers is partially restored while ether bombardment is greatly weakened, as explained earlier. This freezes the motion of the fundamental particles since the electrostatic forces no longer exist. It is not just the soft particles themselves which eliminate the electrostatic field effects. The presence of these captured harder particles greatly reduces the mean free path of bombarding ether particles that normally produce electrostatic forces. This virtually eliminates the differential forces on the fundamental particles of the atoms and molecules that are dematerialized, but the harder electrons contain the dematerializing energies. The capture of harder particles by softer ones mentioned in earlier chapters essentially amounts to a dematerialization of hard particles. The dematerialization of atoms requires a more sophisticated application of soft particles, something nature does not normally provide. The normal motion pattern of the ether particles which produce the electrostatic forces on hard particles is disrupted by encountering the softer particles, which are enormous when compared to the hard particles.

Since dematerializing energies move with the teleported object and the combination has little or no inertia, it follows that the inertial properties of the dematerializing energies have also been nullified. The ether particles are diverted from the paths they take to produce the electrostatic effects. It is a mutual effect involving the smaller and larger ether particles. This means they have no tendency to rotate when the aggregate moves. A definite conclusion can be derived from this. They are locked into the atoms of the dematerialized material. This occurs because the harder electrons they contain tend to congregate around the protons in the atoms. This may seem paradoxical to some, since the electrostatic field effects in the atom have been eliminated. This isn't a paradox because it is the presence of these particles which eliminated these effects in the first place. If the position of the dematerializing particles should change, the electrostatic field effects would tend to return and draw them back to their original positions. Since the hard particles of the atom don't rotate, they prevent the dematerializing particles from rotating. Therefore, no magnetic fields are produced when the object is teleported and consequently it still has no inertia.

The dematerializing energies consist of soft and harder electrons comprised of photons from the ultraviolet to near the gamma range. Dematerialized objects can be pushed along by a beam of light. This beam must be of the right frequencies and at the velocity of light, since it requires little or no force to move these particles. They can also be teleported at almost an infinite velocity by other means. This will be discussed later. When the teleported object reaches its destination, it is impregnated with materializing energies, which drive out the dematerialized energies. These are comprised of soft electrons composed of photons of a slightly lower frequency. They are of a nature that can interact with the dematerializing particles, yet cannot produce appreciable dematerializing effects themselves. When these energies are driven out of the body, it immediately returns to its original condition.

A material body can be rendered invisible and intangible, visible but intangible, and invisible but tangible. The first state has already been discussed. The matter in the second case has been dematerialized, but soft electrons comprised of photons encompassing the visible range of light still permeate the material and thus reflect visible light. This was mentioned in Part III. The third case means that the soft electrons which make matter visible have been driven out. Ultraviolet light of the right frequencies will accomplish this. The energies which make matter invisible must be applied continuously, otherwise the matter will become visible again, since the fundamental particles of matter continuously generate soft electrons.

The ability of ultraviolet light in a certain frequency range to make matter invisible was allegedly discovered during the 1930s. A popular magazine of the time gave an account of such experiments and featured a series of photographs showing a man in something resembling a diving suit being exposed to these radiations. The man slowly became transparent, and the sequence of photos showed him finally becoming invisible, although he was completely tangible. Previous attempts to explain the phenomena mentioned above have been pitiful examples of inept thinking. For example, the standard explanation of invisibility has been the bending of light around an object. It isn't difficult to pick this apart by the most elementary reasoning process. The usual explanation for dematerialization has been stepping up the vibration of molecules. These are worthy of an academic scientists, but since conventional science does not recognize such phenomena, the source must be placed outside the ranks of these scientists.

THE PHILADELPHIA EXPERIMENT

The subject of teleportation brings to mind an experiment allegedly conducted by the Navy during World War II, known as the Philadelphia experiment. The validity of the rumors, which persist after more than thirty years, can be neither confirmed or denied. According to the story, the Navy performed a series of experiments at the Philadelphia Naval Yard designed to make a ship and its personnel invisible. This would have been a great advantage in the war effort if successful. The details are somewhat vague, but the experiments supposedly went beyond their expectations. The ship disappeared from the Philadelphia Yard and appeared suddenly in a harbor hundreds of miles away. Some of the Navy personnel disappeared, and were never seen again. Others went mad when parts of their bodies became invisible again after the experiment. One group of sailors allegedly raided a tavern in Philadelphia while invisible.

It seems possible that this could have happened in light of the principles outlined in this chapter. Assuming that it did happen, the author will attempt to reconstruct the sequence of events from a logical standpoint. The Navy was undoubtedly aware of the successful experiments in invisibility performed a few years prior to the Philadelphia experiment. Logically, if a ship and its personnel could be rendered invisible, they would have a tremendous advantage over enemy warships. However, after invisibility is attained, another problem arises, which is maintaining this invisibility for the desired length of time. Perhaps, in attempts to solve this problem, other frequencies in the ultraviolet range were employed, which produced dematerialization. This would be an effect which they hadn't anticipated. The inertia of the ship in this stage would be nullified. Its sudden appearance in another port hundreds of miles away poses no problem from the standpoint of energy requirements. The reasons it picked out another home port and the manner in which it achieved this do present an enigma. Perhaps one or more of the dematerialized personnel were thinking of this port, and their mind power gave the assembly the necessary impetus to teleport it there. A psychic master is able to dematerialize his body and transport it to any desired spot at near infinite velocity.

The materialization of the ship after its arrival is still more difficult to explain, if it is assumed that only Naval personnel were involved in these misadventures. Not all our visitors from outer space are benevolent. Hostile and mischievous aliens with great technical resources have been with us for ages. They have, no doubt, been responsible for a long list of Fortean phenomena, including mysterious disappearances of large objects and great numbers of people from time to time. It is more than likely they were deeply involved in the Philadelphia experiment, and extended gratuitous "help" to the Navy from time to time.

A book recently published entitled *The Philadelphia Experiments* by William M. Moore and Charles Berlitz provides convincing evidence that the Philadelphia experiment actually occurred. It is highly interesting, but was marred by the implication that Einstein and his "unified field theory" gave the Navy personnel the insight to perform the experiment. What the authors failed to realize is that Einstein did not have a unified theory, and would have been as baffled as the rest of them as to the cause of the phenomenon.

From a mechanical standpoint, invisibility can be maintained for any desired length of time by employing two or more generators of the correct ultraviolet frequencies. They can be positioned so that they render each other invisible, yet at the same time maintain the invisibility of the desired object. The state of invisibility would not affect their operation, and they could be carried along with the object.

There are instances when the teleportation process occurs at near infinite velocity. In such cases, the transmission is not produced by the method just described. It involves the direct use of the mind, which transcends any other process. The mind operates and controls matter by means of a vast network of communication lines connecting all ether particles and all particles of matter. It is also by these lines that thought is transmitted at near infinite velocity. These lines will be discussed in more detail in the next chapter. A dematerialized object, which has practically zero inertia, is transmitted over vast distances by a similar process and at about the same velocity as that of thought. A psychic master with the ability to teleport can dematerialize his body, or another object, or both. He can then transmit his body, and/or objects, to a destination at the speed of thought. Astral projection takes place in an identical manner. It is well known in occult circles that it is possible for one to separate the astral body from the physical, and travel great distances with the astral body almost instantaneously. The soul center has greater control over the astral body than it does over the physical. Those who practice astral projection are able to do the same with the astral body that a master has learned to do with his physical body. In the latter case, both the astral and physical bodies participate in the transmission.

Sit down before fact as a little child,
be prepared to give up every preconceived
notion, follow humbly wherever and to
whatever abysses nature leads,
Or you shall learn nothing.

—T. H. Huxley

CHAPTER 26

THE SCIENCE OF PSIONICS AND THE FIELDS OF LIFE

Psionics involves such things as ESP, radionic healing, radionic pest control, clairvoyance, dowsing, and psychometry. This chapter will analyze and explain some of the most baffling aspects of this research, utilizing the unifying principle. The nature of the aura or the fields of life will also be explained for the first time.

The common denominator of all phenomena and manifestation, as mentioned in Part III, is the life lines, or lines of communication, which exist between the particles of the highest ethers. Each of the infinitudes of particles are permanently joined, either directly or indirectly, to all the other particles of the universe. It is through these life lines that the creative intelligence controls all aspects of the universe. They are actually extensions of the life giving intelligence of the universe. It follows that all psionic phenomena can be simply explained in terms of these life lines.

This common denominator is an excellent starting point, and it begins at a far deeper level than any previous attempts to account for any of the manifestations of the universe. Consequently, it will prove to be far more fruitful. These lines can be likened to the nervous system of a human body or the circuits of an electronic mechanism. This is another application of the hermetic axiom. The primary creative intelligence, sometimes called the Godhead, manipulates the entire universe, directly and indirectly, by means of these lines. It sends commands through the network of these lines to the particles that it uses to create matter and the life forms which it manipulates.

The pattern of this creation follows the pyramid principle, as described in Chapter 24. A soul center is created first in the highest realm, which is the beginning of a major cycle. The creation of this center is analogous to the building of a giant relay station. The creative forces, from which the subsequent development of the universe results, emanate from this central station or center. This primary soul center created the lower ethers, lower frequency matter and other soul centers, or relay stations, by commands transmitted through these life lines. The laws and rules governing creation were transmitted from the primary intelligence, or Godhead, to the first relay station. From there the same rules and plans were transmitted and programmed into subsequent centers. They, in turn, followed identically the same pattern with the centers they directly created in subsequently lower realms. This is in accordance with the hermetic axiom and is actually the origin of this axiom. The manner in which the logos created the planetary systems and the life forms for which they are responsible is now clear.

An analogous situation exists in the generation and subsequent distribution of electrical power from a central source to the myriad of individual consumers throughout many communities. First, there is the origin of the electrical power, such as Hoover Dam, where water power is transformed into electrical power by means of giant turbines and generators. This can be symbolic of the Godhead. From there, it flows to a transmission yard, which is analogous to the first integrated intelligence. The power is then transmitted to various substations, which correspond to the direct subordinates of the main integrated intelligence of the Elders, mentioned in Chapter 24. From there, the power is distributed to lesser stations and so on, to individual homes. The power is originally transmitted at extremely high voltages and, through successions of transformers, is stepped down to lower voltage for various uses further down the line. This corresponds to the development of the lower ethers.

The network of life lines becomes infinitely complex as the higher ethers combine to form lower ethers, and these in turn are manipulated to create matter. The various energies, electromagnetic, soft electrons, etc., associated with the manifestation of any life form, are indistinguishable from those observed with so-called inanimate matter and its interactions. The life sustaining force, the difference between a live body and a dead one, would remain a mystery without the concept of the subtle life lines just described.

All matter, from the highest realm to the lowest, is directly and indirectly an extension of the primary intelligence. Live matter, however, is a specialized manipulation of supposedly inert matter by intelligences toward a greater unfolding and completion of their cycles of development. The "live" matter is the medium through which a center of intelligence functions in the realm occupied by that matter, and it is done through the life lines. When the intelligence is no longer able to use the specialized organization of "inert" matter to advantage, the circuits originally created for the direct control of the body are severed. The body then reverts back to "inert" matter. The reincarnation pattern extends to all life forms including plants. For example, the death of a plant has no effect on the intelligence manifested through it. When conditions are right, the same intelligence will create a new plant. Creation always progresses from the simple to the more complex. This means creation works from the higher realms toward the lower ones, which is in accordance with the flow of energy from a high potential to a lower one. A creative intelligence always creates a body in a lower realm from that in which it has its own existence.

No organization can be operated efficiently without the keeping of records. It follows, by applying the hermetic axiom again, that this is true for the entire universe in every detail. Since the universe is under complete and intelligent observation at all times, every activity down to the level of minute particles is indelibly recorded somewhere. This is done by a vast network of "computers", whose sophistication transcends any produced as yet in this realm. The life lines already discussed are used in all the circuits. Every intelligence has a built-in computer recording all its activities.

The recording and transmission of information by means of these life lines is accomplished in a variety of ways. When an individual makes contact with an object, some of the lines associated with the object become attached to the person who touches it. Likewise, bodies which contact each other exchange lines which are integral parts of themselves. Thereafter, they are in direct contact with each other by means of these basic life lines. Even light reflected from a surface carries some of these lines with it, which had been associated with the object with which it was temporarily in contact. This is not difficult to understand when one considers that when an object contacts another, a minute part of each becomes attached to the other. It may be only a few molecules, cells, or ether particles. The same applies to photons of light.

The concepts and principles outlined in this chapter enable the occult or psionic phenomena to be understood, which have, until now, been beyond human comprehension. The power of this new insight becomes apparent when it is used to explain psychometry. Psychometry is the ability of people to hold an object and determine its past history. If it had been handled or owned by someone else, the one who psychometrizes it is able to reveal much about that person. Direct lines of communication have been established between that object and the person being contacted, even if he or she is deceased. There is a hookup by means of the basic life lines from that individual to the memory banks of a cosmic computer. This computer may or may not be the one belonging to the soul center of the individual or the brains of any of the bodies it projects. The mind of the psychometrizer is able to contact this computer through these life lines, and get a playback of some of the information pertaining to the individual. As mentioned before, an integral part of every soul center is a primary computer. This in turn is connected to the brains of the bodies it projects into lower realms. These brains are also highly intricate computers. Each cell of every living organism, whether it is plant or animal, is in contact with the computer of the intelligence in a higher realm sustaining that life.

Radionic pest control utilizes the same life lines as psychometry. T. G. Hieronymus invented a device, called the Hieronymus machine, to detect the emanations of soft particles from any material, which he called Eloptic energy. He received a patent for the device in 1949, No. 2,482,773.(59) Variations of his device turned out to be useful for radionic pest control. An excellent history of the development of the Hieronymus machine, and other radionic control devices, is given in the book entitled *The Secret Life of Plants* by Peter Tompkins and Christopher Bird.(13)

The Hieronymus device operates by placing a photograph or negative of trees or plants infested with insects into the device. The photo may be painted with a chemical that is inimical to the insects which are to be destroyed. The machine is tuned to a certain "frequency" which is characteristic of the insects. The operator determines the frequency by a detector, which relies upon the tactile sense in his fingers. The detector feels as though it has a greater resistance, or drag, when the resonance point is reached. The infestation is destroyed within a short time, even though it may be a great distance from the machine.

The light which affected the negative of the photograph carried with it the life lines from the living organisms of the insects. These became attached to the negative and, in turn, are transmitted to any copies of the negative. When the negatives are destroyed, pests can no longer be eradicated, since contact through the life lines has been broken. The mind of the operator focuses on the organisms by use of the machine and these life lines. The lines serve as channels or direction finders by which energies producing the same effects as the chemicals can be directed to the insect pests.

The machine merely functions as a focusing point for the energies, since an accurate drawing of the machine has proven to be as effective as the machine itself. It is the mind of the operator which is directly responsible for the flow of energies that does the work. The mind sends the commands through the life lines which control matter and direct the energies, applying the same principle involved in the creation of matter. The Hieronymus machine transforms a novice into an "adept" in the projection of energies. An "adept" can do the same thing without the machine. The Hieronymus invention can also be used for sending beneficial or healing energies to distant organisms.

The principles employed by Hieronymus and others are indentical to those used by practitioners of voodoo and the so-called black arts. The only essential difference is that the masters of these arts have learned to produce the same effects without the use of a machine. The same kind of mind power is used in each case.

Hieronymus, De La Warr, Abrams, Drown and others did important work with radionic healing devices. These machines were used for diagnosing and treating disease, and proved to be highly effective. The diagnosis of disease using blood samples, saliva, etc. follows the same pattern just discussed.

Abrams pioneered the science of radionics early in the 20th century. He found that every type of disease or ailment produced a characteristic radiation. He was able to determine the relative average frequencies of these radiations, and carefully charted them. From the concepts already discussed, such an occurence is to be expected. Every substance has a characteristic radiation. When a part of the body malfunctions or is altered, the actual chemical composition changes, and this will be reflected in the energies it radiates. Actually there will be two kinds of radiation: soft electrons comprised of photons in the visible light range and higher, traveling at velocities well below that of light; and electromagnetic radiations in the radio frequencies. The latter is the kind of radiation with which Abrams was dealing. The former is the type of radiation with which the late Oscar Brunler (who will be discussed later) worked. Both kinds of energy reflect the nature of the organism radiating them. A living organism tends to radiate both kinds, since cells behave like an oscillator. Inanimate objects do not behave in this manner. Therefore, they produce only a stream of ejected soft electrons.

Before anything of importance is created, complete plans or "blueprints" must be formulated. It is apparent by application of the hermetic axiom that this pattern predominates throughout the universe in all realms. The complete blueprints of these future plans exist in the vast network of computers associated with all creative intelligences. For a lesser intelligence, such plans may only include the future construction and projection of a body into a lower realm. In the case of greater intelligences, these plans have greater scope, and this scope becomes ever more inclusive farther up the pyramid of life. Prophecy is based on the ability to tune into some of these cosmic computers and receive a playback. The greater the prophet, the higher up the pyramid he is able to probe. This phenomenon has been the origin of many bizarre and fallacious ideas concerning the nature of time.

De La Warr demonstrated the above principle with what is known as the De La Warr camera.(32) As an example, a seed can be placed in the well of this psionic device. The operator then concentrates on a future development while "tuning" to the so-called vibrational rate of the seed. When the photograph is developed, a clear picture of the requested period of development is revealed. This may be in the bulb stage or as a fully developed plant. Similarly, the future condition of a patient can be determined by placing a blood sample in the device.

The mind of the operator plays a vital role in each of these above cases by tuning into the computers of the life-sustaining intelligence of the organism involved. This intelligence exists in a higher realm. The concepts discussed in this chapter are also involved in a wide range of other phenomena such as telepathy, clairvoyance, map dowsing, etc. Telepathic impressions are transmitted directly by means of the life lines already described. Therefore, the velocity of transmission must have close to an infinite value. Clairvoyance is the transmission of messages from cosmic computers in a manner analogous to that of television or videotape, with the brain of the psychic acting as the receiver. In the case of map dowsing, the map provides the focal point for the mind of the dowser to contact that section of a cosmic computer which relates to a part of the earth displayed on the map. The computer contains a record of all physical aspects of the earth, past and present.

The mechanics of map dowsing are somewhat different from those of dowsing in the field. The dowser in the field picks up the emanations of soft electrons directly from the mineral he is detecting. The soft particles radiated from any material are characteristic of that particular substance.

When psionics finally gains a substantial foothold, many of the techniques of the medical profession will become obsolete. It isn't surprising that the AMA has employed extreme measures to suppress it. In addition to the healing techniques of psionics already discussed, there could be devices which radiate dematerializing energies. Such machines could make bloodless surgery a reality by selective dematerialization of any tissue.

Researchers in psionics have long been aware of a field of energy surrounding all human organisms. It is called the L-field or the field of life, and can be influenced by the mind. Many different types of experiments with this field have led to the conclusion that this field determines the body's form and function. From the previous discussion, it is apparent that this conclusion is not altogether accurate. This field is only a step upward on the ladder of cause and effect. It has already been shown that the life or soul center existing in a higher realm is the prime motivating force which determines all the final outcome of this.

The type of energy manifested as the L-field is nothing other than the soft particles discussed repeatedly throughout this treatise. Their true function is in the promotion of special types of chemical changes which only take place in living organisms. It requires high concentrations of soft particles to promote such chemical changes. This is the main distinction between "living" matter and inert matter. It was the bions generating high concentrations of such energies that led Reich to the discovery of orgone energy. When a living organism dies, abnormal quantities of soft particles are locked in the cells. Heat applied to such matter disintegrates the soft electrons which, in turn, release great quantities of hard electrons. This produces the fire when organic material burns, and is the reason organic material is combustible while inorganic substances in general are not. Soft electrons make possible the building and maintaining of cells, which are really giant molecules. The manner in which the soul center is able to control matter in this realm, and consequently the creation of soft particles, has already been elaborated upon. This involves the step down principle mentioned in the chapter on teleportation. The well known aura is the manifestation of these energies.(62,97) It follows that the aura will reflect the physical and mental state of an individual. It is the same field revealed by Kirlian photography.(65)

The nature of the L-field would remain a mystery without the concept of the soft particle, the law of redistribution of energy, and a proper understanding of the ethers. Previous attempts to explain the L-field leave something to be desired. The L-field regulates the normal bodily functions and is controlled by the so-called subconscious mind. This is the portion of the brain which functions in the same manner as a servomechanism. It has all the characteristics of a standard computer. It has no independent reasoning capabilities, and operates only in the way in which it is programmed. The type of programming it receives is dependent upon the experiences of the individual, including those of the prenatal period. The individual's experiences in previous lives in the physical realm and the reactions to those experiences are the principal factors which govern the type of programming this computer receives prior to birth. In this manner, the person can profit from past experiences and the development process can continue in the manner described earlier. Psychics can tell many things about an individual by looking at his aura or L-field.

The nature of this aura in terms of the soft particle concept readily accounts for certain phenomena never before explained. For example, some radios behave erratically in the presence of some individuals. When such a person changes position in relation to the radio its performance changes. One position can produce excessive static and the static immediately ceases when the person moves away. A return to the original position produces static again. There are many such regions where this phenomenon occurs and it can extend throughout the room occupied by the radio. In some instances, the radio will even switch stations. This occurs mostly on FM. There are varying concentrations and types of soft electrons producing the color effect seen by sensitives. When a highly sensitive or "temperamental" radio is exposed to certain parts of the aura, disintegrating soft particles release excessive numbers of hard electrons in its circuits. This produces the static and in some instances changes the frequency characteristics of its tuning system to the extent of causing it to tune into another frequency.

The properties of the aura also resolve the mystery of the Stradivarius violin, which has baffled experts for over 200 years. Every aspect of the Strad has been duplicated, including geometry, wood, varnish, etc. In other words, exact replicas of the Strad have been reproduced, except for the quality of the sound it produces. What has not been taken into consideration is that certain types and combinations of soft particles can be absorbed by the wood to produce subtle changes in its physical characteristics. Stradivarius no doubt had a unique aura which impregnated his creations with a unique type and combination of soft particles.

The computer has a more direct line to the soul center than the reasoning part of the brain, since the proper functioning of the body depends upon it. The subconscious can only be programmed to the advantage of the individual by intelligent planning of the reasoning mind. When followed assiduously, this procedure can eventually override behavior patterns of the reactive mind which seem to work against the person. Proper meditation has been used quite effectively to achieve this.

The human organism functions in identically the same manner as a highly complex electronic device directed by a sophisticated computer. Where the flows of hard electrons are used to operate the electronic device and its computer, a soft electron flow enables the human body to function. A system of wires carries the electricity for the operation of the electronic device while nerves are the carriers of the soft electron flow in the organism. Organic materials are the best conductors for soft electrons and metals are the best for hard electrons.

It requires a potential difference to maintain an electrical flow for soft electrons as well as for the hard particles. Von Reichenbach showed that the human body maintains a potential difference between the right side and the left. In other words, it is similar to a battery. This supplies the potential for the soft electron flow which enables the body to function. It requires warm temperature for the necessary chemical processes in a living organism. This is supplied by the continuous disintegration of the more unstable soft electrons flowing in the body and releasing the hard electrons.

An electronic device in operation produces electromagnetic radiations. The nature and frequency of this radiation reflects the nature of the device. It is often known as static. It follows that the interactions of soft electron flow in an organism and especially in the brain will also produce electromagnetic radiations. However, soft electrons are far less active than the hard electrons and, consequently, lower ethers are disturbed with the production of far lower frequencies. Since the activity of a particle is directly proportional to the frequency of the photons of which it is comprised it can be concluded that hard electrons are about 10^5 times as active as the soft electrons flowing in an organism. It follows that the interactions of hard electrons will produce frequencies on the average of about 10^5 times as high as that produced by the soft electrons mentioned. Since most of the static produced by electronic devices is in the AM frequency band, it can be concluded that the emanations from the brain will be the ELF radiations. They are what has been known as "brain waves". The characteristics of such radiations are altered by thought. It follows that one's thoughts can be determined by the proper analysis of the "wave" patterns of such radiations. The reader may be shocked to learn that machines have been developed that can read one's thoughts by the analysis of these ELF radiations, also that the CIA has been employing such machines for many years to monitor the thoughts of those they consider a potential threat to the status quo. Their range however has been limited to only a few miles. The author knows personally of a case of an individual who has been victimized by the CIA in this manner. He is the electronic genius mentioned earlier who developed the levitating device that confirmed the nature of gravity already expounded upon. He had also developed a means of magnetizing metals other than ferromagnetic materials.

Shortly after he was scared away from continuing, he was admitted to a hospital for a checkup. While there, an illegal operation under the sanction of the CIA was performed on him. An implant was inserted in his brain in order to amplify his "brain waves" so that he could be monitored from a greater distance. He began to realize something was wrong after he left the hospital when he experienced headaches and loss of memory. X-rays showed this implant but he was unable to find any surgeon who would dare to remove it.

The image of the CIA fostered on the public is a group organized to protect our country's security. Instead it is an organization of miscreants trained in the black arts and deception to safeguard the interests of the power elite who have kept this planet in bondage for ages. Every individual who has shown unusual ability including psychic powers has come under their surveillance. It was then determined at headquarters in Washington, D.C. whether or not it was in the best interests of the power elite for the person to be terminated. Many people over the years have met with untimely deaths in this manner. This includes well over 100 well documented cases of individuals who died under mysterious circumstances and who also knew too much about the Kennedy assassination.

Many have wondered why the author has not met with a similar fate since he has been stomping on the toes of the power structure much harder than anyone else for many years. This is a seeming mystery and paradox that needs to be cleared up at this point.

When the time is propitious for a great new idea to be introduced to the world the power to enforce its introduction will accompany the one who is to introduce it. This power will far transcend that of any man-made organization which would oppose it. It isn't surprising that many CIA hit men have been expended in an effort to eliminate the author. A former acquaintance of the author, with unusual abilities and who had an important mission to fulfill, has had a similar run-in with the CIA. Every hit man sent to terminate him has instead met with a starnge "accident." It is interesting to note that the CIA is now only a shadow of what it once was and all of its best hit men are long gone. Prior to Reagan's inauguration small newspaper articles kept hinting that the CIA was in big trouble. One of them mentioned that director Stanfield had fired (?) nearly 900 agents. Obviously this was a infantile attempt to explain away the disappearance or mysterious death of about 900 agents. The latest of these stated that "The morale and performance of the CIA has reached an all time low and only drastic surgery can save the patient." It is also significant that such rumors and articles followed the runs-in the author and former associate had with such criminals.

A typical CIA agent is an individual with few scruples and also one who is likely to be emotionally unstable. Most are the misfits of society. The above mentioned associate of the author had an experience that confirmed this. An apartment just above the one in which he was once living was, of course, occupied by a CIA agent. As has always been the case, the living quarters of everyone under their scrutiny are thoroughly bugged. For the more "important" cases there is a direct pipeline from this bugging to CIA headquarters in Washington, D.C. Unknown to the CIA at this time was that this former associate was adept in astral projection. One evening the agent who was psychic, as most of them are supposed to be, found out about this ability when he became aware of the fact he was being monitored by the one he was supposed to be monitoring. His reaction was complete panic. He started to call headquarters but dropped the phone and rushed to the bathroom and began sobbing. (Afterwards his clothing had to go to the cleaners.) The proceedings were automatically transmitted to headquarters. Headquarters were then visited by this associate wherein it was decided by CIA officialdom it was in the best interests that he be liquidated. Some prominent individuals in the public eye were there at the time.

Another organization fully as evil as the CIA is the IRS. It was created for two main purposes. First to help feed an industrial empire which specializes in implements of destruction. Where are most of the tax dollars extorted from the public funneled? Second, to legalize invasion of the average citizen's privacy and rights which expedites subjugation and control by the vested interests. It is needless to state that this organization of degenerates will never extract a cent from the author and they will be asking for trouble if they try. The reader may be glad to learn that the IRS has met with a fate similar to that of the CIA. They don't have nearly the clout they once had and the government is trying to cover this up with publicized scare tactics.

In line with the above statements is a quote from a bi-monthly publication of a consultant firm known as "Personal Finance" for which subscribers pay $78.00 per year. Quote: "Tax collections are withering through evasion and internal breakdown within IRS ranks." — unquote.

THE PSIONIC RESEARCH OF GEORGE DE LA WARR

Perhaps the most remarkable research in the psionic field was conducted by George De La Warr in England. One of De La Warr's important discoveries concerned what he called "the spiral stairway of evolution," as described in Chapter 7 of the book *New Worlds Beyond the Atom* by Langston Day and George De La Warr. (32) A sample of material was placed at the north pole of an upright bar magnet. An operator using a De La Warr detector could pick up a point of resonance at a specific place in the vicinity of the magnet, after mentally concentrating on the sample. Each material resonated at a point which was typical of

Figure 31
DE LA WARR'S SPIRAL STAIRWAY OF EVOLUTION

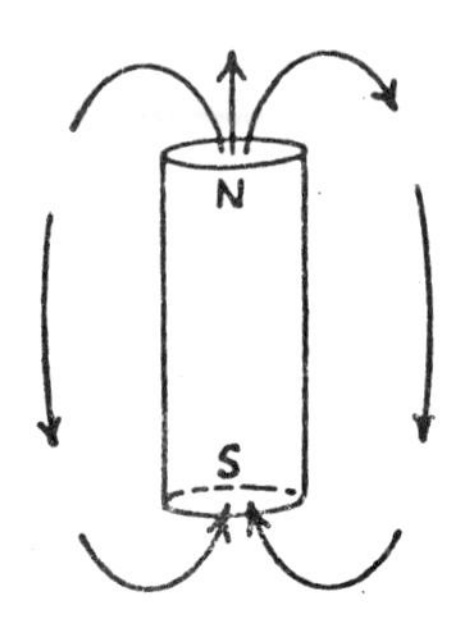

Side view of magnet

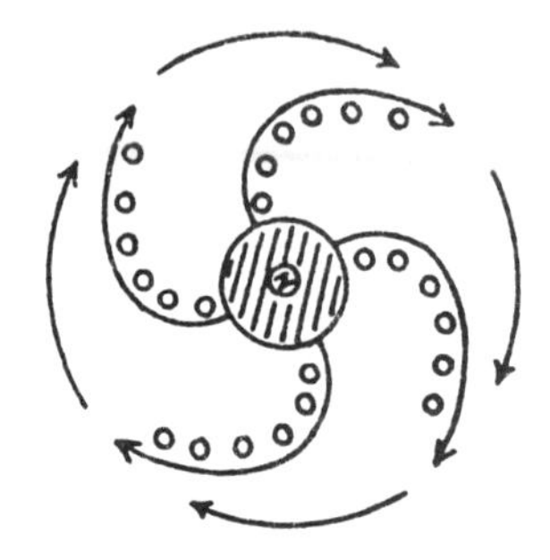

Top view of magnet
Demonstrating the Vortex Motion

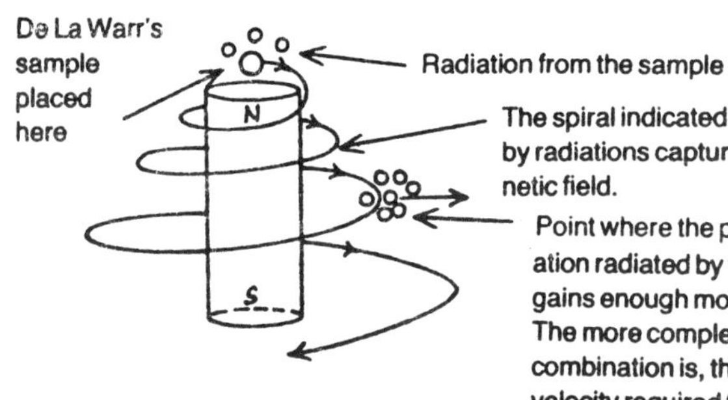

Top view of the De La Warr's Experiment

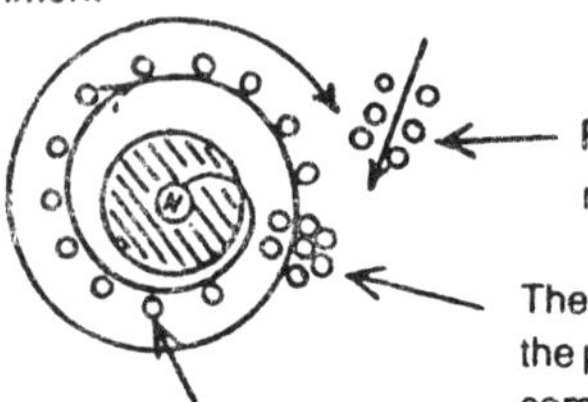

that substance. It was found that these reaction points occurred along a three dimensional spiral, which started at the north pole of the magnet and radiated outward toward the south pole, but at a greater distance from the magnet. It was also found that the magnet had to be rotated in a certain position with respect to the earth's magnetic field in order to get the best reaction. Figure 24 demonstrates the phenomenon.

The pure elements had their points of resonance where the spiral was narrowest. The more complex the specimen, such as chemical compounds, organic material, life forms, etc., the further down the spiral these resonance areas occurred. The explanation follows a pattern similar to the Von Reichenbach experiments. The earth's magnetic field plays an important part in the phenomenon, because of the particles which travel down the field. A concentrated fluid flow tends to follow a vortex or whirlwind motion, rather than a straight line motion. This is also true of a magnetic field. Since most of the particles responsible for producing a magnetic field are negative charges, the vortex motion of the field follows the left-hand rule. A magnetic line of force consists of a minute vortex in the ethers. The path of an individual particle follows a spiral, since the path is the result of two motions, a rotation and a translation. The intensity of the magnetic field depends on the number of such lines per unit, cross sectional area, and the kind of ethers in motion.

The soft particles radiated by a sample placed at the north pole of the magnet are captured by the magnetic field and travel down the magnetic lines toward the south pole and tend to converge at that point. During their travel down the lines, they are constantly accelerated. There are three influences tending to force the soft particles out of the spiral: One is their own momentum; another is the centrifugal motion of the vortex; and the other is the repulsive action of particles already captured and being captured by the field, as well as that of particles traveling down the earth's field. The point of emergence from the magnetic field of the bar magnet is the resonance point picked up by the operator of the De La Warr Detector. Most of the particles are ejected in a definite line at this point, because of the proper orientation in the field of the bar magnet and the earth's field. Without this orientation, the ejection would not be at one point, but would be at different points in the field.

Since the bar is nearly perpendicular to the earth's field, depending on the magnetic inclination at that point, the particles captured by the magnet are subjected to bombardments from particles traveling down the earth's field. The particles captured by the bar magnet travel in a wide spiral path. On one side they travel in the opposite direction to those moving in the earth's field, while on the other side they travel in the same general direction and thus have fewer interactions. The field strength around a bar magnet is seldom uniform. Therefore, the magnetic intensity is greater on one side than the other sides. This is why the orientation of the magnet with respect to the earth's field is important in the De La Warr experiment. The strong side of the magnet should be in the position at which the captured particles encounter the greatest bombardment, so that there will be less tendency for them to be prematurely dislodged from the field and randomly scattered.

The more complex the organism or substance placed at the north pole of the magnet, the greater the range and type of soft particles radiated. This situation forms a stronger interlocking combination of particles, which will remain in the field for a greater distance. Since it is soft particles, and not photons, which affect a photographic plate, it is logical to conclude that these points of resonance can be photographed where the particles are concentrated and ejected from the field in a definite direction. This is what De La Warr did. The phenomenon is briefly summarized as follows: As the particles are radiated from the sample, they travel down the field toward the opposite pole. As they travel, they gain velocity and tend to be pulled together into a group by mutual magnetic attraction. They follow a circular and spiral path during this period. When they finally reach the resonance point where they have gained enough velocity to leave the field, they are concentrated sufficiently to affect a photographic plate.

De La Warr assumed on page 46 of his book *New Worlds Beyond the Atom* that ". . . everything both animate and inanimate had its correct angular relationship to the Earth's magnetic field, . . ."(32) To test this theory, he conducted a series of experiments in which samples placed on a photographic plate in a dark room were rotated until a reaction was picked up by a detector. At that point, a brief exposure resulted in a photo giving clear and well defined forms. De La Warr couldn't be expected to have a clear conception of what he was doing without the concept of the soft particle and an understanding of its nature, as well as that of the magnetic field. Organized structures radiate particles in a significant pattern and direction. When they are oriented so that the particles they radiate collide directly with the particles traveling down the earth's field, this pattern is disrupted. If De La Warr's equipment and photographic plate had been adequately shielded from the flow of soft particles in the earth's field, the results would have been independent of any orientation of the samples, regardless of the earth's field. The earth's field by itself is too feeble to produce significant short range effects. However, the particles can acquire high velocities after traveling long distances in the earth's field.

Although the earth's field is relatively weak, there is much more to it than is indicated by conventional instruments such as a magnetometer. These instruments detect mainly that part which is due to hard electrons. The effects resulting from soft particles produce only minor reactions on conventional detectors. Most of the energy of the field is not detected. Experiments of De La Warr and Von Reichenbach gave indirect evidence of it.

De La Warr, Abrams, Drown, and other researchers in psionics found that a blood sample from an individual is in permanent contact with every part of that person's body, regardless of its distance from the person.(2,27,32,34,59,81) The physics of this has already been discussed. Therefore, the blood sample is an effective medium for both diagnosis and treatment of the individual. De La Warr devised an ingenious method of diagnosing a disease from a blood sample with photography. A lens system was used to focus the radiation from the sample onto a photographic plate. In order to sort out the radiations of a specific disease, a synthetic radiation tuned to the suspected disease or condition was radiated, or projected, so that it intersected the radiation from the blood sample. A photographic plate was placed at the point of intersection. If the disease were not present, the plate would not be affected The synthetic radiations interacted with similar radiations if present in the rays from the blood sample. This resulted in a higher concentration or reinforcement of this kind of radiation than any of the others in the beam; therefore, it was the radiation which produced the image.

It should be noted that in all of the psionic experiments the mind of the operator plays a key role in the results. The important work of the pioneers in psionics has clearly demonstrated a vital fact continually emphasized in this treatise. It is that the primary creative intelligence is in all things, and directs the activities of all things, including the smallest particle of matter. In other words, all things observed and encountered are actually thought forms, and the thought form reflects the nature of the intelligence which produced it.

De La Warr developed photographic techniques in diagnosis and treatment to perhaps a higher degree than any of the other researchers in psionics. Some of this incredible work in recording the past, present and future condition of an organism was mentioned in a previous chapter. The images produced on the photographs were generated in a manner similar to projecting a picture onto a television screen. Physical form in nature is created in a like manner, except that the process takes place in three dimensions, instead of two. In each case, it proceeds under intelligent direction.

The practical applications for the discoveries of De La Warr and other psionic pioneers are practically unlimited. These include finding lost persons and objects and detecting mineral deposits at any place in the earth. Although it has been a quarter of a century since De La Warr conducted most of his important research, the application of his discoveries has been minimal. He repeatedly tried to interest the academic world in his discoveries, but encountered the same quality of mind which Von Reichenbach encountered a century earlier.

COLOR THERAPY

This branch of the healing arts has been shown to be highly effective.(57) Consequently, it has not been endorsed or applied by the medical profession in general. The principles involved are similar to those employed in healing by radionics. In both cases, combinations of the appropriate soft electrons are directed to the afflicted areas. The only essential difference is in the source of the energies employed. It has already been shown that soft electrons accompany light. The types of soft electrons are characteristic of the frequency range of the light they accompany. It is expected that different parts or organs of the body and diseases will be affected by certain colors and color combinations. This is another demonstration of the vital role which soft particles play in all the life and chemical processes.

ACUPUNCTURE

Acupuncture is gaining acceptance in the Western World as a healing method. With capable practitioners, excellent results have been obtained. Paradoxically, the medical profession has been giving it serious consideration.

The acupuncture treatment for a given malfunction involves inserting metallic needles in the body at certain nerve centers. There are hundreds of these centers distributed throughout the body. Knowing precisely where to place these needles requires a technique and knowledge which is not easily acquired, even with a chart at one's disposal. The nervous system can be likened to a complex circuit of some elaborate electronic device. It carries the electricity which enables the body to function. As in a circuit, there are centers where nerves converge at a common point. The proper functioning of the body is dependent upon the energies which are directed from these centers. An afflicted part of the body has a lower potential, or a higher positive charge, than surrounding areas; and a needle placed at the right point can start a flow of electricity to the area. This flow can dislodge obstructions in the circuit and re-establish a normal condition in many instances.

The initial source of the electricity may be from an external source. Once the flow is started, the electricity will continue to flow to the afflicted area in the manner that Reich's cloudbuster draws orgone energy from a cloud to the ground.

Acupuncture has not proven to be a panacea. It requires such precision and extensive training for the practitioner that widespread application does not seem likely in the near future. This resolves the apparent paradox of why it is being considered by the medical profession.

For many of those interested in psionics and who are working in this field, this chapter is likely to be considered too brief. Such an opinion would be justified. Psionics is a broad subject. It would require a large volume to give it the treatment it deserves and to present the contributions and important work, past and present, of many in this branch of science. To offset in some measure the brevity of the above treatment, an analysis of a problem of great concern, and a remedy, will now be given.

The age of electricity and the proliferation of various electrical appliances and devices of all kinds produced unnatural electromagnetic radiations which have caused health problems of mammoth proportions throughout the civilized world. Careful research has shown that the general health of people in areas which previously had no electricity rapidly deteriorates after the introduction of electricity and the subsequent use of TVs, radios, and all of the other modern appliances. The reasons such radiations are inimical to humans and other life forms have never been understood. They become apparent in the light of principles introduced in this treatise.

As already indicated, the human and animal organisms require an abundant flow of soft electrons comprised of photons in the visible light range for their efficient operation. This flow is interrupted in the presence of high concentrations of soft electrons comprised of lower frequency photons such as those produced by unnatural electromagnetic radiations. They tend to capture or gobble up the harder electrons the organism requires. It is a case of the softer particles absorbing the harder particles. This is the reason such radiations are harmful.

Psionic researchers have in recent years found a highly efficient means of counteracting the effects of inimical radiations. It is a device known as a polarizer. It is a complex antenna system compressed in a conical bundle slightly over four inches in diameter and height. It has produced significant improvements after being placed on different parts of the body. The most dramatic effects of all occur when it is placed over an electric conduit or cord which is connected to an active outlet. There have been numerous and vague explanations of how and why it works but, as is to be expected, they have all missed the mark.

The more astute reader has likely deduced its operation already. It functions in the manner of the Reich cloudbuster. It draws and concentrates the beneficial soft electrons to affected areas of the body. It has a much greater affinity for the harder electrons the body requires than for the softer particles radiated by unnatural means. An electrical wire or conduit functions as a sink much in the same way running water forms an outlet for soft electron flow in a cloudbuster. Therefore, when a polarizer is placed over an electrical wiring system a great flow of beneficial soft electrons is the result. A high concentration of such particles throughout the area of the electric system is the result. For the benefit of the reader, more information about the polarizer and how to procure one can be obtained by writing Environmental Polarity Research, P.O. Box 22528, San Diego, CA 92122.

The multiple wave oscillator developed by Lakovsky produces similar results but works on a different principle. Paradoxically, it generates a wide range of frequencies, each of which is inimical to a living organism. However, this combination produces interactions which result in the disintegration of great numbers of very soft electrons, which release the harder particles the body requires. It should be mentioned that the disintegration of soft electrons does not always release the very hard electrons. Often the harder particles released are only a very few octaves harder than the particles which originally housed them. The degree of hardness of particles released depends on the degree of agitation and other factors.

CHAPTER 27

MATERIALIZATIONS FROM HIGHER REALMS

Spirit manifestations includes ghosts, poltergeist activities, and materializations produced by mediums during seances. The materializations in some cases are both visible and tangible. At other times, they are tangible but invisible, or intangible but visible. Principles already elaborated upon render this type of phenomenon understandable. The step down principle is involved, with one essential difference: The object or body existing in a higher realm is itself impregnated with successively lower frequency particles, until it is able to manifest itself in this realm. When the materializing process reaches the stage where energies are in a frequency range close to the physical, it becomes visible. These energies are known as ectoplasm. Since materializing energies come from a higher realm, a high loose charge of very hard electrons frequently impregnates the bodies. There is seldom a perfect balance of positive and negative charges in the materialized object or being. Therefore, any direct, physical contact may be dangerous, as some have learned to their sorrow.

Every planetary system in the universe has thirteen major realms, consisting of twelve astral realms and one physical realm. Since progression takes place in relatively small increments, there are intermediate realms between the major ones. The physical realms of the different planets seem to be in varying degrees of development. There is some evidence that the physical realms of most of the other planets may not be suitable for intelligent life, as we know it. However, all of the planets in this system may possess not only intelligent life, but highly advanced civilizations existing in realms above the physical.

There have been many reports, apparently some reliable, of contactees being taken to planets in this system and others. The common claim is that they were shown advanced civilizations. If these planets do not support life as we know it and the reports are true, then the step up principle needs to be defined in order to explain these occurrences. This will also account for well authenticated and mysterious disappearances occurring from time to time. The step up principle involves the disappearance of a body from the physical realm and its appearance in a realm just above the physical. The process accomplishing this is the exact reverse of the dematerialization process. The fundamental particles of the atom are impregnated with electrons comprised of higher frequency photons than those of physical matter. The manner in which the physical matter becomes dematerialized is different from the dematerialization process described earlier. In this case, the action of the particles is not frozen. Instead, it is greatly increased. It is similar to the process in which soft particles house harder particles. Soft particles are far more active by virtue of the harder particles they contain, than they would be without them. As a result, they interact with physical matter.

During the step up process the spaces between particles stepped up are not impregnated with other particles as is the case with the previously mentioned dematerializing process. As a result, ether bombardments are not impaired. The fundamental particles of physical matter are larger than those of higher frequency matter. This is a key to understanding why molecular motion is more rapid and events take place more rapidly in the higher realms than in the physical, since the kinetic energy of all ether particles is the same. The smaller fundamental particles in the higher realms have much greater surface areas in proportion to their masses. This means they will experience far greater ether bombardments in proportion to their masses than do the fundamental particles of physical matter. Therefore, they will be given greater accelerations. This tendency is enhanced because in proportion to mass they will be hit more often because of the greater activity of the higher ether particles.

The harder photons which interpenetrate the fundamental particles of physical matter are in turn impregnated with still harder photons and so on up the ladder. This process also involves the etheric counterpart. This continues until the physical object becomes visible and tangible in a realm just above the physical and etheric realms. The body maintains practically the same weight and inertial properties in this state as the other matter in this realm and is virtually transformed into higher frequency matter. It should be noted that the harder photons can interpenetrate the protons of physical matter and transform them into what is equivalent to higher frequency protons. The hard and smaller electrons occupy the "solid" portion of the protons and not their holes. This transformed physical matter no longer interacts with the matter of its former state because the activity of its fundamental particles is too great.

There are things that still need to be clarified concerning this process. The fundamental particles and atoms of this transformed physical matter are more massive than those of the higher realms. Yet the bodies of the transformed physical matter will have about the same weight and inertia of those of like bodies in the higher realm. On the surface this seems to be a paradox but it is resolved when one realizes that the bodies of the transformed physical matter contain much fewer molecules than do the bodies of the higher realm. Also, the activity of the transformed particles is considerably increased because of the higher frequency of bombardment by the higher ether particles than was experienced in the physical realm.

The dematerialization process described earlier freezes the motion of the fundamental particles and the matter becomes inertia-less and intangible in all realms. Matter in this case retains its inertial properties but becomes intangible in a higher realm because the motion of its particles has been increased.

It is now clear what happened to many of the contactees mentioned above who were taken to other planets. They were first subjected to the energies described in the above transformation process in order to be aware of the realm on the planet or planets to which they were taken. When they returned to earth, the step up energies were removed and they resumed their original state.

If the step up energies are not applied in the proper balance the body will soon return to its normal state. This would happen if the wrong frequency combinations were used, causing the energies to escape. Evidently, beings in a realm just above the physical are able to project combinations of the step up energies into the physical realm at various times and places. Anyone who walks into a region or pocket of these energies will suddenly find himself in what would appear to be another world. His body would be transformed into a body of higher frequency matter which is tangible in the next higher realm. The combination of energies might be such that they would eventually escape from the body. As a result, the individual would then return to the physical realm.

Such cases have been recorded. A notable instance was described in a recent book entitled *Time Travel: Myth or Reality?* by Richard Heffern on pages 43-54.(58) According to the account, J.P.J. Chapman and his wife Poole, of Dorset, England, were searching for some wild flowers. They ventured into a vacant area near some apartment buildings in their search. Mr. Chapman walked a short distance into the area, and suddenly became aware that the apartment buildings had disappeared. He stated that a "vast open space of nothingness surrounded me". He walked into the direction where the apartment buildings had been seen. The sun was in the sky, the ground was below his feet, but he saw no signs of people or buildings. He retraced his steps and soon found that everything was normal again. His wife noted that he had disappeared, and was worried until the time of his reappearance.

It is significant that the sun was still in evidence during his experience. As mentioned previously, the major celestial bodies exist in all the realms. This means that regardless of the realm one occupies, the same bodies such as the sun, the stars, and the planets will be seen. Energy fields such as the one which caused Chapman to temporarily disappear exist only for brief periods. Otherwise, there would be a rash of disappearances, which would focus world wide attention on such areas. Evidently, Chapman was not in the field long enough for the energies to become locked into his body. When he walked out of the area, the energies quickly escaped.

Many strange disappearances are no doubt the result of teleportation. The person or persons are teleported from one part of the planet to another for undisclosed reasons. Some may have been teleported to other planets. This could account for people disappearing and never being seen again. Such occurrences have given rise to bizarre speculations as to the nature of time and space.

CHAPTER 28

MISCONCEPTIONS OF TIME AND SPACE

Teleportation, prophecy, visions, disappearances and other phenomena have led to weird and illogical speculations concerning time and space. Surprisingly, most of them have come from other than hard core scientists.

A completely adequate definition and analysis of time was presented in Part I. It renders the vapidness of all these wild speculations about time selfevident. If the science fiction version of time travel were a possibility, then cause and effect is not an actuality. Nothing has ever really happened, since time travelers could go back and prevent everything that seemingly has happened from happening. They may have prevented themselves from coming into existence by the same process. A self-contradicting and hence impossible situation exists, a denial of all the laws of creation. This is a demonstration of the worst kind of logic possible. Speculations such as time travel are so devoid of rationality they fall into the category of insanity. Insanity is a state of mind in which the individual is out of touch with reality. The concept of time travel is a denial of reality. Therefore, a belief in this idea is by definition a form of insanity. This is actually another case of doublethink.

All of the seemingly inexplicable occurrences which have been explained away by time travel, time warps, space warps, fourth dimensions and the like, can be simply and logically accounted for. Every detail of everything that has ever happened is recorded in the vast network of cosmic computers. The conscious mind can be tuned to obtain a playback of some of the records. An individual can experience a past occurrence, which seems so vivid and real the person will believe he has been transported back in time. He will seemingly be able to walk around at will in the region involved, and even talk to the participants. However, they will ignore him since his experience is only a playback, and not an actual case of time travel. It is significant that in accounts of those who have had such experiences it was mentioned that the "actors" in the drama paid no attention to them. One can in the same manner have a realistic experience of some future event by tuning into what has been planned for the future.

This type of experience does not account for all cases of a seeming displacement in time. Since particles of matter in higher realms are far more active than those in lower realms, it follows that events in realms of higher frequency matter take place more rapidly. This means that smaller units of time must be employed in the higher realms. The con sciousness automatically adjusts to these changes, so that the inhabitants in these worlds are not aware of any differences. Accounts received from entities residing in an astral realm who have recently lost their physical bodies confirms this. A notable case which the author encountered involves a person who seemingly had spent many months in an astral realm since his demise. At this time, he was informed to his amazement that some guides were going to take him down to the physical realm so he could view his own funeral. This funeral took place only three days after his departure, yet he thought several months had passed. Occult lore is steeped with cases of this type, yet the obvious reason for the time anomalies always escaped those who researched the subject. It is to be expected that the wrong interpretations concerning the properties of time are always placed on such incidents. One of the most popular explanations is the erroneous conclusion that time doesn't exist in the astral realms!

Many events which happen in the intermediate realms between the physical and first astral realm are patterned after those which will occur later in the physical realm, according to plan. This is similar to a rehearsal prior to the real production and follows the hermetic axiom again. An idea or plan generally needs to be tested for soundness and changes need to be made, before it is applied on a grand scale. Many of the regions in these intermediate realms have their counterparts in the physical. Those entities above the mainstream of humanity who have important roles to play in the drama have embodiments in the intermediate realms, as well as in the physical. Therefore, some events which are destined to take place in the physical have already occurred in a higher realm. This and certain cosmic computers are responsible for the accurate visions of future events, which prophets have received throughout history. Som individuals may have been temporarily transported to these realms to obtain glimpses of certain conditions on the earth, as they are supposed to be sometime in the future. These experiences have supposedly included conversations with some of the inhabitants at times. The person in each case thought he was a time traveler or passed through a "time warp" into future time.

Another kind of phenomenon involving a time discrepancy is a series of events supposedly taking place in familiar surroundings, in which the apparent time interval is much smaller than it should be. For example, one might walk from one place to another and be aware of every step taken; yet find that a much smaller interval of time has elapsed, than is actually required to walk the distance. This is a case where the mind of the individual may have been impressed with the thought that he or she had actually walked all the way, but the in dividual was actually teleported to the destination. A state of hallucination could have been artificially induced prior to teleportation. It is possible that a practical joker with certain powers was involved. A significant number have claimed to have had such an experience. This is another type of experience which has spawned the idea of time or space warps.

All paradoxes concerning time and space are well within the scope of concepts introduced thus far. The creation of an activity in any form involves the flow of energy, and consequently the flow of time. Time is inseparable from all of this, and is therefore an integral part of it, including creation. It follows that anything which is independent of time is not a creation. Space comes under this category! It is a formless void of infinite extension in three, and only three, dimen sions. This is all that it is. One becomes aware of its existence only through creation or the flow of energy, which can only take place in three dimensions.

The absurdity of that supposedly profound phrase, "beyond time and space," often used by metaphysical teachers and writers, should be more than apparent by now. An entity is dependent upon both time and space for its existence. It would be some achievement to get beyond time and space.

CHAPTER 29

FALSE ILLUMINATION: AN ANALYSIS OF THE SCIENTIFIC EFFORTS OF WALTER RUSSELL

The major goal of an incarnating soul or intelligence is to attain the stage of development wherein the physical body is in perfect rapport with the higher bodies, including the soul center itself. THis means that all channels from the center of intelligence to the physical body are cleared. These major channels connect to various psychic centers in the physical body, known as chakras. In the higher schools of occult study, this condition is known as illumination. When some of these channels are partially opened, the individual becomes known as a sensitive, psychic or medium. The more these channels are opened, the more perceptive the person becomes and the greater is the ability to pick up psychic impressions. Sometimes only a physical membrane separates a partially cleared channel from a psychic center, and occasionally an injury breaks this membrane. A notable instance is the world renowned Peter Hurkos. Hurkos became one of the world's greatest psychics following a severe injury.(18)

Illumination has been a rare occurence on this planet during recorded history. Generally those who acquire it are not in the public eye. The true masters of the Far East are in this category, and help shape the destiny of the world from behind the scenes. Many cases of partially opened chakras have been mistaken for illumination. This results in a flow of energies throughout the physical body, which gives one a feeling of euphoria or sometimes the impression that the mind has been opened for revelation. These people believe God has spoken to them. The partial opening of one or more chakras does not necessarily give one a clear channel to the higher realms from where real truths are channeled. A person may receive impressions from various sources, which may or may not be true. This is why psychics and mediums are not infallible, as their records attest. Consequently, sound logic and judgement are generally one's best guide.

A classic example of one who thought he had become illuminated but was clearly not is Walter Russell. Many people regard him as the true sage and illuminate of this century. He is still considered an example of the universal man. Russell had little formal education, but became one of the foremost sculptors of his time. He also showed ability in lines of endeavor such as painting and music. Walter Russell was born in 1871 and died in 1963. During his long and eventful life, he became a friend and associate of most of the leading personalities of his day. These included Mark Twain, Theodore Roosevelt, Sir Arthur Conan Doyle, Alexis Carrel, and Nikola Tesla.

When he was 50 years old, he experienced the opening of a chakra and the consequent flow of energies and impressions which led him to believe he had become an illuminate. This is described in the introduction to *Atomic Suicide*, which he and his wife wrote. The book gives an account of the 39 days in May and June of 1921 when it was supposedly shown to him "God's full process of creation".(106) From that time on, Russell thought he was blessed with transcendent knowledge. He expressed his revelations in the form of several books, of which the most notable are *The Secrets of Light* and *Atomic Suicide*. Extraordinary promises are made in the introductions to these books with regard to revealing all of nature's secrets, including the nature of gravity, light, matter, etc.

An analysis of Russell's scientific efforts will be given in considerable detail to fully demonstrate that he was completely misled by his false illumination. In the process of doing this, more acceptable explanations for the phenomena he allegedly explained will be presented, based on the new science given in this treatise.

This analysis begins by confuting a statement made in the first part of the introduction to *Atomic Suicide* on page *xv*, in which he stated that as long as man depends upon the evidence of his senses for knowledge of Cause and Effects — which are the limit of his vision — he will never solve these secrets.(106) This is a direct violation of the hermetic axiom. This treatise is tangible evidence of the fallacy of this dogma. The revelations contained herein were the result of logical analysis of impressions received by the senses, not from divine illumination such as Russell claimed to have received. Russell apparently was not possessed of unusual reasoning powers, since he was unable to logically analyze phenomena received by the senses. Furthermore, considering the fact that he was supposed to be a man of "transcendent insight", it follows that "it cannot be done". Yet it has been done.

The Russell periodic charts of the elements were a result of his "illumination". An analysis of these charts reveals another of the scientific enigmas of this century, which is why they were ever taken seriously by anyone. He was actually awarded a Ph.D. in Science for these charts by the American Academy of Science, in 1941! The Russell charts were based on the wave concept of nature. His wave concept divided the elements into nine "octaves" with the heavier elements on one end of this unfolding wave pattern and the lighter elements on the opposite end. One chart supposedly lists the elements in ascending levels of complexity. Incredibly, hydrogen, which is the simplest and lightest of all the elements, does not appear on the end of this chart. A total of 18 hypothetical elements are between hydrogen and the end of the chart! When the two heavier isotopes of hydrogen, deuterium and tritium, were discovered, Russell claimed to have predicted their existence. Unfortunately, these two isotopes are heavier and more complex than hydrogen and should have appeared above hydrogen on this chart, but they didn't.

Russell's chief claim to scientific eminence was his alleged prediction of the element plutonium, which seemed to appear on his chart above uranium. This was only a coincidence, since his chart has room for only three or four transuranic elements. As nearly every student of science knows, a dozen transuranic elements have already been discovered in defiance of Russell's predictions.

An overall viewpoint of these charts indicates that Russell was about 180 degrees out of phase with reality. Isotopes are listed as elements and many elements such as copper, silver, iron, zinc, gold, mercury, tungsten, etc., are listed as isotopes. An isotope of an element has the same chemical properties as the element. This is an important fact which he completely disregarded. In addition, as already mentioned, according to his chart there are quite a number of elements down the scale from hydrogen yet to be discovered. The old Mendeleyev periodic chart modified by the work of Moseley is vastly superior, since it conforms with reality.

The picture becomes increasingly grotesque as more of Russell's supposed contributions to world knowledge are analyzed. In accordance with academic science, which he largely denounced, he attributed weird properties to space, and talked of curved and warped space. Although he spoke of academic science in a thoroughly disparaging manner, he failed miserably to reveal any of its many flaws and, instead, substituted ideas that transcended even those of academic science in irrationality.

According to Russell, on page 217 of *Atomic Suicide*, he stated that nowhere in Nature does motion in any three-dimensional mass revolve around a common center. All mass is made up of pairs of ring units, which are joined together in parallel planes to create hemispheres.(106) As almost everyone knows, any three-dimensional object which rotates must rotate about an imaginary axis. He later uses this obvious mathematical and physical fact to "prove" other contentions in contradiction to the earlier statement. For example, he states on page 220 of *Atomic Suicide* that if you look at an electrical current in a vacuum tube (cathode ray tube) you will see parallel rings extending from the cathode to the anode, like buttons strung upon a thread. Each of these rings is supposedly controlled by its own center of gravity in its own plane.(106) It is significant that three rings do not appear until an appreciable distance from the cathode. They get increasingly closer together as the anode is approached. The reasons are in perfect conformity with concepts already introduced, and have nothing in common with any of Russell's ideas.

An explanation for the above phenomenon will now be given in detail. The electrons emerge from the cathode with near zero velocity. As their velocity increases, the resulting magnetic field captures large quantities of soft particles, which tend to follow the circular ether flow. As the soft electrons are thrown outward, many disintegrate into their constituent light, as they collide with other particles a short distance from the line of electron flow. The concentration of soft particles is not uniform. The magnetic field concentrates particles within a zone, leaving a void on each side of this concentration. The same pattern was described in the production of diffraction rings and lines in Part III. In a like manner, another group is produced further along the path and so on. As the electron velocity increases, the magnetic field becomes stronger and the concentrations become closer together.

The reason for the discrete concentrations of soft particles along the line of flow of electrons will be given now. The soft particles captured by the magnetic field tend to travel in circles, the planes perpendicular to the direction of the electrons. The spin of the captured soft electrons produces another magnetic field associated with lower ethers, other than that of the magnetic field which captured them. This new magnetic field is in planes perpendicular to those of the original field. The new field concentrates the particles in relatively thin rings, in the same manner that tight clusters of particles are produced in accelerators. The rings are visible only because of the disintegration of some of the particles in the rings. There is a considerable gap between the first ring and the cathode, because in this interval the electrons have not acquired sufficient velocity to produce such an effect.

Another of Russell's many strange misconceptions is taken from pages 222-223 of *Atomic Suicide*:

> According to Russell, the most evident proof that the universe of suns and earths is made up of pairs of rings, and that they disintegrate by throwing off pairs of rings, is to look at such planets, as Jupiter and Saturn, and such ring nebulae as Lyra and the others on that same page. The telescopes, of course clearly show the parallel wrinkles on Jupiter . . . further on he states that you can see planets and suns expanding in planes which are parallel to their equators. This, they continue to do until great holes are bored right through them were their gravity shafts exist to still control them until their motion ceases entirely.(106)

The above passage gathers up phenomena involving different principles, in order to support a pet dogma, which is devoid of a foundation to begin with. He failed to present any logical process by which a planet or any celestial object is able to throw off a ring, let alone explain how it got to be so thin. Jupiter's "parallel wrinkles", or belts, were explained in the chapter on atmospheric phenomena. They are generated for an entirely different reason than Saturn's rings. In actuality, Saturn's rings are a result of debris captured by the planet's gravitational and magnetic fields.

James Clerk Maxwell was the first to show that these rings consist of relatively small individual particles, each of which is in orbit. No one yet has explained why these rings are so thin and encircle the planet at its equator. It is time for this mystery to be resolved.

Saturn rotates very rapidly and has a diameter about 11 times as great as that of the earth. Its rotational velocity is about 25 times that of the earth, which means that its magnetic field is about 25 times as intense as the earth's field. Consequently, the concentration of particles is correspondingly greater. Since the captured particles tend to travel down magnetic lines, the concentration of these particles is lower at the equator than in the higher latitudes. Incidentally, this is one of the reasons that the Aurora Borealis and the southern lights appear in the higher latitudes. The concentration of particles is greater and more collisions result with the disintegration of soft particles into their constituent light.

Debris and fine dust which enter the gravitational influence of Saturn at first tend to orbit in a myriad of directions, but always in a plane which contains the center of mass. The larger particles of the original debris are reduced to fine dust by collisions. As a result, the visible portion of the rings is almost totally comprised of this fine dust. There are no doubt relatively large bodies which are not visible, yet orbit in planes other than that which includes the equator. Most of the orbiting particles encounter the heavier concentrations of charges captured by Saturn's magnetic field. This is because initially most of the orbits extend into the higher latitudes. These concentrations of charges extend for great distances beyond the planet's surface. Such heavy concentrations of charges offer resistance to the passage of the finer particles, which tends to divert them from their original orbits. It is similar to the refraction effects of light. As a result, increasing numbers tend to be diverted to orbits along the zones of lower concentrations closer to the equator. There is always a tendency to follow lines of least resistance. Although this condition tends to produce more particles orbiting along the equator, it does not account for the ultrathin rings. Great quantities of fine debris entering the gravitational field of a planet will eventually form rings similar to that of Saturn, regardless of whether or not it has a magnetic field. Rings will not necessarily form along the equator but in a plane, which is determined by the general direction of approach of the main mass of the debris, the distribution of the particles, and their relative velocities.

Initially, particles travel in many orbits in various planes. This creates numerous collisions, finally forcing all the orbits into one plane. When two particles are moving in the same general direction, but at oblique angles to each other, a collisions between the two will cause each to move in a new direction. However, the angle after the collision will be more acute than the original angle. This is the key to understanding the eventual arrangement of all orbits in a common plane that is extraordinarily thin. As the particles come closer to moving in the same plane, fewer and less violent collisions will occur. Since they must orbit about the same center, the above condition cannot be completely satisfied, until the thickness of the rings equals the average diameter of the particles. This condition would probably require more time than the age of any of the planets.

In the case of Saturn or any planet which has a significant magnetic field, the plane of the orbits will be along the equator because this is the zone of least resistance. Recently it was found that Uranus has rings similar to those of Saturn. They were formed in the same manner. The debris which formed the rings of Saturn and Uranus, pockmarked Mars and the moon, and formed the asteroid belt probably came from the same source. According to legend, there was a planet in orbit between Mars and Jupiter called Maldek, which blew up as a result of an interplanetary war. If so, Mars, Saturn, and Uranus must have been in conjunction with it at the time and received more than their share of the bombardment of debris of various sizes. Our moon may have been Maldek's moon before the disaster. Giant spaceships with colossal gravity-inducing beams can transport planets from one place to another. As mentioned earlier, perhaps Maldek's moon was moved to its present position in orbit about the earth.

The Russell concept of gravity is another example of irrationality in the extreme. On page 139 of *Atomic Suicide* he states:

> ". . . that gravity exerts no force, whatsoever, to either attract or repel. Gravity is, supposedly, a shaft of Magnetic stillness which has been extended two ways from zero in the cathode of the electric current, around which electric motion can stimulate the power — or energy — of its Magnetic zero center. Gravity is motionless and changeless. A gravity shaft is a two-way extension of a point in space where all the power in all the universe is existent, to a pair of points around which motions turn to balance the power extended from their centers."(106)

It seems that Russell was as adept in the art of scientific double talk as any modern theoretical physicist. He would have had a difficult time using this vague concept to explain many of the phenomena concerning gravity, such as levitating beams, the propulsion of UFOs, and the fact that negative charges are repelled by a gravitation field.

From the sample passage given from Russell's works, the reader may have noticed a consistent pattern. Russell always fails to define any of his terms and carries his dogmatism to ridiculous extremes. At no time does he establish or justify any idea. If a teacher knows and understands the subject matter he is dealing with, he can express it in simple, understandable language and, above all, will properly define his terms. Has Russell done this? The less one knows and comprehends his subject, the more vague and nebulous will be his discussion concerning it. In this respect Russell is pre-eminent.

In view of this, it seems unbelievable that he would have such a following even today. He is still hailed as the most versatile genius of this century. There are several possible reasons for this. One of these is the charisma he undoubtedly had coupled with his boldness. With these characteristics, he was able to capitalize on the reputation he had earned as an artist. Nebulosity has generally been associated with profundity even among the so-called intelligentsia. Therefore, he was able to convince nearly everyone that his brand of scientific double talk contained profound cosmic truths beyond the understanding of the vast majority. Strange to say, the author has never encountered anyone, during which time Russell was mentioned, who recognized the truth about him. This is merely a demonstration of the fact that there are few pioneers and original thinkers in any century.

The analysis of Russell's work becomes even more surprising in view of another passage from pages xxv-xxxi of the introduction to *Atomic Suicide* which he obviously endorsed:

> According to this, Walter Russell is a consummate illuminate. God gave him an extraordinary perception which reaches around the entire 360 degrees of light spectrum. He could "see" within the atom, or within all the stars and nebulae of space without need of telescope or spectrocope. More than that he can see and know the geometry of space and the means by which the invisible universe absolutely controls the visible universe. That means that the riddle of the universe which no man has solved, regarding the mystery of the emergence of matter from space, and of its being swallowed by space, is as clear to him as the light of the sun is clear. A consummate illuminate is defined in this introduction as one who is given all-knowledge of the Cosmos. (106)

An important fact which self-proclaimed "illuminates" seem to overlook is that the extent of their assimilation is dependent upon their level of comprehension. In Russell's case, this has been proven to be very limited. In fact, it was apparently so miniscule he was unable to see how nebulous and unsatisfying his ideas were and how they failed to unify any concept.

Sufficient space has been devoted to such an expose. It has been clearly shown that Russell was not illuminated. He was probably victimized by false impressions projected upon him by unenlightened beings, existing either in the intermediate realms or the lower astral. It can be concluded that the only impressive aspect of Russell's books was the quality of paper on which the books were printed. Despite this, they should be rated well below the old-time Montgomery Ward and Sears Roebuck catalogues. They, at least, had some utility value in their day.

Undoubtedly, Russell was a man of high integrity but when he ventured into the realm of science and metaphysics, he was out of his element. His great reputation and prestige were instrumental in leading many others down the same false path he was originally led. This included some of the distinguished gentlemen mentioned above such as Tesla, who declared that Russell's ideas were so advanced it would be more than a century before the world appreciated them. This exercise in exposing Russell's false teachings demonstrates what can happen to a person when his psychic centers are partially opened. Many others have been, and are, continually victimized in a similar way to that of Russell. Most of them are not well known and have little prestige. Consequently, they do not obtain many followers. Many religions and schools of thought outside religion were founded by people who had experiences like Russell's. The importance of clear, logical thinking cannot be taken lightly. This process should never be separated from a person, even if the person becomes illuminated or psychic.

The occurrences just discussed should not be confused with hunches which nearly everyone receives from time to time. Hunches are helpful warnings or suggestions which filter down to one's consciousness from the soul center. They are sometimes called one's guardian angel and are generally beneficial if heeded. They still must be assimilated and logically considered before being acted upon, however.

CHAPTER 30

THE REALITY OF THOUGHT FORMS

The more knowledgeable and discerning researchers in borderland phenomena are aware that thoughts are more than just some intangible aspect of reality. Thought forms have been detected and seen by sensitives under rigid and objective experimental conditions. For example, the late Vern Cameron, one of the foremost dowsers of his day, could detect thought forms with his dowsing instruments with consistent accuracy under controlled conditions.(70) A subject would project a thought form into any part of a room, and Cameron would always locate its exact position and outline. With the exception of certain rare instances, such forms are created from higher frequency matter. The direct effects of thought are not usually discernible in the physical realm, due to disharmony and chaotic conditions which produce cancellation effects. Since the physical realm is somewhat detached from the basic creative intelligences and has not yet reached a sufficiently high degree of development, physical matter is more difficult to control with thought. A logical and penetrating analysis which is in harmony with the concepts already introduced reveals that all creations and occurences are the result of thought. The planetary systems are embodiments and thought forms of the logos.

It follows that the children of the logos, or the human race, are also creators in the same way. This may be the origin of the statement in the Bible about "God creating man in his own image". Their creativity, however, is not as purposeful or on even remotely as large a scale as that of the logos. In general, men are not aware that they are creators in a manner similar to that of their creators. Large numbers of people thinking in unison generate thought forms which are formidable. In this way, life forms or intelligence are produced in the higher ethers, which can exert considerable influence in the physical realm. The soul centers of the created entities exist in realms below that of the soul centers of the humans who created them. It is apparent that organizations conducive to unified thinking will create an entity which will work toward the maintenance of the organization. Since this entity is a definite life form, it has a will and intelligence of its own! It follows that the larger the organization, and the older it is, the more powerful and influential the entity associated with it will be. This means that new members will tend to come under the influence and control of this entity. It is like a Frankenstein monster in many instances. The number of such entities is equal to the number of groups and organizations. Their nature and influence may be either benevolent or malevolent depending on the nature of the group with which they are associated. Therefore, there are national entities, college entities, corporation entities, church entities, race entities, etc. This accounts for the condition that all bonafide members of any one group have certain characteristics in common. In some respects, they even develop certain physical characteristics which are similar, depending on the length of time a given individual is a member.

Perhaps the most powerful and malevolent of these entities is the money entity. This is to be expected since the idea of money is in nearly everyone's consciousness, and acquiring money encourages the development of the worst traits exhibited by humans. The more money or wealth one acquires, the more he or she tends to come under the influence of this entity. It is understandable why the love of money has been called the root of all evil. The knowledge of organizational entities and the money entity, in particular, is probably what prompted Jesus to state, "It is easier for a camel to go through the eye of a needle than it is for a rich man to enter the kingdom of heaven". The actual evidence demonstrating the true meaning of this statement is overwhelming. There are few individuals in history who have acquired great wealth and at the same time shown any degree of spirituality or used this wealth wisely. Generally, their main goal was to accumulate still more of it and also the power which goes with it. The typical man of wealth or big business man is spiritually, intellectually, esthetically, and culturally destitute, besides being greedy and unscrupulous. It is indeed a powerful and high minded individual who is able to completely resist the influence of such entities and act on the volition and dictates of his own higher consciousness. Such a person is not of the mainstream of humanity.

The creation of entities in the higher ethers by no means represents the extent of man's creativity. Many of the lower life forms (usually undesirable) on this planet are probably the handiwork of humans in the distant past. Ancient races probably had a better understanding of the laws mentioned above than modern man, and applied them systematically with more tangible results. They may have been able to create elementary types of intelligences which could project bodies into the physical realm. The legendary demons mentioned in the Bible and elsewhere are also the creations of man. In some cases, they have been able to materialize in the physical realm for a period and wreak havoc.

The intelligence centers of most animals exist in higher realms than those of the entities and other products of human thought, because they are the result of more purposeful thought and are, therefore, created by the higher bodies of the soul centers. Other thought forms result from the thoughts of the physical and astral bodies. The entities produced by the collective thoughts of organizations do not seem to possess bodies as such, since the thoughts which created them are of a more abstract nature. They manifest themselves by influencing and controlling minds, rather than by projecting definite physical forms or bodies. It seems some life forms produced by humans and other offspring of the logos will even have intelligence centers below the realm of tangible physical matter.

Some readers may question the author's statement that animals are creations of humanity or other offspring of the logos. This concept has been an integral part of the higher metaphysical teachings of so-called "Mystery schools" for thousands of years. This fact alone is not completely satisfying. It should be explored from a logical standpoint to see how well it conforms with the overall cosmic plan already outlined.

It was suggested in the chapter on the pyramid of life that the ultimate destiny of those members of humanity who make the grade is to become logos in realms far below the physical. Part of the early training in preparation for this role is in the creation of the more elementary life forms, which in part consist of the entities already discussed. Such forms are the direct result of thoughts projected solely by the astral and physical bodies of people. These elementary entities become very powerful and influential, because of the coordinated thoughts of great numbers of individuals over a long period of time. The form of the intelligence centers of these entities is rudimentary; therefore, their thoughts and influence are restricted to very narrow channels devoid of versatility and logic. Since they are the products of thought projections of the lower bodies of human souls, the intelligence centers of these elementary beings are located in lower realms than those created by the coordinated thoughts of older souls.

As incarnating humans become more advanced, their thoughts become more purposeful with the consequent creation of higher life forms in higher ethers. This means that the higher bodies of humans become better coordinated with the astral and physical bodies. The centers of intelligence of such created entities are more sophisticated than earlier creations and are able to project tangible bodies into the physical realm by the step down process. This means that they also possess astral bodies, as do humans. This is the origin of the animal kingdom. The different species of animals on different scales of intelligence represent the products of different groups of humanity at different stages of development. Throughout the history of this planet, many different races and civilizations have come and gone. Each group was in a certain stage of development during their stay on the planet. Some groups were comprised of much older souls than others. It is not likely that the present animal forms were created by humans incarnating on this planet at the present time, since the vast majority of people are very young souls. Animals have about the same developmental relationship to more advanced humans as such humans have to the logos. The soul centers of most of the animals exist in realms below the higher astral realms. This has been confirmed by those who visited these higher realms and returned. They report that no animals or insects exist in such realms. However, plant life exists in great profusion in the higher realms because it is a creation of the logos.

The consensus among scientists is that man is a comparative late comer who evolved from lower life forms. This exhibits the same quality of thinking and refusal to face facts that has been deplored time and time again in this treatise. Steel implements and other evidence of man's presence on this planet have been found in deposits which are probably hundreds of millions of years old. For example, in his book *Mysteries of Time and Space*, on page 18, Brad Steiger tells of a rockhound, William J. Mersten, who found footprints of a man wearing sandals embedded in a rock formation near Antelope Springs, Utah, which is supposed to be 600 million years old.(113) One of the footprints showed that he stepped on a trilobite. Trilobites have allegedly been extinct for hundreds of millions of years. Steiger's book contains a wealth of factual information which confutes the conventional belief about the length of time humans have inhabited the earth. Such deposits are certainly much older than those our venerated anthropologists and archaeologists have been sifting in a futile effort to determine man's origin or first appearance on earth. Have such findings as those of Mersten's deterred these great men from their efforts to prove that man has been here for only a short time and that Darwin was correct? They have not.

There are other life forms on this planet which aren't the work of man. One of the more important of these is known as the devic intelligence or devic forces. Their realm of existence is mainly the etheric, or that occupied by the etheric double of physical matter mentioned earlier. They play a vital part in making a planet habitable and in maintaining this condition. The regulation of atmospheric conditions and plant life is part of their responsibilities. Their relationship to the planet is analogous to that of the nervous system to the human body. They are considerably more powerful and intelligent than humans, since they are extensions of the logos themselves. Occasionally they make themselves visible to certain humans. This is the origin of the legends about the "little people" including gnomes, elves, and fairies. Things of this nature have, of course, been debunked by our erudite authorities.

Whales and dolphins are other life forms which man did not create. Contrary to dogmatic and popular beliefs, whales and dolphins are more intelligent than most humans. Conventional reasoning is that, since the brains of dolphins and whales are larger and more complex than that of humans, it must be the amount of intrinsic cortex in the human brain which makes man superior to all other life forms. Surprisingly, it turns out that whales and dolphins have a greater amount of intrinsic cortex than humans. Researchers have concluded from these facts that man's superiority is due to factors on a higher level than the physical. What they apparently failed to realize is the physical state reflects what is going on at a higher level and is an aspect of cause and effect. They also give man more credit than he deserves. Man's great accomplishments are due to the vastly superior intelligences which incarnate in the human race from time to time. Were it not for this, there would be no civilizations. Extensive research on human intelligence shows that the majority of people are incapable of abstract thought.(81) Researchers are unwittingly attributing the superior qualities of mind to this tiny minority mentioned above.

According to an article that appeared in a weekly, nationally circulated newspaper some years ago (unfortunately the author cannot recall the exact date or specific publication), a research program on dolphins sponsored by the Navy proved that dolphin intelligence was superior to the vast majority of humans. Many of their findings were not made public. According to the scientist, John C. Lilly, who worked on the project, direct communication was allegedly made with dolphins, and they were able to communicate in English!(76) They have a language more sophisticated and intricate than ours. After the discovery that they were dealing with a higher order of intelligence than their own, the Navy suddenly terminated the project, much to Lilly's dismay and disgust. According to Lilly, the dolphins involved died of a broken heart when the project terminated. Lilly has written a number of books on the dolphin.

Another indication of dolphin superiority is that they have adapted to their environment more efficiently than man, and they habitually display finer character traits and a greater benevolence than most humans. Living in the ocean offers different challenges and experiences than living on land. Whales and dolphins may be embodiments of highly intelligent beings from other planetary systems, who have been seeking new kinds of experiences and challenges in their development cycle. Those who hunt and kill such creatures may be committing crimes worse than murder.

The logos did not begin their creative activities at the same time throughout the universe. There is a great variation in the times the various planetary systems in the physical and astral realms came into existence. In fact, the life cycles of these systems follow the same pattern as human embodiments in accordance with the hermetic axiom. It follows that the offspring of the logos, as well, are in varying stages of development. Some groups are relatively young and some are very old. It generally requires many millions of years for the human soul to reach a stage where it can manifest itself in the physical realm with the total attributes of the soul center. According to Edgar Cayce, the bulk of humanity on this planet is made up of very young souls in about the 100,000 year bracket.(22) They apparently did not all originate from the same logos. This accounts for the many races and differences between them.

THE ORIGIN OF PLANT LIFE

A great deal has been published in recent years concerning previously unsuspected properties of plants. The best and most comprehensive account yet written about the work and research in this field is the previously mentioned book entitled *The Secret Life of Plants* by Peter Tompkins and Christopher Bird.(13) Plants display all of the psychic attributes of highly developed humans and perhaps to even a higher degree! They are telepathic and communicate with each other. They also display emotions similar to those which humans experience. If isolated, they become lonely and tend to deteriorate. They respond in the same way humans do to various kinds of treatment. The great scientist, Jagadis Chandra Bose, proved that their nervous systems are even more efficient than those of humans and react more readily to various stimuli.

The work of Bose in promoting a better understanding of plants far transcends that of anyone before or since. Much of his important research in this field took place around the turn of the century. The ingenious instruments he devised to measure the growth and behavior of plants have never been duplicated for some strange reason. They could magnify these processes by as much as 100 million times! He was a physicist who overshadowed all of his contemporaries in this field, in addition to the great names in physiology and psychology.

Bose also found that so-called inanimate matter responded to stimuli in a manner analogous to that of the living, and that no definite boundaries existed between the physical and physiological. The following statement by Bose is taken from page 116 of *The Secret Life of Plants*: "In my investigations on the action of forces on matter, I was amazed to find boundary lines vanishing and to discover points of contact emerging between the Living and non-Living"(13) These findings verify that all manifestations are creations of intelligences, hence all matter will display life characteristics in accordance with the hermetic axiom.

The monumental research done on plants during the past 50 years brings up an interesting question: Why does the plant, a supposedly lower life form, exhibit attributes which are apparently superior to those of humans? Once again, the answer is simple. Plants are an integral part of the earth and, as indicated before, the earth and other planets are embodiments of the logos. This means that plants are extensions of the logos. If it were not for plants, life as we know it could not be sustained. Through plants there is at least an indirect channel to the consciousness of the logos. Plants probably have a few more surprises in store for us when more profound investigations are made into their nature.

THE NATURE OF THE CREATIVE PROCESS AND TELEPATHIC COMMUNICATION

All of occupied space is permeated with particles of all kinds. Such particles in the physical realm consist of the complete spectrum of soft electrons which house the hard electrons and protons. The camouflaged hard particles are the ingredients from which matter, including planetary systems, is created by thought. Commands sent through the life lines of the basic ethers by an integrated intelligence arrange the basic particles of matter permeating space to produce a thought form. A planetary or solar logos follows this procedure to create matter as we know it. Some of the more advanced adepts on the planet have at times demonstrated this process to create a material object out of seeming nothingness. Any thought activates the basic life lines which control the universe. The activation of life lines automatically affects basic particles of matter in some manner, since life lines are an integral part of all portions of the particles. The manner and degree to which the particles are affected depends on the nature of the thought doing the activating. This in turn is governed by the nature of the intelligence producing the thought.

Commands or disturbances are transmitted down these life lines at a near infinite velocity. The activation of any particle activates a network of life lines connected to each and every constituent ether particle comprising that particle. This activated network of life lines transmits a complex signal associated with the nature of the disturbance through the ethers at a near infinite velocity. A similar particle in the path of this disturbance is also activated in a manner similar to that of the original particle by an identical network of life lines, since each particle is connected to some kind of network of life lines. Unlike particles will not be affected. It is analogous to resonance. This is the basic principle applied to telepathy. When a thought is transmitted from one brain to another, certain cells in the brain of the sender are activated in a highly complex manner associated with that thought. The life lines connected to the cells activated then transmit this signal to a similar combination of cells or particles in the brain of the receiver. The signal is then amplified and transformed into an electric current in a manner analogous to that of a radio receiver. Frequencies are also involved. Each individual transmits thoughts which activate the particles involved within definite frequency ranges. Once again the old hermetic axiom is involved.

This suggests that machines can be constructed which can duplicate the performance of the brain and thus receive and record one's thoughts from any distance. It has been claimed that the late T. H. Moray had built such a device. This has been the testimony of individuals who claimed to have seen it work. The device could pick up conversations at any distance. It was not the sound waves that were picked up, however, but the thoughts behind the words. Moray claimed that his device could do this with people speaking on the other side of the globe. The thought or the activation of the life lines is greatly amplified with the spoken word. As with electromagnetic radiations, the intensity of the signal will decrease according to the inverse square law, unless the thought is beamed directly to an individual. In this case there is little attenuation of the thought signal as it passes from the sender to the receiver. It is apparent that if the inverse square law did not hold for the normal thought processes which are not specifically directed, chaos would reign throughout the universe.

Devices similar to that which Moray supposedly built have been used for interstellar space travel and communication for ages. Space travelers likely have machines that can both send and receive such signals. Certainly radio communication could not be used because the velocity of transmission is too low and attenuation effects too great. The signals would be beamed in a manner analogous to lasers, but with far less attenuation. If Moray indeed built such a machine, he undoubtedly received the instructions for building it telepathically or by a thought form projected to him by an alien intelligence. This is the manner in which Tesla received most of his ideas. Moray was undoubtedly highly telepathic and clairvoyant.

If one were to construct such a device, the following principles and facts would have to be considered. Whenever particles, or a system of particles, are activated, the system of life lines associated with these particles transmits replicas of such activations through the ethers via a like system of life lines at an almost unlimited velocity. Such disturbances pass through matter with no attenuation and with little or no activation of ether particles until they encounter the right combination. The brain radiates ELF electromagnetic particles which travel at light velocity. Simultaneously a system of life lines is activated in a manner which duplicates this pattern of radiations but these signals travel much faster and have a far greater range. It follows that such a machine must function in the ELF frequency range and be capable of generating ELF photons and soft particles.

The principles of the creative process cover the entire spectrum of activity. This is true regardless of whether it involves the creation of matter, a certain life form or the various kinds of communication. The intelligence which motivates the smallest particle of matter is the same as that which motivates the greatest beings or centers of intelligence.

CHAPTER 31

THE LAW OF DUALITY IN REGARD TO MALE AND FEMALE

The law of duality underlines all manifestations. Its application pertaining to male and female has not been adequately defined in metaphysical treatises and lectures, hence misconceptions are still a part of popular teachings. A soul center or a basic creative intelligence has a dual nature. Like the two sides of a coin, it consists of a male and a female portion working together as a unit. It has an analogy in the right and left sides of the brain. Each half of a duality has its own specific functions, but it requires the unified efforts of both of them for the total organism to function correctly.

During reincarnation cycles, the male segment is supposed to take up a male body, while the female part does the same with the opposite gender. Evidence and extensive research indicate that this plan has not been completely followed on this planet for ages. By checking the reincarnation pattern of many individuals, it was determined that nearly all those whose records was traced had embodiments both as males and as females. The consensus among teachers of metaphysics is that this process is in accordance with natural law and divine plan. They assume it is necessary for the individual to achieve balance. The necessary balance these authorities allude to already exists in the soul center. Each part must be a reflection of its source in order for this center to represent itself in the physical realm. For this to be accomplished, the male part must always represent itself as a male and likewise for the female portion. A unification of the male and female segments takes place in the lower realms, when each part has reached a stage where it is in perfect rapport with its counterpart in the soul center. When this stage is reached, the soul center is able to project a body into the physical realm with androgynous properties. It will exhibit a blend of both male and female characteristics, or a replica of itself.

This is in accordance with the 7th hermetic priciple, known as The Principle of Gender, which states that there is gender manifested in everything — the masculine and feminine principle is ever at work. No creation, physical, mental or spiritual, is possible without this principle.

The folly of the fluctuation of gender in embodiments should be evident. It is analogous to switching the wiring in electronic devices of each side of the brain to parts of the body it wasn't designed to control. This would result in a disorganized individual. According to *The Book of Truth*, on page 35, this tendency to change polarities periodically in developing humans was outside of the cosmic plan.(95) Alternate genders were supposedly the result of an experiment by a rebellious former overseer of the development process. He had hoped to speed up the process by this practice, and thereby started a trend which has not yet run its course. Evidently, this overseer's mental processes were not in good working order at the time. In any event, according to the account this director was relieved of his position and punished by his superiors for the violation of established laws. This was the being who became known as Satan

It isn't difficult to see how the periodic change of polarities would result in badly mixed up personalities with disoriented sexual drives. This is the origin of homosexuality and the various degrees of sexual aberration. For example, a female soul finding herself in a male body, after a long series of embodiments as a female, will be far more strongly attracted to males than to females. The same pattern holds true for a male in a female body. Situations of this nature result in personalities which are exclusively homosexual. Those who have had about an equal number of embodiments in both genders in an alternating sequence are more inclined to be bisexual, and so on.

Wide variations in the reincarnation pattern of the inhabitants of this planet have produced a spectrum of sexual behavior which covers the entire range. At one end of the scale are those who are entirely homosexual. Proceeding toward the opposite end, more are encountered who are inclined toward heterosexuality. The bisexuals are in the middle. Pure heterosexuals are found at the opposite end. These are the ones who have had few, if any, experiences in the wrong body. They, as well as the complete homosexual, make up only a small percentage of the population. An increasing number of sex changes taking place today indicates how many unfortunate individuals realize they are in a body of the wrong sex.

They are merely availing themselves of an opportunity to correct it.

The simple and obvious explanation for the conditions mentioned above has apparently escaped all of the leading figures in psychology, parapsychology, and the occult, who have been seeking an answer to this condition for a long time. None of the theories advanced by these experts is plausible enough to be accepted by the majority. It is understandable at this point why academic thinkers have never found the answer, but there is no excuse for those supposedly versed in basic metaphysics. Even those who suspected that reincarnation might be at the root of it failed to see that this phenomenon is contrary to natural law.

CHAPTER 32

THE ORIGIN AND TRANSFERENCE OF DISEASE

For about 100 years, the consensus of academic science has been that germs and viruses are the cause and carriers of disease. Recent discoveries have shown the true nature of disease origin and transference. For example, an account is given on page 212 of *The Secret Life of Plants* in which Soviet scientists placed identical tissue cultures in two hermetically sealed containers separated by glass.(13) A lethal virus was placed in one container, killing the cells within it. The other colony was not affected. When the experiment was repeated with a quartz divider instead of glass, the colonies in both containers were killed. It is significant that there was no way for the virus to penetrate the divider.

The explanation for the phenomenon given by the scientists was incorrect, as plausible as it may have seemed. They discovered that ordinary glass does not transmit ultraviolet light, whereas quartz does. Next, they conducted experiments which showed that as soon as a colony began to battle against a virus infection the ultraviolet radiation they normally emitted intensified. They concluded that the cells communicated with each other by means of ultraviolet radiation. They then reasoned that upon receiving the alarm from the dying colony the originally unaffected colony mobilized for resistance against the phantom enemy, which then proved fatal to them. If preparation or resistance against a threatening force was itself dangerous and inherently destructive to an organism, most life as we know it would soon disappear. Communication between plants and organisms has been known to occur over great distances and through solid barriers. This does *not* occur by means of electromagnetic radiations, but by the medium through which all telepathic communications occur, as described earlier.

Von Reichenbach demonstrated that glass is a powerful barrier to the passage of soft particles, or Od, as he called it. This is largely because glass is completely devoid of a crystalline structure. As mentioned before, it is the soft particles accompanying light which produce many of the effects of light. The photons can do little by themselves, except to stimulate the optic nerve.

The science of radionics has shown that every type of ailment or malfunction has its own characteristic radiation. All substances radiate, and the type of radiation is characteristic of the material or organism radiating the energies. When an organism begins to malfunction, its radiation will change in accordance with the malfunction. The radiation associated with a specific disease is the radiation emitted by the organism in an attempt to combat the disease. By projecting the same energies back into the organism by a radionics healing device, the malfunction can be eliminated, since more energy is being directed toward this end than the organism can generate by itself. By the same method, the action of poisons can be nullified.

Soviet scientists showed that disease is the result of inimical radiations. These are in the form of soft particles. The glass divider prevented them from reaching the colony in the other container, while the quartz allowed them to pass through. Viruses are certain types of molecules. They radiate the kind and combinations of soft particles which completely disrupt the normal chemical processes in healthy organisms. When the virus is isolated, the normal emanations from the virus do not have a high enough intensity to be dangerous. However, when injected into a host, they multiply, and the subsequent radiations reach a high enough intensity to even affect other organisms at a distance.

Radiation, in the form of soft particles, is the direct cause of all diseases. Each disease is the result of specific radiations, which are consistently characteristic of that ailment. Since disease is repetitious and follows the same pattern over extended periods of time, it can be concluded that there is an independent intelligence or thought form behind it. It was shown in the chapter on thought forms that coordinated thought creates entities in the ethers slightly above those associated with the physical realm. Disease entities come under the same heading and are produced in the same manner.

Under the right conditions, a disease entity is able to project energies into a susceptible individual who has not followed all the rules of good health. When this occurs, the person exhibits the symptoms of this disease. This in turn creates suitable conditions for projecting definite life forms, in the guise of germs, which manifest themselves only under these conditions. They radiate the energies which produce the disease. Their manifestation follows identically the same pattern as the Crosse experiments (to be described later), when life was seemingly produced out of inorganic matter. They are projected by the disease entity. That which destroys these organisms severs the channels by which the disease producing energies were injected into the individual. This led scientists such as Pasteur to the partially correct conclusion that it was the germs which were directly responsible for the disease.

One may contract a disease by direct contact with another so afflicted or with something the diseased person has been in contact with. This occurs in much the same manner in which some sensitives are able to psychometrize by handling an object which has had direct contact with another person. Channels are then produced by which the disease producing energies can be transmitted to the individual who made the contact.

It should be emphasized that initially all disease is galvanized by toxemia or the gradual accumulation of toxins and waste material throughout the body brought about by improper lifestyles, eating habits and stresses. This inhibits the normal functions of the organs, rendering the body susceptible to any type of malfunction or invasion of exterior influences associated with a specific type of disease. The body essentially has great ability to heal itself and resist inimical invasions if the rules of good health are rigorously followed.

George Lakhovsky was the inventor of the multiple wave oscillator, which has been highly successful in the treatment of diseases and cancer. He made some significant discoveries pertaining to the causes of these maladies. He outlined his theories and discoveries in a book entitled *The Secret of Life* which was written in 1925.(67) The crux of Lakhovsky's idea was that every living thing emits radiations. This is quite true, but Lakhovsky did not seem to realize that it also holds for inanimate matter.

Lakhovsky compared a living cell to an oscillating circuit, which is actually endowed with self-inductance and capacitance; and thus oscillates when a current flows through it. Microscopic investigations indicated that this was indeed the case. A living cell, supplied with electricity in the manner of a transmitter, emits a characteristic radiation, and will resonate in sympathy with radiations of a similar frequency. Due to their extremely minute size, these cells radiate in the infrared to ultraviolet light range. According to Lakhovsky, microbes produce oscillations which cause oscillatory disequilibrium in a healthy cell, thus producing a malfunction of that cell. Lakhovsky was only partially correct in this conclusion since he was still somewhat shackled by the concepts of orthodox science. It was the soft particles radiated by the microbes or disease entity which caused the subnormal condition, not frequency interference effects.

Colleagues of Lakhovsky verified his theories of cell radiation with resonating circuits, when they obtained radiographs of living cells by placing them directly on photographic plates. A malfunctioning cell could be restored to health by means of radiation of the right frequency. This led to the development of the multiple wave oscillator.

Lakhovsky also theorized that the energy necessary for the production and maintenance of cellular oscillations came from outer space. He assumed that the energy responsible was from the highly publicized "cosmic rays". In order to verify it, he took a group of geraniums, previously inoculated with cancer, and placed them in separate pots. After tumors developed, one of them was taken at random and surrounded with a circular copper spiral whose extremities were separated. All of the other plants died after several weeks, but the one surrounded by the copper wire was free of any tumors and had grown to twice the height of untreated healthy plants! On page 111 of his book, *The Secret of Life*, he states:

> ". . . The copper spiral must have picked up external radiations, atmospheric radiations, and that it created an electromagnetic field which absorbed any excess of cosmic waves in the same manner as the Oscillator in my previous experiments . . .(67)

His ideas concerning the reasons for this phenomenon were somewhat nebulous. For one thing, the idea that absorption is a factor is not logical. After a medium, or field, becomes supersaturated with any type of energy, no more absorption can occur. The surrounding area will then be bombarded with incoming energies, as though the barrier didn't exist.

The spiral wire concentrated beneficial orgone energy, or soft electrons, around the plant much in the manner in which Reich's cloudbuster could draw orgone energy from clouds or surrounding areas. Experimenters have utilized this principle to make gardens flourish, by running a network of copper wire up and down rows of plants.

Cosmic rays have baffled conventional science since their discovery many decades ago. According to the findings of academic scientists, they consist mainly of ultra-high-energy positive charges or the nuclei of atoms. Most of them are protons. Some are supposed to have kinetic energies approximately one billion times that attained by particles in the most powerful particle accelerators! This was determined from the thickness of matter required to stop them. It was found that their intensity de creases during sunspot activity, increases at night and reaches a maximum at approximately midnight. This was explained by the assumption that nearly all come from outer space and are deflected by the sun's emanations, thereby causing many of them to miss the planet.

The idea that only high energy particles can penetrate considerable thicknesses of matter has already been shown to be incorrect. Cosmic rays may actually consist of relatively slow moving, low energy soft particles. They are of varying degrees of stability and tend to disintegrate after penetrating considerable thicknesses of matter. This releases the harder positive charges which are contained in them. The sudden presence of hard protons will rapidly discharge an electroscope.

Hard particles radiated by the sun are nearly all captured by softer particles. These combinations tend to remain intact until they collide with a planet and its atmosphere. The soft particles then disintegrate and release both positive and negative hard particles. Most of the positive charges are neutralized before they reach the surface of the planet. During sunspot activity, this neutralization tendency is accelerated, since particles are ejected at higher velocities. Particles reaching the earth from beyond the sun generally travel at much lower velocities than those radiated by the sun, due to the law of redistribution. Interactions and collisions coupled with the general resistance, which particles encounter in outer space, gradually slows them down. Many of them don't disintegrate when they collide with the earth because of their low velocity. This readily explains why cosmic ray intensity seems to be higher on the night side of the planet. They penetrate deeper before disintegrating and this gives the impression of their having a higher intensity.

From the principle that the frequency of an oscillating circuit is modified by contact with a metallic substance which short circuits it, Lakhovsky reasoned that the same thing should happen to bacteria and thus re sult in their destruction. To test this theory, emulsions containing high concentrations of bacteria were exposed to metallic spirals. All of the bacteria were destroyed after 25 hours. It is also significant that the best results were obtained with the better conductors, such as silver and copper. The metals tend to lose their bactericidal powers when the surface becomes covered with a thin layer of calcareous or organic material. This is also an effective and simple method of sterilizing water without the introduction of chemicals or boiling. It is another of the important discoveries which have never been utilized to any extent. Lakhovsky made significant contributions to an understanding of disease and the methods of curing it. Perhaps in the future his work can be continued and produce rapid healing in conjunction with radionic healing devices.

Cancer takes on various forms and is generally the end result of improper eating and living habits. A disease or other entity may be involved; because the malady seems to have the tendency to take over and control the afflicted person, like some demon entities have taken over people's bodies or minds. It usually takes a long time to develop; and is primarily found in middle-aged and older people, but does occur in children. The body functions much like a battery with two terminals connected to a conductor. Von Reichenbach found that the right side of the body is negatively charged and the left side positively charged. The terminals of this battery can be considered as the two lobes of the brain. They connect to the circuits or nerves by which all of the bodily functions are controlled. The electricity flows continuously, because there is always a potential difference between the right and left sides. This is the source of the electricity which causes the cells to oscillate.

The energies which maintain the charge on this battery come in part from the astral body. These energies are transmitted by means of a highly flexible cable, which is known as the silver cord. It attaches to the navel. From there, it travels up the spine to the brain. The usable energies are produced by the step-down principle described earlier. These energies are not sufficient to maintain the body, which must receive additional energy in various forms from external sources. The major function of the energies transmitted by the silver cord is to carry messages and commands, so that the body responds to the dictates of that intelligence. The additional energies required come from three main sources: the food consumed, oxygen that is breathed, and the soft electrons, which enter the body through various centers or receptacles, known as chakras, located along the line of symmetry of the body. The goal of the soul center is to produce a body in the physical realm, which is in perfect rapport with itself and is independent of external energies for its sustenance. Some of the masters of the Far East have supposedly attained this ability.

The normal oscillation of the cells generates a high percentage of the soft electrons necessary for maintaining chemical balance in the body. As a person grows older, unwanted chemicals or deposits gradually accumulate in the cells, and changes in the chemical composition of the blood also occur. All of this, in turn, changes the electrical characteristics of the cells, and the soft electrons which the body needs are slowly choked off. This combination of events can result in the transformation of a normal cell into a cancerous one, which means a chemical transformation. Cells can be likened to giant molecules and also fit the definition of a molecule. The laws which govern chemical changes also apply to cells. The soft particles generated by the oscillation of malfunctioning cells promote chemical changes, which result in transformation. The transformed or cancerous cell then generates soft particles, enabling it to produce its kind from healthy cells. From then on, the cancer spreads at an accelerating rate.

In many instances, this condition can be arrested by proper diet and living habits, which tend to reverse the process. Many different cures for cancer have been found but suppressed by the medical profession. Some of the cures involve the use of radionic devices and magnetic fields, which counteract the chemical action of the cancer tissues. The fundamental principles of psionics have already been discussed.

The concepts involving psionics, which includes radionic healing methods, and what has been introduced in this chapter lead up to another highly effective healing process known as homeopathy. It is based on a principle known as the "Law of Similars". It has been found that whatever substance produces symptoms in a healthy person will cure these symptoms in a sick one. The science of homeopathy was developed by the German physician Samuel Hahnemann in the late eighteenth century. He reasoned that symptoms are a result of the vital forces within the body combating a malfunction. It would then follow that if a substance which creates a similar reaction in a healthy body can be introduced into such a malfunctioning organism it will produce the same forces already being employed by the body to combat the disease. This means that the two forces will work in sympathy with each other and thus expedite a cure.

As shown earlier, radionic healing devices follow an identical pattern. Even diseases or malfunctions produce a specific type of radiation of soft particles. When the same kind of radiation is turned back into the patient a cure is effected. Samuel Hahnemann, the Wilhelm Reich of the 18th century made another highly significant discovery during his experiments with homeopathy. Since some of the remedies were highly toxic he would dilute the substance in alcohol and water. He found that the more it was diluted the more effective it became while at the same time it lost its toxicity. After a sample was dissolved, a small part of the solution was placed in another container of alcohol and water and then vigorously shaken. This process was repeated many times until scarcely a molecule of the original substance remained in the final solution. Yet all of the original curative powers of this substance were greatly enhanced. This is a paradox that has completely baffled everyone up to this time. Yet it is a fact verified by daily homeopathic practice. The time has come for this paradox to be resolved. This phenomenon is in perfect harmony with concepts already introduced concerning the nature of the ethers and the life lines associated with them and which constitute the common denominator of all phenomena.

The life lines associated with all the ether particles comprising all of the particles of the atoms and molecules of the original substance become intimately associated with a significant portion of the ether particles comprising many of the alcohol and water molecules of the solvent. Vigorous shaking expedites this process. As a result, many of the molecules of the substance are in sympathy with those of the substance dissolved. This means that a greatly increased number of life lines are carrying similar messages or energy impulses. When a sample of this solution is then placed in another container of a similar solvent it carries with it life lines that are connected with all of the molecules of the original solution which are in sympathy with the original substance. The mixing of this sample with the new solvent means that a greater number of life lines will become affected than was the case in the original solution. It is a pyramiding process! It is analogous to the process of radionic pest control discussed in Chapter 26. As is the case with radionics, the mind of the homeopathic doctor or person doing the mixing plays an important role in the process.

This method of treatment proved so effective and vastly superior to conventional methods that it is to be expected the medical profession in general and specifically the AMA would take action against those who practiced this type of cure. As a consequence, homeopathic physicians have been persecuted to the extent that their number dwindled from 14,000 during the late nineteenth century in the United States to a mere handful of 200 at present. There is a closely knit network of organizations such as the AMA, National Cancer Institute, American Cancer Society, the FDA and the various chemical and drug industries that profit from cancer and the general ill health of the population. This well organized group of the worst malefactors to be found among humanity will stoop to any tactic to prevent a cure from being employed for any one of the major afflictions.

The standard medical practice known as allopathy is of course contrary to natural law and is in general harmful to the patient. Drugs administered in accordance with conventional practice work in opposition to the organism's effort to heal itself. The organism adjusts itself to the regular intake of drugs administered or prescribed by allopathic physicians and thus becomes dependent or addicted to them with the consequent weakening of its own vital forces. It is quite significant that in every case where physicians had quit practicing in a given area for a certain period for various reasons, such as a protest against the enactment of a new law or ordinance, the death rate in that area dropped considerably!

Homeopathy and radionics, as indicated above, follow identical principles. However, radionics has proven to be more effective and rapid in the healing process. The main reasons are that more accurate and higher concentrations of the needed energies are employed. Also, radionic diagnosis is more effective. It is to be expected that radionic practitioners have also been more savagely persecuted by the AMA and other vested interests. However, radionic diagnosis requires greater tactile skills than does homeopathy. Therefore, homeopathy can be practiced by more individuals and without need of specialized equipment.

A highly effective therapeutic process has been pioneered by the late Hindu scientist Benoytosh Bhattacharzya in India. His process employs the same principles used in radionic pest control. Diagnosis and treatment are done by means of a photograph or blood sample of the patient in conjunction with a prism. For example, a photograph of a given patient is examined under a prism. A bodily malfunction will be manifested as a definite color effect when the photo is viewed under a prism. By means of the color pattern from which the malady is identified, a cure is effected by flooding the affected portion of the photo with the appropriate color of light. This is the same color that is used in color therapy for treating the same affliction. Interestingly enough, when another photo of the same patient is examined with a prism as the treatment is taking place, changes in this other photo will be seen to occur as the therapy progresses! Colors seen under the prism will change according to the changes taking place with the patient. Of course, when the photo is viewed without the prism no color pattern will be seen because the various colors blend together to produce white light. The prism merely separates them. Various minerals have a different color when viewed under a prism than they are when they are viewed without it. For example, a diamond has the color blue when seen through a prism.

The phenomena just described involving diagnosis and treatment by means of a photo demonstrates the principle discussed earlier concerning the transmission of energies via the network of life lines connecting all ether particles. The necessary groundwork has now been laid for a better understanding of the human organism.

THE NATURE OF THE HUMAN BODY

Much has been written about the various parts of the body such as glands, chakras, the nervous system, blood, the lungs, etc. However, this has resulted at best in only a very superficial conception of the relationship of these various parts to each other and their functions. This is to be expected, since soft particle physics as introduced in this treatise is mandatory in order to gain an adequate understanding of any and all phenomena.

During the study of the human organism it should be noted that the number seven is strangely involved in all of its aspects. For example, to cite a few instances, it is noted that there are seven ductless glands, seven layers of the epidermis, seven orifices, seven main chakras, etc. To carry all this still further, the prism breaks up the light from the sun into seven colors of the visible spectrum.

Sensitives of the type Von Reichenbach employed in his research claim that each of the seven chakras which lie along the line of symmetry of the body radiates a predominant color. Each chakra is associated with a specific gland and distributes light or energy of this particular color to a specific part of the body. The energies each chakra distributes enter the body by means of a ray which enters the body through the crown chakra located at the top of the head. This is associated with the pineal gland. This incoming ray looks like a cone or vortex of white light. This ray changes into a specific color as it encounters the outer aura of the body. This color is dependent on the type of aura of the individual. After the ray enters the body it appears to be broken down into seven different colors by the pituitary gland in a manner analogous to a prism breaking white light into seven different colors. From there it is distributed through the body by means of the various chakras, each one of which deals with energies of a specific color.

Each gland functions in the manner of a transformer or a filter which allows energy or soft electrons associated with light in a certain frequency range to pass through while obstructing the others. It is a refining process. It should be kept in mind that each of the seven colors separated by a prism also contains colors or photons and soft electrons associated with all of the colors of the visible spectrum. The Land experiments discussed earlier demonstrated this fact. The color normally seen consists of a predominance of photons and soft electrons within a certain frequency range. The glands separate these energies into a narrower frequency band.

The cell is a highly complex structure consisting of billions of atoms. The buildup and maintenance of a cell requires the presence of a high concentration of soft electrons consisting of photons of light within a relatively narrow frequency range. That is, all of the soft particles involved consist of light whose frequencies fall within definite boundaries. The process of chemical changes and transmutations is dependent on the disintegration of soft electrons and the subsequent release of harder particles, including hard electrons and protons after they penetrate the substance. The disintegrations are brought about largely by interactions of soft particles especially if they consist of light in comparable frequency ranges. Different kinds of cells require different kinds of soft electrons for efficient construction and maintenance. This means that soft electrons comprised of light within a given frequency range will have a greater effect on certain types of cells than they will on others. Every atom comprising a cell radiates combinations of soft electrons. In most cases the radiated particles either absorb or capture invading particles. If they are harder they will be captured by the invaders. In each case there are fewer disintegrations than would occur if the radiated particles consist of light in the same frequency range as that of the invading particles. Since each major part of the body consists of entirely different types of cells, the kind of soft electrons required for each part will differ from that needed for any of the other parts. The process of filtering out the soft particles needed for the various organs is carried out by the glands. The chakras distribute these particles to the organs that require them.

It has been established that the blood carries nutrients to the cells and also takes away the waste. The red cells carry the nutrients while the white cells extract the waste. The dematerializing process is involved in this function. Oxygen taken into the lungs has a tremendous affinity for soft electrons. The lungs allow the soft electrons carried by the oxygen to enter the bloodstream much in the manner that soft electrons penetrate the insulation of a conductor and allow the hard electrons they camouflage to be deposited at the surface of the conductor. Soft electrons comprised of photons in the infrared range carry with them the harder electrons associated with light in the visible spectrum as well as the lower ultraviolet. This is the combination that is taken into the lungs. The lungs.

being of a spongy structure, provide an enormous surface area for the soft electrons associated with the infrared to penetrate the lung tissue and deposit the harder particles into the bloodstream. Once again the hermetic axiom is involved.

Digested food enters the bloodstream in a similar manner. Vital energies contained in the food, combined with the high concentration of soft electrons radiated by the cells, enable the nutrients to pass through the walls of the veins and enter the bloodstream. The additional soft electron concentration in the blood carried there by the oxygen enables the nutrients to stay in the semidematerialized state until they can be transferred to the various parts of the body for maintenance and the building of new cells.

Dead and broken down cells tend to be carried away by the white blood cells in a similar manner. There are soft particles comprised of light within unique frequency ranges that promote this function. However, in all but very few special cases, the process is not 100 percent efficient. Not all of the broken down cells and waste products are carried away. They gradually accumulate in the cells. As they accumulate, the body functions deteriorate. This is manifested in the aging process.

There is a delicate balance which exists in the processes described above. If it is disrupted, death of the organism soon follows. For example, the soft electron concentration in the blood must be maintained above a critical level at all times. This is why one must breathe almost constantly air above a certain minimum density or pressure. If the soft electron concentration of the right kind were high enough, the breathing process would be obviated. Such an experience was described in the book *Etidorhpa*. In certain areas in the inner earth the beneficial soft electron concentration is so high one can live without the need of an atmosphere! A psychic master does not require food or air for the maintenance of his body. He is able to take his sustenance directly from the ethers around him. It should be noted that all known space is permeated with soft electrons, which harbor the protons and electrons comprising the atom. The creative intelligence can draw on and assemble them to form any material substance desired. It is from this reservoir that planetary systems are created.

The nervous system controls the motor responses of the body. The nerves function in a manner analogous to the circuits in any electronic system. They conduct the flow of soft electrons to the various parts of the body to initiate muscle response according to commands issued by the brain via the life lines connecting ether particles. When a certain muscle or muscle group is commanded to move a given part of the body, an increased flow of soft electrons is sent to that area. This causes the muscle fibers or cells to contract or group together into a more compact bundle. This pulls the tendons to which the muscles are attached, and this in turn moves the part of the body associated with the muscle group. It requires electrostatic forces to cause the muscle fibers to move into more of a spherical bundle. The number of electrons conducted through the nerve fibers is not nearly great enough to produce the necessary force. The electricity required is provided by the blood, which rushes to the affected area. The electricity carried by the nerves merely triggers the response. Since electricity flows from a high potential to a lower one, a muscle contracts by the outer portion's being impregnated with a higher concentration of electrons than that close to the center. A muscle gets tired and refuses to function when these periodic differences in potential can no longer be maintained. After repeated use, the entire muscle group becomes saturated with negative ions deposited there by the blood. When this excess of negative ions escapes and is carried away by blood during a period of rest, the muscle is able to function again. It now becomes apparent why a numbness and paralysis occur when the blood circulation is cut off from the affected portion of the body.

The manner in which cancerous tissues grow at the expense of the surrounding healthy tissues has never been understood. A cancerous tissue develops when the normal cells do not receive the required number or concentration of soft electrons of the right kind for their proper maintenance. This is produced by blockages in the electrical system and the consequent build up of toxins in the tissues. This, of course, is the result of improper eating and living habits. When a normal cell does not receive the required amount of soft particles for its maintenance it is gradually transformed into another kind of cell requiring a lower concentration of soft electrons for its maintenance or else it dies and another cell is created which can survive under the conditions inimical to the original cells. As the blockages in the electric system increase, the supply of soft particles is reduced and, in order to survive, the new cancer cells having a lower potential or stronger positive charge than the surrounding normal cells, will draw from them the electricity they require for their maintenance. As a result, they in turn will transform into cells that can survive under the reduced flow. In this manner the cancer can grow at an accelerating rate.

From the above picture the remedy becomes apparent. A complete change in diet and life style becomes mandatory. It follows that a diet which includes detoxifiers would be most effective. The grape is the greatest detoxifier known and has been employed with effect to cure all forms of cancer. It is a remedy known as 'the grape cure'. It is to be expected that the medical profession has never recommended it. The author can attest to the efficacy of the grape to cure various ailments. He has found that a copious intake of grapes can prevent and even cure the common cold.

The program can be greatly accelerated by subjecting the patient to high concentrations of soft electrons or orgone energy as experienced in orgone accumulators or inside pyramids of the right construction. The therapy can even be more effective by eliminating exposure to radiations of man-made electricity. The so-called polarizer mentioned earlier is effective in counteracting this condition. Reich was highly successful in curing cancer with orgone accumulators. A far greater number of cancer cures have been affected by these means than the intolerably corrupt AMA and its affiliated organizations would have the public believe.

The dematerializing process taking place within the body as mentioned earlier accounts for the ability of certain individuals psyched up to chew up and swallow glass and metallic objects without injury. If it were not for the dematerialization process, fatal injuries would obviously result.

A flesh and blood robot or android can be created according to the pattern described above. The body does have a self sustaining battery which supplies the electricity needed for the 'operation' of the body. The right side has a higher potential than the left as already mentioned. An android is not under the direction of higher forces and a soul center. It operates according to programmed responses of its computer which is the brain. There are subtle differences in the bodily construction of the android and the human which are not evident in outward appearances. This enables it to be self sustaining. In the case of the human, if the energy and communications lines from the astral body are severed, the physcial body will no longer function. It is intended that the physical body be under remote control of the soul center. As already stated, there is a line that connects the astral and solar plexus of the physical body known as the silver cord. By application of the step down principle, energies of higher frequency matter are stepped down such that they are usable in the physical realm. Along with it, of course, commands are transmitted via the life lines. The silver cord is used for the primary maintenance of the physical body. Energies are also sent directly to the pineal gland by the step down process. This is involved in the motivation and destiny of the body. It is directly associated with the conscious mind while the energies and commands transmitted by the silver cord involve the subconscious or reactive mind.

There is a wide gap frequency wise existing between the soul center and the astral body for direct motivation of this body. Therefore, the step down principle is accomplished by several bodies, each one functioning in successively lower ethers until the astral body is reached. In other words, the astral body which sustains the physical is in turn sustained by a body functioning in still higher ethers and so on up the ladder until the soul center is reached. Experts in the esoteric studies not fully understanding the nature and function of these bodies have tacked various names to them such as mental body, emotional body, etc. They operate much in the manner of relay stations.

The human body is an ingenious and highly complex organism. The above treatment serves merely as a brief outline of some of the basic principles in its creation, maintenance and motivation.

"The author's recent experiments with orgone accumulators have demonstrated the validity of concepts introduced in this chapter. This includes the fact that the body is essentially an electrical system that requires copious amounts of soft electrons covering the entire visible spectrum of light. These energies are largely supplied by the food we eat and the water we use. It is the shortage or the blocking of some of these energies that results in ailments and the breakdown of the body. It follows that if water can be impregnated with a high enough concentration of these energies comprising the entire spectrum, the need for food would be virtually eliminated! Such water would be a panacea since it would allow the body to eliminate toxins without additional poisons being added. It would simulate conditions experienced by the protagonist in the book *Etidorhpa* who was exposed to a high concentration of these energies in the inner earth. As a result the need to eat was practically obviated and he experienced a rejuvenation. It was likewise stated in this book that food functions as a carrier of the vital energies.

The author first covered a five gallon water jug with 19 layers of aluminum foil and newspaper (two sheets or thicknesses of newspaper to a layer). The water from this accumulator proved to be far superior to pyramid water, or water that has been placed under a pyramid. The author then covered a gallon jug with 18 layers of copper foil and newspaper. The water from this accumulator proved to be even better than that from the accumulator using 19 layers of aluminum. The taste is not only superior, but it has been found that those who drink the water regularly must cut down drastically on their food intake. The water is superior because copper has a more beneficial radiation than aluminum which is absorbed by the water. Also copper is more effective in stopping and accumulating soft electrons than aluminum."

CHAPTER 33

THE WORK OF BRUNLER IN THE MEASUREMENT OF BRAIN RADIATIONS AND INTELLIGENCE

Some of the most important research in the field of psionics was done by the late Oscar Brunler concerning a certain type of radiation which emanates from the thumb and from around the head.(80, 81) This work of Brunler had its origin in the invention of an instrument called the biometer by a French scientist named Bovis, in the early 1920s.(13) Brunler was a distinguished physicist with impressive credentials in other fields. He teamed up with Bovis in research on disease diagnosis. During their work in diagnosis, they found that each part of the hand had a direct connection to a certain organ or part of the body. Therefore, they could measure the radiation of any body organ by taking the radiation from a certain part of the hand. This is the basis for a branch of therapy known as reflexology.

The biometer was used with great success in various forms of diagnosis. Basically, it consisted of a pendulum in conjunction with a measuring stick placed along a wire, either metallic or nonmetallic. The sample to be tested was placed at one end of the rod, and the right hand of the operator held the pendulum at the other end. The subconscious self of the operator would then cause the pendulum to swing in a definite direction as the sample was moved along the wire toward the pendulum. When the sample reached a critical distance, the pendulum would suddenly change its motion and swing in a direction perpendicular to the wire. This distance was found to be proportional to the fundamental frequency of the radiations coming from the sample. The term "fundamental frequency" refers to the frequency of the photons comprising the major portion of the soft particles radiated by the sample.

An explanation for the phenomenon will now be presented. All the energies radiated by the sample leave their origin with the same initial velocity for the same reason that the velocity of light is independent of its frequency. As indicated earlier, the field intensity around an electron is directly proportional to the frequency of the photons comprising it. When soft particles leave the sample, they encounter a medium which tends to slow them down. This retarding medium is uniform and consists of hard and soft particles, which permeate the atmosphere around the earth. The rate at which this medium slows down a soft particle is inversely proportional to the field intensity around the particle. The distance a soft particle ejected from the sample will travel before coming to rest is the value $\frac{1}{2}at^2$ where a is the rate of derellevation and t is the time consumed in the process.

Since the soft particles radiated have the same initial velocity, it follows from the relation, distance equals $\frac{1}{2}at^2$, that the distance a particle travels before coming to rest is directly proportional to its field intensity, or the frequency of the photons comprising it. For example, if the field intensity doubles, a is one half as great, but t becomes twice as great since the velocity is a constant. Therefore, the value $\frac{1}{2}at^2$ doubles. Bovis found that this was the case. His pendulum always responded where a high concentration of these energies occurred. This was the point where they accumulate after coming to rest. A variety of energies emanates from a sample, but the combination is held together by magnetic attraction in the same manner that clusters of particles form in particle accelerators. It is the average field intensity of the combination which determines the point of accumulation.

Each organ of the body has its own characteristic radiation, as determined by radionics. The average field intensity of the radiated particles is the same for any perfectly functioning organ, regardless of the individual. It was found that the biometric radiation from a normal organism always concentrated at a distance 20 cm from the object radiating it. The average "wavelength" of the light comprising this radiation was found to be 6400 angstrom units. It was rated at 100 degrees on the biometric scale. It follows that a radiation of 3200 angstrom units would be 200 on the biometric scale, and so on. When an organ was malfunctioning, this radiation was always less than 100 degrees biometric. In fact, each malady had its significant measurement which never varied. This coincides with the findings of radionic research, which approaches the phenomenon from another direction and employed the electromagnetic radiations produced by living organisms.

One type of biometric reading taken from every diagnosed patient puzzled Brunler and Bovis. It emanated from the thumb and was always more than 100 biometric degrees. It varied from patient to patient and ranged all the way from about 200° to well over 400°. One day they tested a low grade imbecile and obtained the lowest reading ever. It was only 118 degrees biometric. Brunler then realized what this particular radiation meant. It was not associated with any organ but came from the mind and was independent of the physical condition of the patient. This was confirmed when Brunler checked back on the records of their patients. He found there was a distinct correlation between the radiation from their thumbs and apparent mental levels. Brunler soon found that the same radiation emanated from around the head. From that time on, he devoted the rest of his life to this particular research and measured about 30,000 people in various walks of life. He empirically developed this research into an exact science and was able to accurately predict the achievement level of any individual.

The emanation of this energy from around the head brings to mind an incident Brunler often mentioned in his lectures. This involved experiments conducted by a French scientist at the turn of the century. It was found that electromagnets placed around the heads of individuals produced beautiful halo effects in a dark room. At the time, he was using the laborers and cleanup men around his lab for subjects. He then arranged a demonstration for a group of scientists but, unfortunately, used one of his colleagues for the subject, and no halo appeared when the magnet was turned on. He was soundly ridiculed and consequently abandoned all experiments of this nature.

The reason for this outcome is apparent. The radiations from the heads of his original subjects were in the lower frequency levels. When some of the radiations were disintegrated into their consitituent light by the powerful electromagnet, the resulting light was in the visible range. This meant their biometric levels were all below 250__. The radiation from the head of the colleague he used in his aborted demonstration was in the ultraviolet range and therefore invisible. Evidently, this researcher did not have the fortitude of Brunler, Reich, or any of those mentioned in this treatise, since any one of them would have been inspired to search out the reasons for this interesting paradox. He would have continued, regardless of any derision heaped upon him by his unimaginative colleagues.

The Brunler-Bovis biometer told Brunler considerably more about an individual than just his mental potential. The overall wave or energy pattern emanating from the brain indicates the character of the individual. This is registered on the biometer by the behavior of the pendulum. For example, a fully clockwise and rotary motion indicated that the person had an excellent character and was highly constructive. A fully counterclockwise motion indicated a character the exact opposite. The pendulum would respond in a variety of other ways to indicate other traits, which Brunler was able to correlate in a definite and consistent manner.

Radionics has demonstrated that direct contact with an individual can be made through a blood sample, photograph, or saliva sample from which a complete diagnosis can be made. It follows that the same can be done by means of a signature, or any creation of the individual. It is then to be expected that a complete biometric analysis can also be made from such samples. It wasn't long before Brunler found this to be the case. The physics of this has already been discussed. The carriers are channels which link the sample to the individual. They the basic lines of communication, which the primary intelligence uses to control the entire universe and link all ether particles together. When the operator wants to obtain a biometric analysis from a signature, the mind contacts the memory banks of a cosmic computer associated with the brain of the subject. This can be done regardless of whether the subject is living or deceased, since all of the characteristics and history of the individual are recorded. By means of these links, he obtains a playback of the wanted information through an energy flow which manifests at the sample. The process is similar to that in which a higher body sustains a lower body.

After testing thousands of individuals directly and indirectly, Brunler was able to work out a scale of intelligence from which he was able to classify individuals according to their measurements. The average reading of primitive people is about 200°. The average of Europeans and Americans is around 250°, while people of the more backward countries is around about 225°. Another highly significant finding was that those below 280° are incapable of abstract thought. This resolved the mystery of why most people can be so easily fooled and be readily made to accept any idea, regardless of how infantile or irrational it may be. It also follows that the great majority on such levels will lack good esthetics, discrimination, and other attributes necessary for higher levels of thinking. The popular types of music, literature, television programs, and so on, reflect this level of intelligence which Brunler proved is so predominant on the planet. When one takes into consideration the number of people born every minute, it is more than apparent that the late P. T.

Barnum made the classic understatemt of the age.

The level between about 360° and 400° was what Brunler called the pure reason or professorial range. Most college professors fell into this category. The term "pure reason" is not as complimentary as it may seem to be on the surface. Those on this level seldom escape the academic straightjacket after achieving an academic degree. Their thinking is generally restricted to narrow channels, as prescribed by authority and textbooks.

Some of the top figures in conventional science in this century are as high as 500° and slightly above. It is apparent that one must be far above the 500° level to defy academic authority under any and all conditions and do important original work outside the domain of orthodoxy. Reich, Brunler, and others already mentioned did so, even though they went through the academic mill.

Brunler came to the conclusion through statistical analysis that only one out of 100,000 people is over 480° on the biometric scale. What he termed genius was 660°. During this time, only 10 in the world were known to be over 600° and it was estimated there were possibly another 10, who had not yet been found. Brunler measured most of the prominent physicists of this century. Only one of those he measured was up to the genius level of 660°. He was C. V. Raman. Although Raman was a Nobel Prize winner, he was in no way bound by orthodoxy and carried out extensive research in India which transcended orthodox science. In fact, he was a great mystic as well as a scientist. He was undoubtedly the best mind that ever won a Nobel Prize. It is a certainty that Brunler did not measure Bose. Had he done so, he undoubtedly would have been shocked.

A question which might be in some readers' minds is: What was Einstein's measurement? After what has been presented, it should come as no surprise that he was a long way from the genius level. His biometric measurement was 467°. The characteristic of his radiation also showed that the real Einstein was somewhat different from the image of the wise, benevolent old patriarch which has been fostered on the world.

Brunler was able to find only a small number among the living with extremely high readings. In order to complete his scale of intelligence, he carried out an extensive program in securing the readings of great men from the past. He did this by testing original manuscripts, paintings, sculptures, etc., they left behind. The second highest reading he obtained was 725° from the work of Leonardo Da Vinci.(81)

Brunler's research adds credibility to the authenticity of the shroud of

Turin. The shroud has received a lot of publicity lately, and scientific tests have indicated it is indeed authentic. The radiation from the shroud was the highest Brunler ever found. It was 1050° biometric. For the benefit of the uninformed reader, the shroud was the linen cloth Jesus was supposed to have been wrapped in when he was taken from the cross. A book entitled *The Sacred Shroud* by Thomas Humber gives a detailed account of the known history of the shroud and the scientific tests which have been made on it.(60) The shroud has a semiphotographic image of Jesus impressed on it, complete with all of the inflicted wounds according to the New Testament. It also has many blood stains. One of the mysteries surrounding the shroud is how the image of Jesus was produced. Tests have shown that a dead body or inanimate object could not produce an image on a cloth of like material, but a live body could! It was shown in previous chapters that a live or animate body radiates far more intense energies of a different nature than a dead or inanimate one. The energies radiated by a live body have been shown to affect a cloth of the nature of the shroud. This indicates that Jesus must have come back to life after being taken from the cross, and wrapped in the shroud. This is in conformity with the account of his having risen from the dead. The recent scientific tests of the shroud in conjunction with Brunler's previous biometric measurement have established the authenticity of the shroud almost beyond doubt.

Brunler's extensive work in biometrics was not free from error, even though he was highly intelligent, with a 700° reading. For example, when examining old documents, it is entirely possible to measure the radiation of a close associate of the creator who handled the manuscript or painting, and thus get a wrong reading. Brunler, of course, was aware of this possibility and took many precautions. In spite of this, Brunler made at least one extreme error of inordinate proportions. The reading he attributed to one particular individual was such a disparity, when compared to this individual's known achievements, that it is hard to believe a person of Brunler's endowment let it pass undetected.

The answer to why Brunler overlooked some important disparities is resolved when it is realized that the inhabitants of this planet may be influenced and, in many instances, manipulated by outside intelligences. Even though one doing important work and fulfilling a destiny may be harassed by evil and powerful influences, he can also be monitored by powerful beings, who may be intent on having him fulfill the work he came here to accomplish. If one does not have a complete picture of the cosmic scheme, too many facts can sometimes be a deterrent to the person's work. This seems to be the case with Brunler. He had a fixation that 1050° was the ultimate and the only radiation higher than Leonardo's. An exposure to a radiation above these might have caused him to lose faith in his ability. This would likely have had a detrimental effect on his work.

Brunler obtained evidence that Leonardo might have had an encounter with a better mind, or that at least such a person handled some of his paintings. From one of Leonardo's creations, Brunler obtained a reading of well over 900°. Since this wasn't consistent with the rest of his works from which 725° was obtained, Brunler managed to shrug it off as some unexplained anomaly.

Leonardo's achievements were impressive, but the assumption that he was the greatest all-around genius is not justified, and many scholars do not accord him this honor. He was overshadowed in several endeavors by others. For example, he tried his hand at mathematics, but showed no outstanding ability in this direction. Although he showed great inventiveness, he was surpassed by men such as Roger Bacon, Archimedes, and by none other than Aristotle.

The Rosicrucian organization possesses ancient documents and copies of these, which can't be found in public libraries. A friend of the author with a high position in the organization told him of some of these manuscripts few are privileged to see. Among them are the works of Aristotle, which would confound an academic historian. For example, one of them proved that Aristotle understood cellular structure well over 2000 years before the world of science did. Another indicated that Aristotle was a mathematician second to none, since he invented a calculus 2000 years before Newton! He did this in order to solve certain problems the mathematics of his day was unable to cope with. With this calculus, he determined the number of cells in the brain, deviating only two percent from modern calculations. This also suggests that he might have invented the microscope. Conventional history does not give him credit for knowing anything about mathematics or physics.

It is not surprising many fallacies infest the popular version of world history. Consequently, some ridiculous ideas have been attributed to Aristotle, contradicting the evidence mentioned above. In spite of this, enough of his work covering nearly every field of human thought has been made available to scholars to convince many that Aristotle was the supreme intellect of all time. It has been claimed that he wrote about 1400 books, most of which are probably lost. Aristotle was far more versatile than Leonardo. He explored realms with great profundity where

Leonardo never ventured.

Brunler's investigations carried him into areas where there has been considerable speculation. One of these involves authorship of the Shakespearean plays. In some circles, there is doubt that Shakespeare was the real author. Brunler apparently settled the issue when he checked Shakespeare's radiation. The biometric analysis indicated that Shakespeare had the characteristics of a great actor, but did not possess the mental equipment necessary to create the plays which bear his name. Brunler's conclusion was that Francis Bacon was the author with a measurement of 640°. This has also been the consensus of many others. This conclusion showed bad logic from two standpoints: First, if Bacon wrote them, why didn't he claim authorship? There is not a semblance of a reason for him not to. The plays indicated a greater ability than did Bacon's known writings. Bacon was a man with an enormous ego, who coveted power and recognition. Secondly, the writing style of the plays is altogether different from Bacon's style. All great writers and composers have individual styles as distinctive as a fingerprint.

If Bacon did not write the plays, who did? Scholars have commented on the strange similarity of writing style between Christopher Marlowe and Shakespeare. Of course, Marlowe has been ruled out, since he allegedly died before the Shakespearean plays came into existence, or did he? Marlowe and Shakespeare were born in the same year. It is strange that Shakespeare didn't produce any of the great writings attributed to him until after Marlowe's supposed demise. It is known that Marlowe did undercover work for the king. Intrigue and cloak and dagger work were a part of life in government circles in those days, even as they are now. Marlowe was supposed to have been killed in a bar room brawl. Was this staged and the illusion created that Marlowe was dead in order for him to carry on his activities in this vein more effectively? If that were true, his subsequent writings would have to be produced under another name. He was a friend of both Shakespeare and Bacon. The Shakespearean plays are indicative of the writing style of a more mature Marlowe, who did a lot of traveling. The plays show an uncommon knowledge of geography which was not available in books at that time, and could not have been obtained by one who spent all of his time in England. An undercover agent would undoubtedly do a lot of traveling.

Brunler theorized that through many incarnations people evolved to a higher level of intelligence. This would account for some having much higher biometric readings than others. He finally concluded that 1050° was the goal which all must reach before going on to something higher.

By taking the readings of famous men at various stages in their lives, he found evidence that there was an apparent evolutionary growth during a lifetime of about one degree on the average, and sometimes as much as five or six degrees. This means that the number of incarnations needed would be between 500 and 1000. Brunler's conclusion was based on pure mathematics. It is apparent that Brunler lacked an overall view of the cosmic plan. Many of the great men measured, or supposedly measured, are outside of the human development process. In many cases, these embodiments are not for evolvement, but to function as teachers or guides to help developing humans. A great being such as an Elder, whose authority and influence transcends even that of the logos, can incarnate in many bodies at the same time. These separate embodiments do not necessarily have the same brain radiations and biometric readings. Each embodiment or personality is endowed with whatever mental equipment is needed in order to carry out the specific mission it was projected down into the physical realm to accomplish. Some missions require a higher order of intelligence than others; therefore, some embodiments of the same Elder possess higher intelligence than others.

When and if the biometric readings of other incarnating Elders are accurately checked, including Aristotle, a reading well above 1050° will probably be found. Elders have a tremendous responsibility involving countless planetary systems. If one of them were to focus all of his attention on just one body on a single planet, it is difficult to imagine what kind of biometric measurement would result.

Since Brunler was doing research on individuals, which included those outside the mainstream of humanity, his calculation on the average amount of progress made by a human during a lifetime is not valid. The precision in getting a measurement wasn't as great as he believed, either. It was possible for him to be several degrees off in a measurement. For example, a friend of the author obtained a reading from Brunler in absentia through his signature. About two years later he met Brunler and received another reading directly. The second one was five degrees higher than the first one derived from his signature.

As stated previously, the bulk of humanity on this planet are very young souls in about the 100,000 year old category or less. Edgar Cayce unwittingly confirmed this, along with other aspects of a human's development. Brad Steiger's highly informative and thought provoking book entitled *Atlantis Rising* gives an interesting account of Cayce's revelations using about 650 life readings of individuals over a period of 21 years.(112) According to Steiger, on page 55 of that book, "Never once did he confuse a date or jumble events he had ascribed to a particular era in Atlantean history in readings given years before''.

Cayce's findings, among other things, concerned how the physical body of homo sapiens came into being. According to Cayce on pages 56-57 of the same book:

> ". . . when man first appeared here, he was in soul form, rather than sheathed in a physical body, . . . by endlessly and carelessly projecting themselves into matter, eventually found their ability to project out of matter waning. Gradually, materiality hardened around these Souls, and they found themselves caught fast in a physical form.
>
> Occuring at the same time was the division of the sexes. According to Cayce's entranced teaching, the Soul is androgynous . . . It was in Atlantis, therefore, if Cayce is to be believed, that sex came into being, due to the separation of these two principles.(112)

Cayce, like many other prophets, possessed only a miniscule comprehension of metaphysical laws and principles. It is understandable that he would misinterpret impressions which he received, and assume that what happened to human souls was an unfortunate accident outside divine order. It is apparent the pattern he presented is a marvelous confirmation and description of principles presented in previous chapters. The chapter on the pyramid of life was written before the author read Steiger's book. Cayce was actually describing a new soul's first attempts to project a body into the physical realm. Cayce also confirmed that the majority of souls now incarnated on this planet first came into being during Atlantean times. The Atlantean culture was the product of much older and more advanced souls who occupied this planet for untold millions of years. It has been suggested that after millions of years of development, children of the logos became guides and teachers of younger souls prior to the time they will, themselves, become logos of systems below the physical realm. It is apparent that Brunler greatly underestimated the number of embodiments a normal human requires to reach a higher station in the cosmic plan.

Brunler's work in the science of biometrics is of inestimable importance. Like other great discoveries, it has been suppressed by the status quo of science and by those in high places. Once again the reasons are apparent. Its universal application could completely revolutionize this planet. It would stamp out politics and deception by those in responsible positions. Everyone would find his or her proper niche in society, and only the most qualified would be in the more important positions. It is only natural for those in positions of power and influence to be reluctant to have their true character traits and mental capabilities revealed. Although this science has been suppressed as far as general usage is concerned, the U.S. government has probably been using it extensively to their own advantage for decades. The author met two individuals who had worked for the government in the use of the biometer. They had letters of commendation from high government officials, including Eisenhower.

Machines can be developed to measure one's radiation without the need of a pendulum and sensitive. It is based on the concept of the soft particle. The basic principle of the machine is quite simple, and was suggested by the author many years ago. Soft particles radiated from the brain or the thumb are caused to disintegrate into their constituent light. This can be done by powerful electromagnets in conjunction with ultrasonics. The light produced by the disintegration of the soft particles is then directed to produce the photoelectric effect. The voltage of the resultant electricity is directly proportional to the average frequency of the light employed. The biometric measurement can then be calibrated in terms of voltage and read directly from a dial. The characteristics of the electrical flow can be projected on an oscilloscope to show subtle character traits of the person being examined.

A more complete presentation of Brunler's findings will now be presented.(81) Individuals below the 280° level comprise about 75 percent of the population. As mentioned before, they are incapable of abstract thought. Therefore, they are unable to form strong opinions about anything deviating from the most mundane and concrete. They are wholly dependent upon authority and convention and are easily swayed. The finer aspects of great art, music, and philosophy escape them completely. The range from 280° to the low 300s includes those able to think well enough to be skilled laborers or go into some of the minor professions. Of course, they are still tightly bound by orthodoxy and are unable to be anything but followers. Between the low 300s and about 360° is known as the intuitive range. Those on this level are inclined to be highly intuitive. They depend on intuition more than logic, and it is well that they do, since their ability to think abstractly is still very limited. Many psychic readers are in this range. Since their level of comprehension and ability to evaluate is not of a high degree, the type of messages they are given fall into categories which can be understood by mediocre intelligence. Therefore, no great seers are found on this level.

The next level has been mentioned before and is a highly significant one. It is called the professorial or pure reason range, and is between about 360° and 400°. Those in this level form the major bulwark of the status quo. These are the ones who unwittingly serve the powerful and devious forces which have kept this planet in subjugation and ignorance for ages. People in this range are able to think abstractly and reason just well enough so the intuitive aspect, depending on their academic training, tends to be ignored or stifled. Although they can think much better than those in the lower ranges, they are not bright enough to be independent thinkers, and no great pioneers will be found among them. They are still bound by authority and orthodoxy and thus go entirely by the book. Their level of consciousness is not high enough to recognize their true limitations; and, especially, if they have a strong academic background. Therefore, many of them tend to overestimate their intelligence. This renders those steeped in the academic tradition the most obnoxious that can be found in any of the levels.

Since those in the professorial level are not original thinkers, it follows that they are inflexible. Once they have been thoroughly trained in one mode of thinking, they are attached to it for the rest of their lives. This makes them perfect tools for the malefactors who control the academic system from behind the scenes. What may have been revolutionary in a previous time becomes the orthodoxy of the present, and this is what these individuals safeguard. In order to get out of the rut, they must return at a time when the orthodoxy they left behind is replaced with something else. Many scholars are also found in this range. A well integrated person on this level can give the illusion of being more intelligent than a poorly integrated individual in a higher range. In fact, some people with excellent memories are skillful in solving certain kinds of problems and are mistaken for geniuses by those without a high degree of discernment. They obtain very high scores on standard I.Q. tests. Brunler's widow, who carried on his work after his demise, mentioned a case in which an individual with a biometric rating of only 300° had a genius rating, according to I.Q. tests. Individuals like these, who have not made any real achievements, usually think of themselves as a misunderstood geniuses who never had a break or just got a "bad deal". They are correct in one sense. Perhaps the most glaring example of an erudite individual in the public eye, who exemplifies all of the traits just described in the pure reason range, is the famous science fiction writer, Isaac Asimov, mentioned in Part I. It was clearly shown that his mental faculties were somewhat less that astute. He has long been a mouthpiece for the scientific community by championing all of the popular dogmas of academic science, while attempting to debunk everything outside the domain of this distinguished body. This includes such things as telepathy, ufology, psionics, etc.

It is difficult to believe that anyone who is supposed to be scientific and objective, and has not led a completely sheltered life, could in good faith take such a stand (especially in view of all the overwhelming evidence that confutes such allegations). Some interesting questions arise from this. Is Asimov in the professorial range? All external evidence suggests that he is. If so, then he might be excused for his indiscretions. He is simply not bright enough to realize he has been anything but scientific and objective in his approach to things academic science cannot explain.

If Asimov is not in this range, then he is in the lower portion of the next higher level. If this is the case, then it can be concluded that Mr. Asimov is not sincere in his professed beliefs that borderland phenomena and UFOs have no sound evidence to support their reality. He is merely trying to do his part to maintain the status quo of science.

This calls to question his integrity. It has already been proven time and time again that many prominent members of the scientific community are not paragons of integrity. The reader is left with two possible conclusions involving Asimov. Is he honest but stupid, or is he dishonest, as well as not being excessively bright?

The level between about 400° and 460° is known as the ego range. Those on this level are more flexible and not as tightly bound by orthodoxy. As a result, they are more open-minded. The personalities who reach this level of consciousness have a better conception of their place in the cosmic scheme, and are generally excited about it. They are usually more talkative than those in any other category. Many writers are found on this level.

The personality range is between 460° and 575°. At this stage of development, the soul center has so much control over the physical body that the body radiates energies which greatly affect others. These people have what is called a magnetic personality. Many outstanding leaders are found in this range. This personal magnetism, combined with better mental faculties, makes them highly effective in public relations. Many famous personalities and certain movie stars are on this level, in addition to some of the more famous writers such as Charles Dickens. This is the range Walter Russell (discussed earlier) was in, and this accounts for his ability to influence and sway others.

The level between 575° and 660° is called the power range. Very few people in any generation are in it. This range includes outstanding pioneers in various fields who are close to what could be termed genius, and some are considered such.

Brunler called the level above 660° the genius level. It is very likely that there are no more than a half-dozen on the planet in this range, unless some are incommunicado, waiting for a propitious time to reveal themselves.

Brunler made another highly significant discovery in regard to this science of biometrics. He found that all those above 575° on the biometric scale usually have altruistic tendencies. This means that all malefactors, criminals, etc. are below 575°. This would take in practically all politicians past or present. It follows that those involved with the so-called forces of darkness are also below 575°. This fact is obviously utilized by the governing powers of the universe to keep things under control. Therefore, the forces of light are always more powerful and intelligent than the forces of darkness.

The advantages of the universal application of this science are not difficult to imagine. For example, numerous evils of our civilization, such as politics, could be wiped out. Only the most qualified individuals would be placed in responsible positions. If a person's true potential were known, the best kind of education and training for that individual could be determined. This could eliminate the trial and error procedure, and the disastrous effects on an individual's personality. Its applications in the fields of psychology and psychotherapy could revolutionize these sciences. At the present time, the methods employed by most practitioners in these fields leave something to be desired. This brings to mind some experiments of a particular psychologist with retarded children a few decades ago. One of the achievements of which he was most proud was raising the intelligence of a high-grade idiot up to that of a low-grade imbecile! The reader can, no doubt, visualize other reforms and ramifications which could result from the proper use of Brunler's research.

Some of the more recent and revolutionary training and educational techniques used on some children have indicated that the potential of humans is considerably higher than originally assumed. This has lead some educators to the conclusion that ordinary children can be turned into geniuses. This is false, of course. The same disparities would show up if all of them were subjected to the same training. The proportionate differences would still be in evidence. The implication that a child or baby, taken at random, could be transformed into a Mozart, Bach or Archimedes is sheer nonsense. The facts brought out by Brunler render this more than obvious.

Each human soul was created according to a certain blueprint or plan. No two are identical. All have different mental characteristics. Some are created with larger and more complex mental equipment than others. The universe can be likened to a gigantic and complex electrical circuit. There are plug-ins for a near infinitude of light bulbs of varying wattages and color schemes. The light bulbs represent humanity and the various life forms. The range of wattages is very great. Each bulb receptacle is for a specific light bulb. A 100-watter couldn't be plugged into a receptacle for a 10-watter or vice versa. This brings to mind a mental blooper committed by the founding fathers of the U.S. Constitution and the writer of the Declaration of Independence. It was the endorsement of that famous remark, "All men are created equal". For ambiguity and dogmatism it has never been exceeded by anything uttered by a Walter Russell. From the standpoint of asininity, it has never been surpassed even by a conventional scientist. Yet, the founding fathers supposedly represented some of the best minds of the period.

At 700°, Brunler was one of the great minds of his age. He made one of the most important contributions to science in this century.

"Failure exists only in the grave. Man, being alive, hath not yet failed; always he may turn about and ascend by the same path he descended by; and there may be one that is less abrupt (albeit longer of achievement), and more adaptable to his condition." — The Magic Story
By Frederic Van Rensselaer Dey (1900)

Hold fast to dreams
For if dreams die,
Life is a broken winged bird
That cannot fly.
— Langston Hughes

"Ere many generations pass our machinery will be driven by powers obtainable at any point in the universe . . . it is a mere question of time when men will succeed in attaching their machinery to the very wheelwork of nature."
— Nikola Tesla (1891)

"Our ears, accustomed from early childhood to hearing their false stories, and our minds, imbued with those preconceptions for centuries, preserve those fantastic suppositions as if they were a sacred trust . . . so that truth seems incredible, and adulterated stories have the appearance of truth."
— Written by Sanchuniathon four thousand years ago

CHAPTER 34

MISCELLANEOUS TOPICS

THE GENERATION OF LIFE FROM "LIFELESS" MATTER

Another remarkable phenomenon which the scientific community continues to debunk or ignore is the production of life forms from seemingly inert matter. Many objective experiments have confirmed the reality of such occurences. The first recorded case involved the experiments conducted by Andrew Crosse, an amateur scientist in the early part of the nineteenth century.(38) This event was completely unexpected and came as a result of experiments in the formation of artificial crystals, involving weak electric currents in solutions for long periods of time. Various inorganic chemicals such as copper nitrate, copper sulphate, and zinc sulphate were employed in acid baths.

After several weeks, small insect forms gradually emerged from beneath the surface of the solutions, and crawled out of their place of origin! After once emerging, they would quickly die if dropped back into the acid. Other scientists soon duplicated his experiments with similar results. There were certain rules which governed the success of the experiments. When sterile equipment was used and an electric current was allowed to flow through the solution, the insects always appeared. The stronger the current, the more quickly they formed. If no current was used, there would be no development of these forms. The number of insects increased by increasing the amount of carbon in the fluids.

This, of course, produced the usual calumny and disbelief in scientific circles, which finally ceased when Michael Faraday reported that he, too, had conducted similar experiments with the same results. Faraday was evidently afflicted with some of the irrationality or insanity of the typical scientist when faced with a seemingly inexplicable event. He was unable to decide whether they were created in the solution or were brought back to life by action of the current.(38) How could anything or any form which obviously wasn't present in the beginning of the experiment be brought back to life?

The conditions which caused these life forms to develop were almost identical to those in the bion experiments of Wilhelm Reich, discussed in Part III. Elementary intelligences or life centers existing in realms slightly above the phyical tend to project bodies into the physical realm, whenever conditions are favorable for this to occur. The hermetic axiom applies in the creative life chain, as well as in other areas.

Certain conditions in the physical realm greatly facilitate the projection of a body into that realm. For example, the fertilization process by male and female enables the centers of intelligence in higher realms to manifest in thc physical. It is a cause and effect relationship. Like can only produce like. In other words, the body reflects the nature or desire of the projecting intelligence. An insect or animal intelligence cannot project or influence the creation of a human body. This is why a given intelligence which desires to project into the physical realm generally seeks out the cooperation of similar intelligences already manifested on this plane.

It isn't mandatory that perfect conditions be first introduced into a lower realm for a center of intelligence to produce a body in that realm, or for the fertilization process to take place. If this were true, the creative cycles could never have started in the first place. This was demonstrated in the Crosse experiments. It then follows that the human being doesn't necessarily require incarnation in a womb. This principle concerning the projection from a higher realm into a lower one resolves the old enigma, "What came first, the chicken or the egg?"

The channels which feed and promote the growth of a body prior to birth are severed after it is removed from its origin of birth. Thereafter, the body cannot return to this place of origin and survive. This is why the life forms generated by the Crosse experiments died when they were placed back in the solution. New channels and circuits are created after the organism emerges from the place of birth, so that it may continue in the growth cycle.

THE TRANSMUTATION OF ELEMENTS

A significant amount of research has confirmed that certain elements are transmuted into other elements within biological organisms utilizing limited quantities of energy. Conventional science has been able to accomplish transmutation only after the expenditure of tremendous quantities of energy. Orthodox scientists try to give the impression that their methods of transmutation are the only means to do it.

In Chapter 17 of *The Secret Life of Plants*, an account is given of some of the research work of Louis Kervran on biological transmutation.(13) He performed experiments which proved many different transmutations are continuously being carried out in living organisms with little expenditure of heat or energy. Controlled experiments demonstrated that the feces and egg shells which chickens produce contain many times the calcium provided in the food and water the chickens consume.

Certain mineral processors with whom the author has been acquainted repeatedly recover many times the quantity of precious metals that was originally contained in the ore they process. The late T. H. Moray, of Salt Lake City, published journals on a method he developed for significantly increasing the mineral content of ores such as gold by bombarding it with high energy radiations.(84,85) However, he did not divulge the exact method or nature of the radiations for proprietary reasons.

Transmutation, as described above, increases or lowers the atomic weight of certain atoms, which means that electrons and protons are added to or subtracted from them.

This is accomplished by soft particles which carry hard protons and electrons into the atom and deposit them there. All space is permeated with hard electrons and protons camouflaged by softer particles. There are certain types of soft particles radiated by body tissues and also contained in the radiations Moray mentioned, which are able to deposit hard protons and electrons in certain atoms and transform them into heavier atoms.

The most significant and revolutionary discoveries concerning transmutation in modern times seem to have been made by Louis Kervran and George Ohsawa. Their work is of greater importance than that of scientists given infinitely more acclaim. The following is a brief outline of a book condensation by George Ohsawa called *Biological Transmutation*.(61) It includes articles by Louis Kervran and an account of some of Ohsawa's revolutionary discoveries. During thirteen years of experimentation, Kervran proved that elements are transformed into other elements in biological bodies. For example, magnesium transmutes into calcium, sodium into potassium, potassium into calcium, sodium into magnesium, nitrogen into silicon, etc. Kervran gave the first legitimate explanation of an enigma which has puzzled chemists and others for a long time. It was noted that those who breathed the air which had been in contact with an incandescent metallic surface suffered symptoms of carbon monoxide poisoning. Workers doing blowtorch welding have often been poisoned by carbon monoxide. Yet, countless tests have shown that no carbon monoxide, CO, is present in the atmosphere during such activities. Kervran's conclusion was that the nitrogen in the atmosphere, which had been in contact with hot metal, was transformed into CO after it was inhaled. CO has practically the same molecular weight as nitrogen, or N_2.

George Ohsawa confirmed Kervran's conclusion by transmuting elements outside organic bodies at low temperatures and without high pressures. For example, in 1964, he transformed sodium into potassium inside a specially designed vacuum tube. When oxygen was introduced into the tube containing sodium, the spectrum of sodium disappeared immediately, and the spectrum of potassium replaced it. Shortly thereafter, Ohsawa claimed to have discovered a theory of how other elements could be transmuted. Prior to this, he transformed carbon into iron by "plasmizing" carbon powder into incandescence and placing it in contact with atmospheric oxygen. The oxygen combined with the carbon to produce iron.

It is significant that all these transmutations take place with low energy and pressure. This has always been considered impossible by academic scientists. They have only been able to transmute minute quantities of light elements using high energy bombardments. Their totally unimaginative approach to exploring the structure of matter by building bigger and more worthless atom smashers is typical of the general quality of their scientific thinking. This trend of academic thought is identical in principle to one who puts eggs under increasingly larger drop hammers in the hope of learning more about what is inside them.

Ohsawa applied Eastern philosophy involving yin and yang to science much in the manner that the hermetic axiom has been applied throughout this book. Yin and yang concern the law of duality. They are exact opposites such as positive and negative, two sides of a coin, etc. By following this approach, he was able to predict combinations of elements which would transmute and those which would not. Some elements are considered yin and others are called yang elements. An excess of yang produces yin. These and other general rules have been found to apply in all of the biological transmutations investigated. The difference between yin and yang elements was not defined in the above mentioned booklet. However, elements such as oxygen, chlorine, potassium, calcium, sulphur and phosphorus are listed as yin elements, while hydrogen, sodium, and carbon are yang elements. This supplies a clue for determining the difference.

From the standpoint of the new science presented in this treatise, a yin element is essentially one that has a high affinity for hard electrons, while a yang element tends to give up hard electrons. As explained earlier, water has a high affinity for electrons of all kinds. This is what makes it a great ionizing agent. It contains a high concentration of soft electrons which camouflage harder electrons. Thus a yin element in solution draws hard electrons around its individual atoms, while the corresponding yang element tends to give up electrons to the water. Common salt or sodium chloride is a good example of this. The sodium represents yang, while the chlorine corresponds to yin. The bond between the sodium and chlorine atoms is broken when salt is placed in water. This is because of the high concentration of soft and hard electrons permeating the sodium chloride molecule. The difference between yin and yang elements is not always as marked as this. Some are more yin than other yin elements, while some are more yang than other yang elements. For example, potassium is listed as a yin element, but it is not nearly as yin as chlorine, as evidenced by its behavior when potassium chloride is placed in solution.

As indicated earlier, it requires a high concentration of soft particles to promote transmutation. This enables atoms to interpenetrate much in the manner that the dematerialization process takes place, or that hard electrons penetrate insulators. The interpenetration allows the nuclei of atoms to get into intimate contact, so that a combination or readjustment can occur. The process of transmutation also requires an additional supply of hard electrons, which the soft particles furnish.

Soft electrons must be present for all chemical reactions to occur. However, biological processes require a much higher concentration and variety of soft particles than do inorganic chemical changes because biological changes and processes are correspondingly more complex. An individual creative intelligence is required to produce the soft particles necessary to sustain the organism. In the case of plants, it is the sun which provides the necessary soft particles. As indicated earlier, the sun is the chief logos of the solar system, and plants are projections of the planetary logos. Plants receive soft particles from the sun, which in turn cause photosynthesis to take place. It is the cooperative efforts of the solar and planetary logos which produce plants.

Transmutations are not only taking place continuously in animals, plants, and humans, but also in the earth. The process involved is similar in each case. The soft particles bombarding the earth carry with them the hard particles, which enter the atoms and produce certain transmutations. It is a slower process than in the case of organic transmutations for two basic reasons: First, the concentration of soft particles is less. Second, the transmutations occuring in organic bodies must necessarily take place more rapidly; therefore, the soul essence creates and projects specialized particles for such a process.

It follows that mineral deposits in the earth are grown and not deposited in the manner theorized by geologists. Their explanation for the petrification of organic materials, such as wood, is typical of other illogical theories of orthodox science. It is reported that there are areas where dead animals can be buried and in a matter of weeks can be exhumed and found to be petrified. It has also been claimed that atomic explosions have produced radiations causing petrification of certain organic substances. The earth is an embodiment of an intelligence and, as such, can be expected to experience growths and deposits of an inorganic nature in a manner analogous to an organic body.

Before closing this chapter, a more detailed account of how many transmutations take place is in order. A high concentration of soft electrons bombarding and permeating a substance can cause the atoms to periodically transform back and forth from one element into another. For example, consider mercury. Concentrations of soft electrons can deposit electrons in the nucleus of a significant portion of the atoms. A proton can be transformed into a hydrogen atom or a neutron can be ejected from the atom. During the process, some of the other neutrons can also be ejected and the mercury atom is transformed into a gold atom. Likewise, the gold atom can, in turn, capture neutrons ejected from surrounding atoms. If one of the neutrons loses its electrons by the subsequent interactions, and the electrons stripped off are recaptured by soft electrons, then the gold atoms change back into a mercury atom.

Suppose small particles of gold are present in the mercury when this occurs. As soon as a nearby mercury atom is transformed, it will be captured by the gold aggregate. Gold is more stable than mercury and the cohesive fields around a gold atom are far more extensive and powerful than around a mercury atom. Therefore, the captured gold atom becomes a permanent part of the gold aggregate. By this process, all the mercury can be eventually transformed into gold. Hydrogen will also be produced during the transformation.

A similar process takes place when the mineral content of certain ores is increased by radiation bombardments. Traces of the element whose quantity is to be increased must be present. As atoms and molecules of the surrounding material are temporarily transformed, they are then captured by the traces of the element already present.

The treatment thus far on transmutations has been little more than an outline of the process. A more detailed analysis is in order. The yin and yang approach can at best provide only a very superficial understanding of what is taking place. Soft electrons can capture hard particles only when they are at rest or are traveling at relatively low velocities. The reason is apparent. At high velocities the hard particles escape the influence of the softer particles before they can be slowed down. It is noted that it is largely the nucleii which are involved in the transmutations. The orbital electrons of an atom are always traveling at very high velocities and, therefore, cannot be captured directly by soft electrons which, except for those associated with the ELF frequencies are much smaller than atoms. The nucleons are different. Their activities are confined to only a relatively minute region. Also their motions follow a stop and go pattern since there are sudden 180 degree changes in direction of movement. This sudden and complex shift in velocity is what produces the atomic spectra by disturbing the ethers and creating the wide variety of photons.

The nucleus is not held together by some mysterious binding force, but by two easily understood factors. There is a tremendous interplay of electrons and protons within the nucleus which results in transformations of protons into neutrons and vice versa. There is always an excess of electrons present for this process, resulting from the disintegration of soft electrons in the region. The powerful magnetic fields resulting from this activity keeps the nucleons confined to a very small region. The magnetic fields produced by the motion of protons are far more intense and concentrated than those generated by electrons. The consequent pinch effect on the nucleus is colossal. The result can be likened to an extremely small atom with an abnormal positive charge.

Since the nucleus is restricted to a very small volume and the average velocity of the nucleus is relatively low (often individual particles are at rest or nearly so) it is far more susceptible to capture by soft electrons than the orbital electrons. The right concentration and combination of soft electrons can readily penetrate the cloud of orbiting electrons and carry away the nucleus. This results in the rapid dispersion of the orbiting electrons. When two or more soft electrons with captured nuclei interact and disintegrate, the captured nuclei can combine to form the nucleus of a larger atom. The disintegration of the soft particles also releases large quantities of hard electrons which become the orbital electrons of the transformed nucleus. Before the particles containing the captured nuclei disintegrate, the nuclei of the different atoms are brought into very intimate contact with each other. This is possible since, in the captured state, electrostatic repulsion between nuclei has been nullified.

It is highly significant that in the transmutation experiments of Ohsawa electric currents were applied. This supplied the necessary soft electron concentration for the reactions to occur since, as shown earlier, soft electrons concentrate along an electrical flow. There is another basic rule which governs transmutation processes. If the transformed atoms have stronger and/or more exensive cohesive forces than the others involved, such atoms will multiply at the expense of the others involved. Isolated atoms are more readily captured by soft particles than aggregates. This applies to both synthesis and reduction processes. The reduction process in the case of mercury and gold has already been mentioned.

It is interesting to note that the iron produced by the combustion of carbon and oxygen in the Ohsawa process resists corrosion far more than ordinary iron and also has a higher melting point. The reason is not difficult to discern. The transmuted iron is completely free of contaminants. Therefore, the forces of cohesion between atoms is stronger. Consequently, there is a greater tendency to resist the invasion of oxygen atoms. Also, the greater and more extensive cohesive forces enable aggregates of such atoms to remain solid at higher temperatures.

In conclusion, the transmutation of elements is an integral part of all life processes. It occurs in both organic and inorganic materials and involves intelligence.

THE REASONS THE EARTH'S MAGNETIC POLES ARE NOT LOCATED AT THE GEOGRAPHIC POLES

The fact that the earth's magnetic poles are far removed from the geographic poles, and that they tend to shift, has always been a puzzle to geophysicists and other experts. The concepts revealed in this treatise provide a simple answer to this dilemma. A magnetic pole is defined as the point where the magnetic inclination, or the angle at which the compass needle points downward, is 90 degrees. This is the direction of the magnetic lines of force or the general flow of ether particles. At the north magnetic pole the flow is downward and is upward at the opposite pole.

In actuality, the so-called poles are not sharply defined. The lines, along which the inclination is very close to 90 degrees, are quite extensive and follow a closed path around the lip of each of the large egresses into the hollow earth. The flow of ethers which produce the magnetic field will follow lines of least resistance, as is the case with any fluid. Since the openings produce a void, so to speak, the flow of ethers, concentrated in the higher latitudes, will concentrate at these openings. The concentration of soft electrons at any area fluctuates. Consequently, the so-called magnetic pole will also have a tendency to shift.

A high concentration of soft electrons is radiated out of the openings from the interior. This means an inordinate concentration exists around the openings. Since the openings are not located at the geographic poles, they will assume the rotational velocity of the earth in these areas. Therefore, an additional magnetic field will be produced in these regions and in the same direction as the general flow of ethers. Similar nodal points, or lines, encircle the earth at the lower latitudes, as mentioned in Chapter 20, because ether flows tend to follow circular paths going in and out of the earth's shell. Such nodal lines will be much weaker. A similar case exists along a bar magnet of considerable length.

UFOS THAT ARE LIFE FORMS

An analysis of UFO behavior suggests that a high percentage of UFOs are actually life forms. Trevor James Constable has written two books concerning his research into this highly controversial subject. His book entitled *The Cosmic Pulse of Life* is perhaps the most important and comprehensive book written on Ufology.(25) In a more recent book entitled *Sky Creatures; Living UFOs*, Constable presents a condensation of his previous book and the extensive evidence he has accumulated to date, supporting this contention.(26) In spite of the overwhelming evidence, he has encountered the same brand of obfuscation and vacuity in the academic world as many other pioneers discussed in this treatise.

The purpose of this ehapter is to analyze the nature of living UFOs and their place in the cosmic scheme. These "creatures" are normally invisible and intangible to our five senses, but interact with infrared and radar frequencies. Constable was able to photograph them with infrared film, using a photographic technique he developed. Many of them resemble giant amoebas or unicellular structures. They assume a wide variety of shapes, and even become visible and tangible for brief periods under the right conditions. Constable's research findings in conjunction with the concepts presented in the treatise provide an insight into the true nature of these entities.

Life forms created by the logos include their direct offspring and the planetary life necessary to render a planet habitable. Other life, or thought forms, encountered on or around a planet result from thoughts produced by the offspring of the logos. These offspring may or may not be human. These life, or thought, forms include various demon and other entities capable of independent thought which can exert considerable power and influence.

The demons which were cast out of humans by Jesus and others, as described in the Bible and occult lore, are examples.

Demons have been known to enter and even take control of a human body for brief periods. This implies the body of a demon is associated with ethers somewhere between those of the astral and those associated with the physical body. Therefore, the body of a demon consists of harder particles than those comprising the physical body. This also suggests that a demon body will interact with light of a higher frequency than that in the visible range. This light is undoubtedly in a range between the lower ultraviolet and the X-ray range. Individuals suspected of demon possession could be subjected to radiations of various frequencies and simultaneously photographed with film sensitive to such radiations. Various forms of exorcism could be applied during the process. The relationship and characteristics of these entities with sky creatures is becoming apparent.

Since the sky creatures Constable photographed normally reflect infrared light, it follows that the fundamental particles comprising their bodies are associated with slightly lower ethers than that of normal matter. The reason for this becomes apparent from the discussion in Chapter 21 on the manner in which the fundamental particles of matter create soft particles, which render matter visible. Therefore, since sky creatures are normally visible under infrared, the fundamental particles of their bodies must be softer than the fundamental particles of ordinary physical matter. On occasion, they become visible and tangible. The step-up principle described in Chapter 27 is the mechanism allowing them to do this.

The exact purpose of sky creatures is difficult to ascertain. However, it is probable they are thought form creations of man, and take on forms reflecting the nature of their creators. Perhaps they serve a very important purpose in the cosmic scheme. More extensive research may reveal this ultimate purpose. It is likely they contribute to the overall development of beings on the pyramid of life.

TERRIFYING METAMORPHOSES AND DISPLACED INTELLIGENCES

Tales of werewolves, vampires, and the like have persisted down through the ages and up to the present. Those who have researched the subject to any extent have found a wealth of evidence to support these beliefs. In fact, a Hindu scientist wrote a book on the subject of werewolves, giving a full account of his research and encounters with such horrific creatures. It included photographs of some of them in the transformed state. The photos made the movie version of a werewolf look like a Clark Gable, according to a friend who read the book. He held a high position in the Rosicrucian order and had access to this book in the Rosicrucian archives, not available in any public library. According to this Hindu scientist, the werewolf's physical strength is about six times as great as in the human form. Other findings indicate they can run as far and as fast as the six-million-dollar man when in this state.

Three former acquaintances of the author claimed to have seen such a creature. One of them stated he even saw the transition back to human form. Before the transition, it was seen to jump from the ground to the roof of a garage in one leap. Another observer corroborated this person's account.

There was a werewolf scare in the Los Angeles area in 1962. Many claimed to have seen one, and a husky teenager was supposed to have had an actual encounter with it. He first thought it was someone wearing a werewolf mask with special makeup, including artificial talons. To his horror, he found the mask wouldn't come off when he grabbed it. He ended up in the hospital in a state of shock. During the brief encounter, most of his clothes had been torn off, and he suffered an assortment of bruises and scratches. The incident created a stir, and was discussed on radio and television. The Hindu scientist mentioned above claimed that about two people out of a million are werewolves. This means there might be a dozen of them roaming the Los Angeles area.

Although the evidence for the exitence of these enigmas seems to be overwhelming, no legitimate explanation for this phenomenon has ever been offered. The following explanation is in accordance with concepts already presented. Many different life forms exist through out the universe. Some of them are bizarre and even frightening, according to human standards. Such beings occasionally incarnate on this planet in the human form. The soul centers of such beings have become adept in projecting bodies of the types described above in the physical realm. During an incarnation in the human form, the soul center will, under certain conditions, transform the human body into the form to which it has been accustomed during past lives. This requires a tremendous surge of energies from the higher realms to the physical by the step down principle described in a previous chapter. These additional energies account for the great increase in physical strength during the metamorphosis and afterwards. There may be either an increase or decrease in body size after the transition.

This may also account for the periodic appearance of Sasquatches and the Abominable Snowmen seen all over the world, and why they are so illusive. The strength displayed by Sasquatches on occasion has been far out of proportion to their great size. One was reported to have thrown a car wheel, tire and all, a distance of about 500 feet! As usual, the scientific community refuses to consider the existence of the Sasquatch, or Big Foot, despite all of the convincing evidence. One TV commentator stated that the scientists' attitude is more astounding than even the Sasquatch itself. This confirms a comment made earlier to the effect that in some instances, a scientist's idea of sound evidence is that and only that which stimulates all of the five senses simultaneously. A scientist's direct encounter with a Sasquatch may or may not satisfy such a condition, but it is likely that at least four senses would be stimulated. Big Foot is reported to have a very bad odor.

There are a number of well authenticated and famous cases of lower animals displaying mental abilities well beyond most humans. In some instances, they demonstrated a degree of seership which the better mentalists might envy. Typical examples are the wonder horses of Elberfield, the talking dog of Manheum, a talking mongoose, etc.(38,41) These are usually passed off as unusually smart animals like an exceptional human being. As is usual with attempts to explain enigmas, this reasoning is very shallow.

It is significant that many of these unusual animals were dogs, which are among the least intelligent of animals. The source of these unusual performances should be self-evident. They were merely takeover, or the control of an animal by a higher intelligence. Such cases of possession occur more frequently among humans. This results in split personalities and cases in which the individual commits acts completely contrary to his or her nature.

The possession or control of a body originally created and inhabited by another intelligence may be of a temporary, periodic, or permanent nature. There may be any number of reasons for a possession. One possibility is that discarnate spirits are attempting to communicate with people in the physical realm or to save a life. Another is that these spirits might be seeking revenge for some foul deed perpetrated upon them when they were living.

FIREWALKING AND TELEKINESIS

Firewalking and telekinesis are well-authenticated phenomena which have baffled everyone for ages. As with other previously unexplained anomalies, these are easily resolved by the new science. Hordes of firewalkers have repeatedly demonstrated the abiity to walk slowly through white-hot coals barefooted without injury.

An extremely hot body radiates an ultra-high concentration of high-speed soft electrons of many different kinds. Another body placed in contact with it is immediately impregnated with these particles, tending to disrupt its molecular structure. Most of the damage is done by the harder electrons released by the soft electrons as they penetrate into the substance and disintegrate.

Since the feet of firewalkers are not affected by direct contact with a hot body, it follows that the particles radiated by the heat encounter a strong electrostatic field which repels the high speed particles. This electrostatic field permeates the skin and extends for a significant distance outside the skin. The particles producing the field must be the same kind as the high-speed particles in order to produce maximum repulsion. Many of the particles radiated by the hot body are stopped or disintegrate completely before they reach the skin, while the others are slowed down to such an extent that they can do little damage when they penetrate the tissue. Slow particles have little tendency to disintegrate, and do not release the damaging harder electrons. The more unstable high speed particle disintegrate when they encounter the electrostatic field outside the skin.

Prior to a firewalking demonstration, firewalkers always go through a mental conditioning ceremony. This conditioning causes the feet to be impregnated with a high concentration of soft electrons, which will repel the high speed particles radiated by the hot body. This principle is implicit in an incident described by Max Freedom Long in his book *The Secret Science Behind Miracles*.(79) A scientist who was investigating the phenomenon was invited to participate in a firewalking demonstration. He was told he would be protected by the firewalkers and rendered immune to the heat. He consented but insisted on wearing his heavy boots instead of walking through the hot coals in his bare feet, although he was warned that only his feet would be protected, and not his boots. His boots soon disintegrated from the intense heat but his feet remained cool during the entire walk.

The validity of this principle has already been unwittingly confirmed by experimenters. An account of such demonstrations appeared in the Saga Special UFO Report, Vol. III, pages 54 and 55. It tells of a picture on the cover of the October 27, 1969 issue of "Design News". This picture shows an ordinary box of tissues with one extended. A flame is touching the tissue, but the paper will not burn. There is a challenge in capital letters which asks, "Why Doesn't The Tissue Burn?" According to the text, its discoverer, Inter Probe, Inc., of Chicago, has placed a high-voltage electric probe where the burner is striking the paper. It supposedly sets up an electrostatic field, which somehow reduces the energy level of the flame, nullifying the effects of the heat. Of course, they were unable to explain why it works, only that it does.

They also found that this cooling by electrostatic field works on red hot metals as well. Inter Probe plugged a 900-watt heater coil into an electrostatic outlet until the temperature was about 2000° F. As soon as a high-voltage current was passed through the same electric probe mentioned above and held close to the heated coils, the portion of the coils directly in line with the point of the probe was cooled.

Telekinesis is moving distant objects without direct physical contact. It requires a force to move an object. In the final analysis, it has been shown that only two kinds of force exist in the physical universe, electrostatic and magnetic. For example, gravitation is produced by electrostatic forces only. It is not a force distinct from electromagnetism, as is the consensus of academic science. This means that the phenomenon of telekinesis is caused by the generation of either a magnetic or electrostatic field in the vicinity of the object which is moved. Magnetism is ruled out, since bodies composed entirely of nonferromagnetic materials can be moved with considerable force. It follows that telekinesis is the result of electrostatic forces projected into a body. Experiments have shown that a strong electrostatic field will attract an uncharged body. If the field is positive, the free electrons in the body are attracted to the field, and tend to carry the mass with them. When the field is negative, the body also tends to be attracted because so-called uncharged matter possesses a net positive charge for reasons already presented.

An "adept" who is proficient in the art of telekinesis is able to project a shaft of soft and hard electrons toward the object and produce a strong field in the vicinity. The outline and intensity of this concentration of charges can be made to fluctuate, so that a steady force is exerted on the object in the desired direction. The same effect can be produced by a sharp beam of gravity-inducing radiations directed only on the body to be moved.

A similar process is involved in bending spoons or distorting metal objects, as demonstrated by mentalists such as Uri Geller. Certain combinations of soft electrons temporarily weaken the cohesive forces to such an extent that the object may collapse under its own weight. A Uri Geller type can project a beam of particles and impregnate a metallic object such as a spoon, a knife, or any other body, and thereby greatly weaken the cohesive forces holding it together. Some strong men have been able to bend and break horseshoes, large spikes, coins, chains, etc. that would normally require a force far beyond their muscular ability. During the bending or breaking process, they unconsciously project energies into the object they are working on, and temporarily weaken it to the extent that they are able to create the illusion of superhuman strength. The soft particles escape from the material after the feat is accomplished, and the material resumes its normal state. If it were not for this, the force required to duplicate the feat would be sufficient to tear the flesh from the bones. There is always a great disparity between the lifting ability of the performer and the apparent strength required to duplicate the bending and breaking feats. A famous strong woman could break straps which had a tensile strength of 8000 pounds. Evidently, she was a far greater mentalist than a strong woman.

The author recently participated in a knife, fork and spoon bending session presided over by an expert in this field. Several dozen novices were involved. After following the instructions of this expert, nearly everyone in the room, including the author, was able to bend these implements into various shapes with little application of force. Some of the persons accomplishing this feat were feeble old women. The process consisted of gently stroking an implement and concentrating. In most cases the metal soon became soft and pliable. The large gathering, of course, increased the concentration of soft electrons in the area, which facilitated the process. Often during such sessions a heavy stainless steel knife has been known to bend under its own weight.

The various brands of irrationality and stupidity exhibited by members of the so-called intelligentsia have been outlined continually throughout this treatise. In numerous cases, it has been of a magnitude difficult to believe. A mind boggling fact is that all of the above mentioned cases of mental ineptitude and aberration have been at least equalled by two individuals who are very much in the public eye. One is a supposedly respected member of the scientific community by the name of Paul Kurtz and the other is a famous magician, known as the Great Randi. What is even more unbelievable is that they do not reside in any mental institution.

They deserve to stand beside the most famous Isaac Asimov, who has also managed to avoid such a fate. These distinguished gentlemen have been carrying out a long crusade in an attempt to debunk the reality of psychic phenomena. This includes, of course, ESP, telekenesis and other types of phenomena described and explained in this treatise. No doubt, most members of the scientific community still have doubts about the reality of such things. With the exception of figures such as Asimov, they are not brazen enough, however, to flaunt their stupidity to the world at large by denying the reality of something proven valid beyond any question. There is scarcely anyone who has not experienced a demonstration of it sometime in his or her life or, at least, has a trusted acquaintance who has had the experience. An intelligent person does not need a personal experience to be convinced of the reality. A logical and unbiased examination of the records and the facts is all he needs.

The magician has offered $10,000 to anyone who can prove such things are a reality. He has allegedly tested many people gifted with unusual abilities and none have been able to win the $10,000. There is a catch to this apparently none of those who have tried to collect the $10,000 are aware of. A demonstration of an ability such as telekenesis can be nullified by the presence of someone who also has unusual power along the same line. That he has the power to nullify the ability of an individual to perform telekenesis was more evident in a recent TV show.

It featured such an expert from Salt Lake City who showed he could turn the pages of a telephone book by slowly passing his hand over it. This was done without the presence of the magician. Later in the show, the magician was introduced and immediately claimed that air currents the expert produced caused the pages to turn. He then poured some light, foamy material around the phone book that would be disturbed by any air current. The mentalist was then invited to turn the pages again with his mental power. He failed. He went through the same motions as before. It is significant that the foam was not disturbed during his efforts, thus proving he did not turn the the pages previously in the manner claimed by the magician. He was both surprised and chagrined that he was unable to duplicate a feat he had performed many times in front of large gatherings.

It is very apparent that this magician does possess powers that he denies the existence of. There are three possible conclusions that can be derived concerning this magician and the other crusader who is a close associate of his: (1) They are fully aware of the reality of the things they denounce and, as a consequence, are charlatans of the most detestable kind. (2) They are sincere in their contentions and therefore, are abysmally stupid as well as being psychotic, or (3) They are charlatans and also insufferably stupid. The third conclusion is the one most likely to be valid.

It is hoped that they, at least, read this part of the treatise. The author challenges them to confute what he has stated in their behalf. It is not likely either one of them would read this treatise to this point. The concepts introduced in it are likely far beyond the ability of either one of them to comprehend.

The Great Randi and other would-be debunkers of natural phenomena claim that the famous Uri Geller uses tricks in his demonstrations bending such objects as spoons by just lightly stroking or staring at them. Randi claims he can duplicate Geller's feats but uses only trickery. He did bend a spoon on TV by gently stroking it. The fact that the same thing can be duplicated by ordinary people using no tricks proves that Randi was deliberately lying and that he bent the spoon by using identically the same process employed by the novices the author mentioned above.

Randi's recent attempt to debunk firewalking backfired on him in full view of TV cameras which were recording the event. After closely observing a procession of firewalkers slowly walking a long expanse of red hot coals and carefully examining their feet afterwards, he was forced to admit he was stumped.

LEVITATION PRODUCED BY SOUND

There have been many well-authenticated instances of levitation being produced by sound. Walter P. Baumgartner cites a highly interesting case in an article entitled, "A Tibetan Leviation Technique," which appeared in the April-June, 1978, issue of the publication, *Energy Unlimited.* A Swedish doctor by the name of Jarl, had the privilege of witnessing such a phenomenon performed by Tibetan monks at a monastery in 1939. Huge blocks of stone were levitated to a cliff ledge 250 meters above the resting place of the stones. The stones to be lifted were partially surrounded by a combination of drums and trumpets. After several minutes of playing, a given stone would begin to oscillate and then shoot into the air. It is highly significant that occasionally a stone would burst into pieces during its flight.

In view of principles already elaborated upon, the explanation is simple. The combination of sounds being focused on the object started a high rate of disintegration of soft particles permeating the stones, as they do all objects. This released harder electrons, which gradually decreased the overall positive charge effect of the stone. As this process continued, the resultant charge of the stone became negative. Consequently, the earth's gravity repelled it upward. Something akin to the Reich cloud-buster effect, to be discussed in the next chapter, also took place during the process. The disintegrating soft particles in and around the stone created a void and a consequent rush of soft particles to the area. This added to the negative charge. Sometimes, too many hard electrons would be released, causing the stone to shatter.

Carl Von Reichenbach, whose work has already been discussed, actually showed that sound causes soft particles to disintegrate. He found that color effects are produced by sound, and the resulting colors are characteristic of the sound producing them. The colors, of course, are the result of soft electrons breaking up into their constituent photons of light.

It is not necessarily the hard electrons associated with atoms and electricity that are released during the levitation process. In fact, the gravity inducing radiations react far more strongly with soft electrons associated with ethers closer to that of the gravity producing electrons. Many of the soft particles permeating matter are of the extremely soft variety which are comprised of photons well below the infrared and the gravity range. These particles, as well as most of the others of a harder nature, are not firmly locked within matter, and thus have little or no nullifying effect on the overall positive charge effect of matter as far as the gravity radiations are concerned. When such particles disintegrate, harder particles are released, which do become more intimately locked within matter to give it an overall negative charge.

Nullifying the net positive charge effect of matter will not necessarily affect the inertial properties to any great extent if the negative charges are not homogeneously and closely distributed throughout the mass. In fact, the inertial properties can even be increased, as is the case with the spinning top. The central portion is positively charged, while the outer part has a strong negative charge. A rotating top has greater inertia and less weight than is the case when it is at rest.

Levitation, of course, can also be produced by beaming soft electrons at the right concentration and comprised of photons of the correct frequency range into a body. This is likely the method employed by the ancients with what were called levitation discs, which were supposedly made of copper. Such metal of the right shape and mass, when struck to ring like a bell, could excite the atoms to the extent that a concentrated beam of levitating soft electrons would be ejected. Perhaps in conjunction with this levitating inducing sounds would also be produced. Gravity inducing radiations obviously have their limitations as far as levitation is concerned. Objects are affected only along the line of propagation and could not be employed for lifting objects directly above the ground unless the levitating device were to be held directly above them. This, of course, is not the case with the other methods.

THE MYSTERY OF THE CRYSTAL SKULL

The crystal skull was discovered in the ruins of a Mayan city during a 1927 archaeological expedition. It is a large, clear, quartz crystal, fashioned perfectly into the size and shape of a human skull. Observers claim that strange sounds, light effects, and even odors emanate from it at times. One of the most interesting aspects of the skull is that it maintains a constant temperature of 70° F regardless of the surrounding temperature, even when placed in a refrigerator at -28° F. Many people have contended the skull has exerted influences that produce bad luck. One owner maintained a positive attitude toward it, and seemed to lead a charmed life during the years it was in his possession.

The explanation of the phenomena associated with the skull falls well within the scope of concepts discussed in this treatise. Many high priests of the past were evidently "adepts" in the so-called black arts. They were able to create powerful entities, or thought forms, programmed to protect objects, such as rare gems or tombs they considered sacred. This accounts for the long list of misfortunes connected with such things as the Hope diamond and King Tut's tomb, which cannot be explained away by coincidence.

Experts estimate that it required about 300 years to carve the skull from the original crystal. Since a lot of tedious work seems to have been expended in creating the skull, it is logical to conclude that an entity endowed with unusual powers was created to protect it. This is more than evident because the crystal tends to maintain a constant temperature. This could not be accomplished without intelligent and purposeful application of external energies.

Soft electrons from a heat source would normally enter the skull and disintegrate, releasing large quantities of hard electrons. This could raise the temperature of the crystal to damaging levels. However, the crystal skull automatically provides a very high concentration of soft electrons tending to concentrate on the outer surface. This surface charge then repels external soft electrons projected from a heat source, and maintains the crystal at a constant temperature. As mentioned before, firewalkers employ the same principle to protect their feet.

When the skull is exposed to a low temperature, it provides a continuous flow of unstable soft electrons, which disintegrate inside the crystal. This generates heat, compensating for the heat losses to the outside. Some "adepts" have similar abilities, and can generate and draw high concentrations of such particles into their bodies, and thus render themselves immune to extreme cold. They are able to lie naked in snow banks at subzero temperatures and melt the snow around them.

Other evidence supports the conclusion that the crystal is embodied by an entity. Sensitives see a fluctuating aura around the skull. This aura often extends further from the skull than the aura of an ordinary crystal of the same size. In addition, the skull tends to respond to one's thoughts and attitudes by the various light effects mentioned earlier.

The phenomena associated with the crystal skull are in conformity with the properties of crystals discussed earlier and the research findings of Reichenbach. The major characteristic distinguishing a life form from a so-called inanimate object or dead body is its ability to produce large concentrations of soft electrons. The high concentration is required to promote the complex chemical processes involved in normal organic functions. Crystals concentrate abnormally large quantities of soft electrons and display other characteristics of life forms. Certainly, an embodying or protecting entity could function more efficiently through a crystal and produce the effects described above, than through an ordinary rock.

SPONTANEOUS HUMAN COMBUSTION

Spontaneous human combustion cannot exactly be termed an extremely rare occurrence, since there are more than 70 cases on record. In most cases, the body was reduced to ashes, yet the clothing and surrounding material was hardly scorched. In view of principles already discussed, it is not difficult to account for the nature of the burning. Such a phenomenon could occur only if a highly concentrated beam of unstable, soft electrons entered and concentrated in the body. The cells of the body, comprised of a high percentage of water, would have a great affinity for such a beam.

The soft electrons, being in a highly unstable condition as they enter the body, would quickly disintegrate after the concentration exceeded a certain critical level. The high concentration of hard electrons released would disintegrate the cells. The clothing would not concentrate a sufficient quantity to produce a disintegration. They would tend to pass through the clothing before disintegrating. Sometimes parts of the chair, or bedding, or rug on which the victim was sitting or lying would be burned. In such cases, the beam of soft electrons would pass through the body after much of it was consumed, and disintegrate as it entered the material on which the person was positioned.

The source of such a beam of soft particles remains to be accounted for. In most cases, the person was undoubtedly the target of a practitioner of so-called black magic. All beings are creators in varying degrees. This ranges from the creation of matter in different realms and in various forms to the production of soft electrons, as is the case with bions and the orgone they radiate. In each case, messages or commands are sent along the life lines connecting all particles. The nature of what is created is dependent on the nature of the command and the number of life lines affected. This, in turn, is dependent on the nature of the intelligence, or the being, making the command. Creation covers a near-infinite range of activities. The projection of a beam of soft electrons to an individual is a unique form of creation. It is something analogous to telepathy. In each case there must be a definite connection from one individual to another by means of a special combination of life lines. Through this line, special commands are sent which, in turn, affect surrounding ethers for the creation of a beam of soft electrons of a certain kind to be sent along this connection.

In many cases this connective line exists when the sender has something belonging to the victim, or something the victim has handled. Such a condition is necessary for a younger and less advanced soul to project energies to another individual. An older, and more advanced, being usually doesn't require such a prop in order to project energies to a certain target. Through many experiences and travels around large parts of the universe, many connections to these parts of the universe have been established. Since his sphere of influence has greatly expanded, the chance of establishing a contact with an individual he hasn't seen or been connected with in a physical way is thereby greatly enhanced. By indirect commands to the region occupied by the target, a direct connection can often be established.

It is not difficult to see that the sphere of influence of an Elder would be transcending and unlimited. They can project energies to any part of the universe.

Perhaps some of the cases of human combustion were accomplished by mechanical means. A special type of laser, comprised of a high concentration of soft electrons of a certain degree of instability and directed to the victim at close range, would accomplish the same thing.

THE ORIGIN AND FOUNDATION OF ASTROLOGY

The history and origin of the techniques of astrology are extremely nebulous. All that seems to be known is that astrology has been handed down from generation to generation, for untold ages. It appears to have no scientific foundation, yet in the hands of experts, it displays a consistency and accuracy which transcends human understanding.

Astrology involves the relative positions and relationships of planets in the solar system to each other. These relationships do not seem to be the direct cause of the influences which shape tendencies and destinies; therefore one must look for another explanation. The logical answer is to be found in the policies of the creators of the planets, or the logos. After all, it is the logos who direct the destiny of humanity and individual humans. Therefore, the influences which are attributed to the relative positions of planets really come from the logos. Planetary positions function as timetables for coming events. The relative positions are analogous to the bus schedules of a transportation system.

Once again, the hermetic axiom enables one to gain a better understanding of the function and purpose of astrology. Consider a perfectly functioning organization. The directors of this organization are analogous to the logos. They are responsible for every aspect of its operation and future, which includes the training, performance, and development of each of its employees. This means that a perfect bookkeeping system must be initiated involving every one of its employees. Every phase of each employee's development is carefully planned. Every intelligently planned operation involves a timetable and, in this case, it is infinitely more sophisticated and intricate than any employed in the physical realm. This timetable maintains order in the entire system. Each incarnation of every human is carefully planned as to time, place, and potential drives and tendencies of the embodied personality. Such drives and tendencies direct him or her into the type of experiences necessary for that individual's achievements in that life. Since the planets are in accurate and stable orbits with precise orbital periods, their relative positions correspond to exact time periods. It is logical to expect the logos would use these relative positions for planning the future trends and activities of individuals, countries, organizations and planets.

The logos realized that a knowledge of the blueprint in conjunction with the timetable would be beneficial to developing humans. This knowledge was imparted to humanity by incarnating teachers, as has been described in previous chapters. Such teachers may have been either embodied Elders or much older souls than the mainstream of humanity. Astrology is an outline of the overall plan, which the logos have for humans incarnating on a given planet. Each planet has a different destiny, and therefore will have a different astrological system. Since astrology involves a logical and well ordered plan, it follows that astrology may be employed for the charting of future events. Prophets who have given accurate and detailed accounts of future events through visions have been able to tune into cosmic computers, which contain blueprints for future plans. Astrology provides a means for doing the same thing by following an orderly system which is mathematically precise.

It is apparent that astrology has a scientific foundation as sound as that of any other valid concept. It is also clear the best authorities on the subject still have much to learn about it. The number 12 plays a significant role in the system. The logos probably use a numbering system based on 12 instead of 10. Some mathematicians have noted that this system would have definite advantages over the present one. It would greatly simplify notations and calculations. Interestingly enough, space visitors claim that there are 12 planets in this system, including the remnants of a blown-up planet forming the asteroid belt. There are also 12 signs in the zodiac and 12 months in a year. The master and his 12 disciples are probably symbolic of the sun and its 12 planets. It may be that all solar systems follow a similar pattern, and that each has 12 planets.

It is clear that those who denounce astrology as a superstition and pseudoscience are displaying crass ignorance, arrogance, and stupidity. This is perhaps the most offensive and obnoxious combination which can be found in human nature.

THE NATURE OF RADIOACTIVE CONTAMINATION

Radioactive contamination has developed into a major problem during the past several decades. Carelessness in the production of nuclear devices and fuel for reactors has resulted in ever increasing levels of radioactivity in the atmosphere and water supplies throughout the country and elsewhere. During this period, the U.S. government has continued to lie to the public about the dangers involved. The reasons are not difficult to discern. The manufacture of radioactive substances has become a multi-billion dollar industry.

Our highly touted nuclear physicists have no conception of the real nature of radioactivity, despite their masquerading as authorities on the subject. Why is it that after being exposed to a highly contaminated area, the ramifications do not usually manifest until after a long period and then continue for the rest of the individual's greatly shortened life? The symptoms cover a wide range of ailments and malfunctions. Academic science has no answer for this or how to treat those afflicted. It follows that none of our distinguished authorities know how to dispose of nuclear wastes, let alone how to neutralize them.

The concepts introduced in this treatise supply all of the answers to these problems. According to academic science the products of nuclear reactors and radioactive substances are gamma rays and alpha particles. Alpha particles are supposed to be the nuclei of helium atoms. Gamma rays, of course, consist of ultra-high-frequency photons and hard electrons with no preferred direction of spin. In this respect, and in addition to not being hollow, they differ from the hard electrons of atoms and electricity. Such particles tend to disrupt normal chemical processes and are especially inimical to living organisms.

High concentrations of protons are also ejected by nuclear processes and from radioactive substances. Such particles have been interpreted as alpha rays or the nuclei of helium atoms. They also tend to disrupt ordinary chemical reactions and are injurious to living organisms. As indicated earlier, positive charges tend to be harmful and negative charges beneficial with the exception of the harder electrons of high frequency radiations. A malfunctioning organ has a higher positive charge than a healthy one.

Gamma ray particles and protons are soon captured by soft electrons and become camouflaged. The soft electrons containing these harmful particles are quickly absorbed by the cells and tissues of living organisms. The reason for the delayed reaction of individuals exposed to radioactive contamination now becomes apparent. As shown in previous chapters, living cells have a strong affinity for soft electrons. Soft electrons which have captured the radioactive particles emanating from contaminated surroundings are readily absorbed by the cells. Over along period there is a steady disintegration of these soft particles which results in the release of the damaging protons and harder electrons associated with gamma rays in the tissues. The less stable particles disintegrate first, while the more stable ones remain in the tissues until they finally disintegrate. The hard electrons, being more active than the protons, will tend to be released sooner and more often. After many years, it is mainly the camouflaged protons that remain in the tissues. The effects produced by the particles turned loose in the cells cover a wide range of ailments and are in part dependent on the physical condition of the host.

An understanding of the nature of radioactivity and its effects opens the door to dealing with the problem. Since radioactive poisoning amounts to the absorption of high concentrations of soft electrons housing the destructive particles ejected by radioactive materials, the remedy becomes almost self evident. Such particles can be driven from the host by the heavy bombardment of soft electrons from a source such as a pyramid, orgone accumulater and especially from the device described in Chapter 13 utilizing repeated reflections from a combination of mirrors. In the latter case the soft electrons are more stable and are traveling at higher velocities. Therefore, they will be more effective in driving the dangerous soft particles from the afflicted individual. During the process many of the soft particles absorbed by the tissues will disintegrate, but the effects are mitigated by the hard electrons of ordinary electricity that are released by the bombarding soft electrons. The protons released become relatively harmless hydrogen and helium atoms while the hard electrons associated with gamma rays are rapidly driven from the cells by the hard electrons released by the bombarding particles.

All individuals exposed to highly radioactive substances should spend much time under pyramids or inside orgone accumulators if no other devices which radiates high concentrations of soft electrions is available. The exposure to powerful magnetic fields will also be effective. Magnetic fields tend to draw or expel radioactive particles from the tissues. Reich and his assistant showed that such treatments were effective after they absorbed lethal doses of radioactivity. When the source of the dangerous radiations was removed, they soon recovered. They were continuously exposed to high concentrations of orgone energy in their laboratory and living quarters.

The remaining enigma is the neutralizing of atomic wastes, which has become a far more serious problem than the public has been led to believe. This problem was solved by Wilhelm Reich about 30 years ago and was elaborated upon in detail in his book *The Oranur Experiment*. It is incredible that his discovery has never been utilized, in view of the widespread and growing concern over this dilemma. There are no invectives in the English language adequate to properly describe the behavior of the scientific community and officialdom in the U.S. government in regard to this and the subject of atomic energy in general. It is one of the many dark chapters in the history of academic science and the U.S. government.

The remedy is a ridiculously simple one. All atomic wastes and nuclear devices should be enclosed in lead shielding, then placed in multi-layered orgone accumulators and buried. After only a few years they will have been rendered harmless. All of the atoms of the radioactive materials will have been transformed. In the meantime, the production of nuclear material should cease, since there are infinitely better and cheaper sources of energy than atomic. Also, the government has weapons at its disposal that render nuclear devices obsolete. The trouble is they are much cheaper and easier to produce than nuclear devices and therefore not as lucrative to vested interests.

All research and work conducted in the field of atomic energy and related subjects displays the most abysmal type of stupidity. Three possible conclusions can be derived concerning anyone who advocates atomic energy. One, he is grossly ignorant and incapable of independent thought. Two, he is a miscreant of the most detestable kind who has little regard for the welfare of anyone but himself and, in addition, suffers from myopic vision. Such people constitute those who benefit financially from the production of such abominations, including many in government circles. Three, he is a combination of both of these. There are many in this category.

Those responsible for the development of atomic energy, including the atomic bomb, have allegedly been the elite of the scientific world. True, many of those involved, which include most of the illustrious names of academic sciences in the 20th Century, were very clever and articulate men, mostly in a narrow sense, however. The term "genius" has been too loosely applied. None in this distinguished group was a genius in the true sense of the word. They were all well below 660° on the biometric scale. None of them was in the class of a Reich, Brunler or Raman, who were not involved in this crime against humanity.

A REVOLUTIONARY GREENHOUSE

The author has recently been introduced to the most practical and ingenious device for human survival he has ever encountered. It is primarily a greenhouse, but bears no resemblance to the conventional type. As an accumulator of beneficial and life-promoting energies, it is superior to both the orgone accumulator and the pyramid! It is an invention of Gene Davis of McMinnville, Oregon. The conventional greenhouse has its limitations. It is not only fragile, but is not effective during cloudy or stormy weather. The Davis greenhouse has proven to be effective under all weather conditions. Even on cold and cloudy days the temperature inside remains at a comfortable level. The light inside is brighter than is experienced on the outside, especially on dark and cloudy days. Interestingly enough, there are no shadows inside. The light comes from all directions. This means that several times the space can be utilized for plant growth than with conventional greenhouses of like size. As to be expected, plants grow much faster in this greenhouse than in a conventional one. It is also virtually indestructable. Even a .22 rifle bullet will only penetrate it when fired at close range and in a direction perpendicular to the surface. Otherwise, it will glance off. In addition, it is extremely light, weighing only a fraction as much as a greenhouse of similar dimensions. It can function not only as a greenhouse, but as a highly desirable habitat.

It is needless to state that its performance has completely baffled everyone, and especially academic experts. During its construction, Gene Davis has applied some of the principles and concepts that have been introduced for the first time in this treatise. In fact, its performance is a fine confirmation of the validity of the new concepts concerning the properties of light and the nature of soft electrons. The panels of this greenhouse are comprised of several layers of a unique fiberglass resin. It consists of tiny pieces of glass interspersed with air pockets. A special wax permeates the mixture to improve light reflection. As a result, light which enters this greenhouse has been reflected back and forth many times. This means that a high percentage of the photons accompanying the light have combined to produce soft electrons. It has already been noted that living organisms including plants are equivalent to electronic devices except, instead of hard electrons, they employ soft electrons for their operation. Each type of cellular structure requires soft electrons comprised of light within a specific frequency range. For example, the human body requires seven different kinds of soft electrons, each of which corresponds to one of the colors of the spectrum. Plants in general require soft electrons that are comprised of light in the green portion of the electromagnetic spectrum. Davis permeates his glass resin with a green dye. As a result, a higher percentage of the photons of the incoming light in the green portion of the spectrum are transformed into soft electrons than with photons in any other frequency range.

There are two other important factors which contribute to the performance of this marvelous device. It has a triangular cross section but the sides are curved much in the manner of the adjacent sides of a spherical triangle. This gives the structure strength and rigidity, but it has a still more important function. The curvature and the very smooth outside surface tend to trap the light which enters the unit much in the manner that the prisms in prism binoculars trap the light which enters the objective lens. These two factors plus the countless reflective surfaces of the glass particles allow the soft electron and photon concentration in the interior to build up. The subsequent increase in soft electron interactions results in disintegrations and the release of hard electrons, which raises the temperature inside. The photons released during the process also increase the intensity of light. This greenhouse actually simulates conditions which exist deep in the earth's interior!

The reasons for its superiority over the pyramid and the orgone accumulator are now clear. The two latter devices tend to filter out incoming photons and concentrate the soft electrons. The Davis greenhouse not only concentrates the soft electrons but also collects photons and transforms many of them into soft electrons of a desirable nature. As far as the author knows, this is the only device ever conceived which approximates conditions existing in the earth's interior. This invention has other desirable features. If the reader wishes to know more about it and how to acquire one, write to:

Oregon Greenhouse Inc., P.O. Box 653, McMinnville, OR 97128

CHAPTER 35

THE HUMAN CONDITION

A discerning look will now be taken at the present condition of man. This is necessary in order to provide a prospective of where civilization is headed in the development process. The presentation may appear to be unduly pessimistic, however, the author does not wish to underestimate the amount of reform necessary to keep man advancing in the upward direction. In the long run, man will advance according to the great plan, but this still requires the positive contributions of intelligent people in a unified effort.

Technological advancements have been most impressive during this century. Unfortunately, cultural and spiritual values, as well as general mental acumen, do not seem to be proceeding in the same direction. This may seem paradoxical, since it requires intelligence to develop new gadgets and sophisticated equipment. The degree of intelligence required in such endeavors is not as high as one might suppose. After some creative individual supplies the basic ideas, there is a lot more trial and error than sound thinking involved in developing its various ramifications. It has already been demonstrated throughout this treatise that most of the elite of the scientific world do not have a high order of intelligence.

The present trend in the human condition is apparent in music, the various arts, literature, and general education. For example, the percentage of illiterates graduating from high school is alarming. Obscenities in literature, movies, and other media are becoming progressively more acceptable. Grammatical blunders and nebulosity are projected more and more by supposedly intelligent and educated people. Proceeding along with this is an apparent loss of self respect and distorted sense of values. For example, the complete use of small letters for proper names and titles is becoming ever more popular. This is a form of stupidity and lack of good esthetics that is difficult for an intelligent and well-balanced personality to believe. It is not only demeaning to the individual whose name is treated in this manner, but is the worst violation of the rules of written language that can be committed. Those who practice it show no respect for themselves, or anyone else, and merit only the utmost contempt.

There is no area where diminished creativity is more apparent than in the realm of music. Musical creation reached its culmination during the baroque period with the music of such masters as J. S. Bach and Handel. From that time there has been a decline in the general quality of music composed. The facts confirm this general statement. It should be understood that the author is not including all musical composition in this category.

Numerous experiments have been performed on plants using different kinds of music. These verify the contention that the general level of music has deteriorated. An excellent account of many of these experiments is given on pages 161-178 in *The Secret Life of Plants*.(13) One researcher in particular, Dorothy Retellack, exposed plants to various types of music, ranging from classical to rock. She found that the plants leaned away from the source of the rock and towards the source of the classical. In addition, plants exposed to the rock music had a tendency to deteriorate and die, while those exposed to the classical generally flourished and experienced more rapid growth. Music does not even have to be heard to produce this effect. The transmission of sound patterns through the ethers by means of electromagnetic radiation produces the same combination of energies as the sounds.

Reichenbach demonstrated that Od or soft electrons accompanied sound when objects and instruments were struck.(102) The sensitives he employed saw the soft electrons disintegrating into their constituent light as a result of the vibrations. There are combinations of these energies which are beneficial and others that are inimical to life. The type of energies radiated reflect the kind of sound which is generated. It is clear that music and other creations reflect the nature of the mind creating them. It is a cause and effect relationship. One can expect great things from a great mind and lesser creations from a lesser mind. What should be expected from the mind of an ape? About two decades ago, the paintings from a certain "artist" consistently won first prize in art exhibits. Later it was found (much to the embarrassment of many critics who had praised the work) that these works of art were the daubings of someone's pet monkey! This exemplifies the deterioration of the arts to an all-time low level.

The above examples of the backsliding condition of civilization seem to go hand in hand with the level of automation of society. Radio and television have reduced the need for written communication and steered many adults and youth away from reading. Organizations have been set up to market convenience products and services, so that an individual only has to be able to pay the bill. Even paying bills has been simplified and is evolving into a moneyless operation. Creativity is no longer much of an option in most aspects of society. Man's creativity has been limited by the mass entertainment media, the bureaucracy and taxation of government, and the computer. If a person can sign his name, he can do almost anything. This may even be obviated in the future. Jobs in society are also becoming more specialized and the corresponding creativity in those jobs is less. It is clear that conformity and creativity are not compatible and that creativity would not generally be looked upon with favor in a society of conformists. Paradoxically, creativity is discouraged by a highly materialistic, technologically advanced society. It follows that great art or music would not be readily accepted, since it would deviate too far from the norm and would not be appreciated by the masses. Since the profit motive dictates the nature of entertainment in the mass media, great compositions and sophisticated movie themes are not encouraged. Consequently, creative individuals have little incentive or probability of becoming well known.

There is a definite correlation between good esthetics and the level of intelligence. The great majority on this planet are very young souls. They cannot be expected to be highly discerning or discriminating. The patrons of music during the baroque period were largely members of the intelligentsia with more refined tastes than the average individual. The conditions during this period were exceedingly propitious for the greatest musical minds to incarnate on this planet and give the world the finest musical scores it now possesses.

As the population increased and transportation facilities improved, larger numbers from among the general population began to get into the act. Consequently, later composers began to appeal to the tastes of the average man. This was partly out of economic necessity. The effect upon the general quality of music being composed was small at first, but gradually a vicious circle developed. Lower quality music produces energy effects which are not conducive to high order creativity. This in turn results in still lower grade music, with still greater detrimental effects upon further creativity. With the advent of radio, and finally television, this tendency was enormously accelerated. The masses became involved and the negative energy effects resulting from largely low-grade music being broadcast through the ethers compounded this effect. The reasons for this general decline of civilization are now more understandable. The adverse energy combinations and thought forms which permeate the lower atmosphere of this planet tend to stifle constructive thinking. Very few individuals seem to be capable of rising above these conditions with sufficient mental power left over to see things in their proper perspective. For example, in spite of their technical knowledge, most musicians and conductors seem incapable of distinguishing between good and bad music. The cacophonous "music" of modern composers is treated with the same reverence as that of great compositions by masters of the past.

The principles mentioned above have been exploited to the limit by miscreants who wish to strengthen their position of subjugation and control. The general impairment of the mental faculties of the population insures the success of such an endeavor. Many valuable contributions have been suppressed as a result.

The deterioration of classical music and declining numbers of those who have any appreciation for the finer music is giving way to the onrush of popular so-called music. Outside of a few news broadcasts, the abomination constitutes nearly all that can be picked up on radios. Less than one percent of radio stations broadcast classical music to any significant extent. Various types of boobs who promulgate the horrendous drivel that has always been popular, including those who write it, are idols to millions. This is ironic, since all of them are intellectually, spiritually, culturally and esthetically destitute. One of them, a rock idol, has become a legend. Although he has allegedly been dead for several years, his popularity, if anything, has increased and there are efforts to make his birthday a national holiday. What better proof is there that the great majority of people are very young souls?

The above statements are not meant to imply that all of those who listen to popular "music" are devoid of good esthetics. Many people have never been exposed to any other kind of music, and have been brainwashed into thinking such an atrocity is good music. The devious thought forms and energies unleashed on this planet have distorted nearly everyone's sense of values. The real test of an individual's development comes when he or she is exposed to all kinds of music and is free to decide which is preferred. In lieu of a biometric measurement, the type of music one prefers and the extent of one's discrimination is a highly accurate gauge of how far one has progressed toward mastership in the reincarnation cycles.

Such varying stages of development can be depicted by the following type of diagram which was used earlier to illustrate the different aspects of sexuality. One end of the scale is black, while the opposite end is white. There is a gradual transition in between from the darker shades of grey to the lighter shades, as one advances toward the pure white from the black. The black, of course, represents the youngest souls. To them, fine music is totally repugnant. Among them are to be found the most ardent rock fans. From the black toward the middle there is an increasing tolerance of better music, but there is still a preference for the low grade music, regardless of exposure to the finer music. In the middle ranges are those who profess to like all kinds. Such people think that they are being very broad minded and catholic in their views. They fail to realize they have not advanced to the stage of being discriminating, which is vital for a higher degree of appreciation. This, of course, carries over into other realms of thought and comprehension as well as creativity. Many classical musicians are to be found in middle ranges, including conductors of symphony orchestras. It is small wonder that the "music" of modern pseudo composers (and practically all modern "composers" come under this category) is treated with the deference that it is. Few of them ever give decent renditions of the great masterworks because, in general, they lack taste and intelligence despite their considerable technical knowledge. They often like to add their own gaudy adornments and cheap embellishments during an interpretation of such works. Apparently they are trying to improve on the master they are interpreting by deviating from the score. Although many composers are often victimized by such outrages, perhaps the biggest loser among them has been Handel. It is apparent the phenomenon of doublethink is not confined to experts in the realm of science but is practiced to fully as great an extent in art and music. The lack of discrimination of conductors and respected musicologists and musicians demonstrates how susceptible the great majority is to the brainwashing process. How often has one of them commented on the beautiful melodic content of a composition of some modern pseudocomposer? This is identical in principle to the praise that was given the smearings of the pet monkey mentioned earlier. It would not be surprising if some of the highly touted contemporary scores turned out to be the scribblings of some pet baboon. Many of them are of the same degree of merit.

The white end of the scale represents the consummate connoisseur of music. To such an individual the popular brands of music are obnoxious and offensive. He has an instinctive revulsion toward the popular music, even if he has never heard any classical music. The true value of the music of the greatest masters is appreciated by him soon after he has heard it. This is a vital aspect of consciousness that must be reached before an individual can ever attain true mastership and reach the stage described previously in this treatise.

There are other factors to be considered in the deterioration of the mental and moral fiber of the inhabitants of this planet. The condition has been helped along by many powerful but evil entities, discarnate and otherwise, which come to a planet during stages of its development. There has been an inordinate number of them in and around the planet in this century, especially during recent years. They prey on highly creative individuals who are a threat to the status quo. The greater one's potential, the greater the target he or she becomes. One hope such an individual has for achieving anything significant is to be under the protection of powerful beings who are positively oriented. In some instances, this is not sufficient. Therefore, these people must learn how to develop and direct forces against such entities for protection. If successful, there is a considerable mental and physical improvement, with a high probability of fulfillment, despite the adverse conditions around the person.

The author, from personal experience, can attest to the potency of these devious forces and the terrible frustrations and setbacks that can result from their influence. As a consequence, this treatise has required several decades longer to create than it would have otherwise.

The reader may wonder why the logos and overseers of a planet allow such conditions to occur. Evil entities have their place in the cosmic scheme. They are used to test certain individuals. The manner in which they react or cope with the situtations created by these entities determines the future trend of their incarnations. A large influx of such entities on a given planet generally occurs during the end of an important cycle, just prior to the beginning of a new age. Apparently, this planet is about to come into such an age with an entirely new set of conditions.

The present world organization consists of isolated groups of pseudo-intellectuals. This isolation and specialization of interest groups is partly responsible for the present human condition. Each of these groups is practically oblivious to what is going on in other lines of endeavor. The prerequisites for remaining a member in good standing are great skill in the art of doublethink, blind loyalty to the organization carried to the extent of either ignoring or denouncing all facts which threaten to undermine the foundation on which their rigid trends of thought are based, and the deep rooted conviction that the standard textbooks are the last word and are never to be questioned. The much publicized brainwashing techniques of Communists are not basically new. They have merely been applying the same principles employed by academic institutions for ages.

The reader may wonder about the type of minds which could be brainwashed to the extent of consistently reacting in the irrational manner described in these pages. As a matter of fact, all but a small handful on this planet are susceptible. There are only a few physicists in the 500° range of Brunler's biometric scale. Most of these physicists are still steeped in orthodoxy and are, therefore, in this susceptible category. Since only about one individual in a million is above 500°, there are only about 200 such people in this country.

The reasons for the above statistics involve the nature and history of the human race. The so-called subconscious or reactive mind of an individual operates in the manner of a computer or servomechanism. It regulates and directs the energies from the higher realms which sustain and motivate the physical body. This highly complex computer is programmed prior to birth and carries a complete record of the individual's past in its memory banks. The nature of the programming depends on the individual's past record and what he or she is supposed to accomplish in the following incarnation.

The individual would be unable to function in the physical realm without this computer. He would be unable to think without a memory, and his body could not be sustained, since the conscious or thinking mind is not equipped to control the various bodily functions. This computer, of course, is incapable of independent and logical thinking. The so-called conscious mind is the projection of the soul center into the physical realm. It functions as the pilot of the individual. It has free will, and is supposed to make all of the decisions in regard to the person's conduct.

The logos creates this computer for the embodying soul's use. A young soul has little control over its computer or reactive mind. The soul center's lines of communication to the physical realm are highly inadequate. Therefore, the reactive mind's response to various stimuli will tend to override any dictates of the conscious mind which are contrary to programmed responses. This computer illogically translates many stimuli into necessities for survival. The conscious mind of a young soul is relatively weak and almost devoid of reasoning power, because the signals from the soul center are badly scrambled by the time they reach the physical brain. These souls are more dependent on the reactive mind than older souls.

It has been known for thousands of years that the reactive mind is susceptible to reprogramming when the conscious mind is in a completely relaxed state. This is the basis for meditation. The physical body requires only an infinitessimal flow of energy to maintain its normal processes in this situation. Therefore, the reactive mind becomes nearly inoperative.

The reactive mind is directly created by the logos and has a clearer channel to these intelligences. The embodying soul is similar to a baby who is completely dependent on its parents during the earlier stages of its development. Some soul centers eventually reach the stage where they are able to project bodies into the physical realm which are in perfect rapport with themselves. By this time, they do not require reactive minds to aid in the maintenance of the physical body. They are able to sustain their physical bodies directly, and do not require the sustaining energies provided by a planet. Such individuals are known as ascended masters. They have become masters of themselves. They are no longer hampered by irrational behavioral responses to various situations triggered by an illogical reactive mind, over which they previously had little control. They no longer indulge in such practices as doublethink and the promulgation of false and highly illogical theories and concepts. Their taste in art and music is impeccable. They reflect the true nature of their soul centers. No two souls are alike. Each was created according to a certain blueprint in accordance with overall cosmic plan. Each has its own unique set of abilities and talents. Ascended masters serve as guides and teachers of younger souls. This is accomplished through reembodiments among the mass of humanity or by subtle influences without direct contact with the general population. This progresses for a period before they continue the creative process in realms below the physical.

It has been stated and shown repeatedly that a cyclic pattern governs all activities. The cycle, as with other things, has a dual nature. A period of rest follows a period of activity where growth and development are involved. Cycles are also directly interwoven. For example, reincarnation cycles embrace not only the periods of embodiment on the physical plane and periods of transition in between, but also the general pattern of physical incarnations. Times of tribulation and extreme hardship must be interspersed with experiences which are the antithesis of this. Physical incarnations which run smoothly and harmoniously are important in a soul's progress toward self-mastery. Embodiments in various planetary systems also occur. Life conditions on some planets are more desirable than on others. Likewise, planets themselves go through cycles encompassing periods of destruction and depravity and periods of harmony.

This planet has evidently passed through many such cycles. Civilizations have come and gone, some far in advance of the present one. The earth has been periodically inhabited by intelligent beings for about one billion years. As mentioned previously, human footprints have been found which, according to all geological evidence, were made hundreds of millions of years ago. Due to academic scientists' proficiency in doublethink, such facts have not dampened their enthusiasm and acceptance of the Darwinian concept and other specious theories currently popular.

The present cycle is rapidly coming to a close. A coordinated effort of the best minds on the planet is needed to make the transition from the low part of the cycle to an upward trend. As late as 1960, ten people in the world were known to be over 600° on the biometric scale. According to estimates, there were possibly another ten who had not as yet been found. It is possible there are considerably more than this who have chosen to remain in the shadows. Amazingly, only this small group of high-powered individuals is capable of making radical changes on the planet, because positive, effective change can only occur using sophisticated benevolent means. These geniuses are the only ones capable of coordinating the activities of an entire planet, so that everything works in a rational manner. We have seen how ineffective the superpowers are in running the world.

This is to be expected. A handful of the worst miscreants have held this planet in bondage for ages. They have controlled and directed the policies of the various institutions during this period. They hold no allegiance to any country. One of their major programs has been the belief they have fostered on the people of the larger nations. It is that they must maintain their armed forces for their protection. Consequently, a large percentage of the resources of each country is directed toward maintaining a war machine. Periodically, such men arrange a war to remind them that their greatest priority is their army. It also serves the purpose of lining their pocketbooks, since they own the munitions plants supplying the war materials for both sides.

Consequently, hundreds of billions of dollars of the U. S. national budget are supporting a parasitic military organization. This is done in the name of national defense. It is ironic that they have infinitely more sophisticated weapons at their disposal than (assuming a defense were mandatory) obviates all the weaponry and a military organization, for which these vast sums are funneled. It is deplorable that practically everyone in the U. S. believes it is a good thing such a high percentage of the budget is channeled in this manner. Once again, this reflects the level of intelligence predominant in this country and elsewhere. Obviously, this trend cannot continue if this earth is to become a decent place to live.

The knowledge presented in this treatise needs to be used to aid in the development of mankind. There is enough material in this book to keep hundreds of thousands of researchers at work for eons to come.

In spite of all that has been accomplished in this book, there is still much to be done to further clarify certain topics which were touched on only briefly. For example, a more detailed analysis of the chemical elements and their properties is necessary. This will involve a revolutionary new look at the laws of chemistry and their applications. The present system of mathematical logic is woefully inadequate for such an endeavor. An entirely new system of logic, free of all the weaknesses of present mathematics, is mandatory. The universe operates by such a system and involves a duality made up of the qualitative and quantitative aspects. This treatise has dealt mainly with the qualitative functions of the universe. A method for determining all of the quantitative functions needs to be developed. This is, undoubtedly, the most difficult and illusive part of the duality to resolve. This, the author hopes and expects to accomplish in the not too distant future.

SUMMARY OF PART IV

This section applied concepts and principles introduced earlier to generate a deeper understanding and explanation of phenomena largely ignored by the academic world. The topics covered were teleportation, telekinesis, telepathy, firewalking, levitation, psionics, and other equally baffling phenomena. It was shown that the phenomena discussed are a confirmation of the validity of principles introduced in the first three parts.

Also included was an analysis of the accomplishments of great but neglected pioneers such as Reichenbach, De La Warr, Heironymus, Brunler, and others. Obviously, this planet could be a much better place to live if their discoveries were applied on a large scale.

In conclusion, it can be stated that to a reader with any degree of rationality who has read this far it should be more than obvious that the new concepts introduced in this treatise have done everything that could possibly be expected of a valid idea. It has not only conformed with all the known facts but has proven to be infallible in accurately predicting a wide range of phenomena. This is completely unprecedented. This new science has done all of this so well that it can safely be taken out of the category of mere speculation and theory.

BIBLIOGRAPHY

1. A Magnetic Physician. *Vital Magnetic Cure: An Exposition of Vital Magnetism.* Health Research, 1878.
2. Abrams, Albert. *New Concepts in Diagnosis and Treatment.* Health Research, 1916.
3. Adamski, George. *Inside the Space Ships.* New York: Abelard-Schuman, Inc., 1955.
4. Adamski, George; Leslie, Desmond. *Flying Saucers Have Landed.* New York: The British Book Centre, 1953.
5. Allen, Wm. Gordon. *Enigma Fantastique!* Health Research, 1966.
6. Allen, Wm. Gordon. *Overlords, Olympians, & the UFO.* Health Research, 1974.
7. Appel, Kenneth; Wolfgang, Haken. "The solution of the Four-Color map Problem," *Scientific American*, October 1977, pp. 108-121.
8. Barker, Gray: editor. *The Strange Case of Dr. M. K. Jessup.* Clarksburg, West Virginia: Saucerian Books, 1963.
9. Barrett, Sir William; Besterman, Theodore. *The Divining Rod.* New Hyde Park, N.Y.: University Books, 1968.
10. Beasse, Pierre. *A New and Rational Treatise of Dowsing* Health Research, 1938.
11. Bernard, Dr. Raymond. *The Hollow Earth.* Health Research,
12. Berry, Adrian, "Faster-Than-Light-Spaceships," *Saga Magazine*, March 1972, pp. 38-82.
13. Bird, Christopher; Tompkins, Peter. *The Secret Life of Plants.* New York: Avon Books, 1972.
14. Boadella, David. *Wilhelm Reich, The Evolution of His Work.* Chicago: Henry Regnery Company, 1973.
15. Brown, T.T. *Elektrokinetic Generator.* Washington, D.C.: Patent Office, Patent No. 2,949,550, 1960.
16. Brown, T.T. *Electrokinetic Apparatus.* Washington, D.C.: U.S. Patent Office, Patent No. 3,022,430, 1962.

17. Brown, T.T. *Electrokinetic Apparatus*. Washington, D.C., U.S. Patent Office, Patent No. 3,187,206, 1965.
18. Browning, Norma Lee. *The Psychic World of Peter Hurkos*. New York: Signet, 1970.
19. Byrd, Richard E. "Our Navy Explores Antarctica," *The National Geographic*, October 1947, pp. 429-522.
20. Byrd, Richard E. "All-Out Assault on Antarctica," *The National Geographic*, August 1956, pp. 141-180.
21. Carter, Mary Ellen. "Edgar Cayce's Ominous Predictions of World Upheaval," *Saga Magazine*, April 1969, pp. 78-82.
22. Cayce, Edgar Evans. *Edgar Cayce on Atlantis*. New York: Warner Paperback Library, 1968.
23. Clark, Adrian C. *Cosmic Mysteries of the Universe*. West Nyack, New York: Parker Publishing Co., 1968.
24. Clark, Adrian C. *Psycho-Kinesis: Moving Matter with the Mind*. West Nyack, New York: Parker Publishing Co., 1973.
25. Constable, Trevor James. *The Cosmic Pulse of Life*. Santa Ana, California: Merlin Press, 1976.
26. Constable, Trevor James. *Sky Creatures: Living UFOs*. New York: Pocket Books, 1978.
27. Crabb, Riley: editor. *Radionics, The New Age Science of Healing*. Vista, California: Borderland Sciences Research Foundation, 1974.
28. Crookes, Sir William. *Researches in the Phenomena of Spiritualism* Health Research,
29. Crookes, Sir William. *Researches in the Phenomena of Spiritualism*. Litchfield, Connecticut: The Pantheon Press, 1971.
30. Daniken, Eric Von. *Gods From Outer Space*. New York: Bantam Books, 1970.
31. Davison, Charles. "Luminous Phenomena of Earthquakes," *Discovery*, XVIII, 1937, pp. 278-279.
32. De La Warr, George; Day, Langston. *New Worlds Beyond the Atom*. Yorkshire, England: E. P. Publishing Ltd., 1973.
33. Desmond, Shaw. *The Power of Faith Healing*. New York: Award Books, 1969.
34. Drown, Ruth. *The Drown Radio-Vision and Homo-Vibra Ray Instruments and Their Uses*. Vista, California: Borderland Sciences Research Foundation, 1938.

35. Dudley, H.C. *Apparatus for the Promotion and Control of Vehicular Flight*, Washington, D.C.: U.S. Patent Office, Patent No. 3,095,167, 1963.
36. Dyson, Freeman J. "Innovations in Physics," *Scientific American*, September 1958, pp. 74-82.
37. Eden, Jerome. *Planet in Trouble — The UFO Assault on Earth.* New York: Exposition Press, 1973.
38. Edwards, Frank. *Strangest of All.* New York: Signet, 1956.
39. Edwards, Frank. *Stranger Than Science.* New York: Bantam Books, 1959.
40. Edwards, Frank. *Strange People.* New York: Signet, 1961.
41. Edwards, Frank. *Strange World.* New York: Bantam Books, 1964.
42. Emerson, Willis George. *The Smoky God.* Health Research, 1908.
43. Encyclopedia Britannica, 1963 ed., S. V. "Star".
44. Encyclopedia Britannica, 1973 ed., S. V. "Star".
45. Flanagan, G. Pat. *Pyramid Power.* Glendale, California: Pyramid Publishers, 1973.
46. Fort, Charles. *The Book of the Damned.* New York: Ace Books, 1919.
47. Fort, Charles. *New Lands.* New York: Ace Books, 1923.
48. Fort, Charles. *Lo!.* New York: Ace Books, 1931.
49. Fort, Charles. *Wild Talents.* New York: Garland, 1932.
50. Fredman, Daniel Z.; Van Nieuwenhuizen, Peter. "Supergravity and the Unification of the Laws of Physics," *Scientific American*, February 1978, pp. 126-143.
51. Freeman, John. *Suppressed & Incredible Inventions.* Perris, California: A. H. Fry, 1976.
52. Fry, Mr. Daniel. *The White Sands Incident.* Louisville, Kentucky: Best Books, Inc., 1966.
53. Ginzburg, V.L. "Artificial Satellites and the Theory of Relativity," *Scientific American*, May 1959, pp. 149-160.
54. Goggin, Kathy; Kerrell, Bill. *The Guide to Pyramid Energy.* Santa Monica, California: Pyramid Power .V, Inc., 1975.
55. Goodavage, Joseph F. *Magic: Science of the Future.* New York: Signet, 1972.
56. Gray, Edwin V. *Pulsed Capacitor Discharge Electric Engine.* Washington, D.C.: U.S. Patent Office, Patent No. 3,890,548, 1975.

57. HEALTH RESEARCH, editor. Color Healing.
Health Research 1956
58. Heffern, Richard. *Time Travel: Myth or Reality*. New York: Pyramid Publications, 1977.
59. Hieronymus, T.G. *Detection of Emanations From Materials and Measurement of the Volumes Thereof*. Washington, D.C.: U.S. Patent Office, Patent No. 2,482,773, 1949.
60. Humber, Thomas. *The Sacred Shroud*. New York: Pocket Books, 1935.
61. Kervran, L.; Ohsawa, G. *Biological Transmutation*. Oroville, California: George Ohsawa Macrobiotic Foundation, 1971.
62. Kilner, W.J. *The Aura*. New York: Samuel Weiser, Inc., 1911.
63. King, Serge V. *Pyramid Energy Handbook*. New York: Warner Books, 1977.
64. Kraspedon, Dino. *My Contact With Flying Saucers*. Cedar Knolls, N.J.: Wehman Bros., Inc., 1977.
65. Krippner, Stanley; Rubin, Daniel; editors. *The Kirlian Aura*. New York: Anchor Press/Doubleday, 1974.
66. Krippner, Stanley; White, John: editors. *Future Science*. Garden City, New York: Anchor Press, 1977.
67. Lakhovsky, George. *The Secret of Life*.
Health Research, 1935.
68. Land, Edwin, "Experiments in Color Vision," *Scientific American*, May 1959, pp. 84-99.
69. Lane, Earle. *Electrophotography*. San Francisco: And/Or Press, 1975.
70. Layne, Mead. *The Cameron Aurameter*. Vista, California: Borderland Sciences Research Foundation, 1972.
71. Lear, John. "The Hidden Perils of a Lunar Landing," *Saturday Review*, June 7, 1969, pp. 47-54.
72. Lee, Gloria. *Why We Are Here*.
Health Research, 1959.
73. Leonard, George. *Somebody Else Is on the Moon*. New York: Pocket Books, 1976.
74. Life, editor. "First Color Portrait of an Angry Earth," *Life*, November 10, 1967, p. 107.
75. Life, editor. "Intrepid on a Sun-drenched Sea of Storms," *Life*, December 12, 1969, pp. 34-39.
76. Lilly, John. *Lilly on Dolphins — Humans of the Sea*. Garden City, New York: Doubleday, 1975.

77. Litster, John. *The Oregon Vortex*. Gold Hill, Oregon: Mildred Litster, 1953.
78. Lloyd, John Uri. *Etidorhpa or The End of Earth*. ; Health Research, 1896.
79. Long, Max Freedom. *The Secret Science Behind Miracles*. Marina Del Rey, California: DeVorss & Co., 1949.
80. Long, Max Freedom. *The Secret Science at Work*. Santa Monica, California: DeVorss & Co., 1953.
81. Long, Max Freedom. *Psychometric Analysis*. Marina Del Rey, California: DeVorss & Co., 1959.
82. Mann, W. Edward. *Orgone, Reich & Eros*. New York: Simon and Schuster, 1973.
83. Menger, Howard. *From Outer Space to You*. Clarksburg, West Virginia: Saucerian Books, 1959.
84. Moray, T.H. *The Sea of Energy in Which the Earth Floats*. Salt Lake City, Utah: Research Institute, Inc., 1931.
85. Moray, T.H. *Cosray Biological Principles*. Salt Lake City, Utah: Research Institute, Inc., 1940.
86. Moray, T.H. *Electrotherapeutic Apparatus*. Washington, D.C.: U.S. Patent Office, Patent No. 2,460,707, 1943.
87. Musya, Kinkita. "On the Luminous Phenomenon That Attended the Idu Earthquake, November 26th, 1930," *Bulletin of the Earthquake Research Institute*, IX, 1931, pp. 214-215 (English Abstract).
88. O'Byrne, F.: Reichenbach's Letters on Od & Magnetism. Health Research, 1852.
89. Ord-Hume, Arthur W. *Perpetual Motion: The History of an Obsession*. New York: St. Martin's Press, Inc.
90. Orwell, George. *1984*. New York: Signet Classics, 1949.
91. Ostrander, Sheila; Schroeder, Lynn. 2Psychic Discoveries Behind the Iron Curtain. New York: Bantam Books, 1970.
92. Ostrander, Sheila; Schroeder, Lynn, editors. *Handbook of PSI Discoveries*. New York: Putnam, 1974.
93. Ostrander, Sheila; Schroeder, Lynn, editors. *The ES Papers*. New York: Bantam Books, 1976.
94. Pettit, Ed; Schul, Bill. *The Secret Power of Pyramids*. Greenwich, Connecticut: Fawcett, 1975.
95. Randall-Stevens, H.C. *The Book of Truth*. London: The Knights Templars of Aquarius, 1956.
96. Reed, William. *The Phantom of the Poles*.

97. Regush, Nicholas M. *The Human Aura.* New York: Berkley Medallion Books, 1974.
98. Reich, Wilhelm. *The Function of the Orgasm.* New York: Pocket Books, 1942.
99. Reich Wilhem. *The Cancer Biopathy.* New York: Farrar, Straus, and Giroux, 1948.
100. Reich, Wilhelm. *Selected Writings.* New York: Farrar, Straus, and Giroux, 1951.
101. Reichenbach, Baron Charles von. *Physico-Physiological Researches on the Dynamics of Magnetism, Electricity, Heat, Light, Crystallization and Chemism, In Their Relations to Vital Force.* : Health Research, 1851.
102. Reichebach. *Reichenbach's Letters on Od and Magnetism.* : Health Research, 1852.
103. Reichenbach, Baron Charles von. *Somnambulism and Cramp.* Health Research, 1860.
104. Frank J. "The Luminous Portents of Earthquakes," *Fate Magazine*, November 1965, pp. 90-94.
105. Russell, Walter and Lao. *The Secret of Light.* Swannanoa, Waynesboro, Virginia: University of Science and Philosophy, 1947.
106. Russell, Walter and Lao. *Atomic Suicide.* Swannanoa, Waynesboro, Virginia: University of Science and Philosophy, 1957.
107. Science Digest, editor. "An Unscientific Phenomenon: Fraud Grows in Laboratories," *Science Digest*, June 1977, pp. 38-40.
108. Sears, Paul M. "How Dead Is the Moon?" *Natural History*, February, 1950, pp. 62-65.
109. Sigma Rho. *Ether Technology: A Rational Approach to Gravity Control.* Lakemont, Georgia: Rho Sigma, 1977.
110. Sigma Rho, "Radiesthesia: Science of Tommorrow?" *Fate Magazine*, December 1965, pp. 80-89.
111. Smith, Warren. *The Hidden Secrets of the Hollow Earth.* New York: Zebra Books, 1976.
112. Steiger, Brad. *Atlantis Rising.* New York: Dell Publishing Co., 1973.
113. Steiger, Brad. *Mysteries of Time and Space.* Engelwood Cliffs, New Jersey: Prentice Hall, 1974.
114. Terada, Torahiko. "On the Luminous Phenomena Accompany-

ing Earthquakes," *Bulletin of the Earthquake Research Institute.* IX, 1931, pp. 225-255.
115. Tesla, Nikola. *Lectures, Patents, Articles.* : Health Research, 1956.
116. Three Initiates. *The Kybalion.* Health Research, 1908.
117. Time, editor. "Flight Plan of Apollo II," *Time Magazine*, July 18, 1969, pp. 18, 19.
118. Time, editor. "The Moon — A Giant Leap for Mankind," *Time Magazine*, July 25, 1969, pp. 10-14.
119. Velikovsky, Immanuel. *Ages in Chaos.*
120. Velikovsky, Immanuel. *Worlds in Collision.* New York: Doubleday & Co., Inc., 1950.
121. Velikovsky, Immanuel. *Earth in Upheaval.* New York: Dell, 1955.
122. Watson, Lyall. *Supernature.* New York: Bantam Books, 1973.
123. Young, P. "Time and Space — Adding Credence to Einstein's Work," *Science Digest*, August 1977, pp. 33-36.

* * * * *

RAYS AND RADIATION PHENOMENA by Dr. Oscar Brunler (1950). Some of the most important research in the field of psionics was made by the late Oscar Brunler. "Energy can never be destroyed. The quality of energy stored up in matter — in the atom, the protons, the electrons, the neutrons — gives us the amount of power or energy which can be liberated from condensed energy into the primordial essence. This primordial essence is shapeless, formless, matterless; an all-pervading ocean of energy which we call Ether, Divine Essence or Bio-Cosmic Energy.

"The radiation around our head or around our body as seen by clairvoyants, or visible to anyone by looking through a Kilner Screen, is a dielectric radiation." — *Dr. Oscar Brunler*

APPENDIX

It has been mentioned that the superstructure of the new science elaborated upon in this treatise is based upon the ancient Hermetic philosophy. A more detailed outline of Hermetic principles as they have been handed down and preserved by mystery schools for thousands of years is in order. In the process it will be shown where and how teachers of this philosophy have consistently deviated from reality in some areas by the improper application of its principles. As a consequence, none of the exponents of Hermeticism, and, of course any other philosophy past or present, have resolved the mysteries clearly explained in this book.

The following outline has been derived from a rare book entitled *The Kybalion*, written anonymously by three individuals known as "Three Initiates", who are obviously well versed in these teachings. The book was first copyrighted in 1912 and later in 1940.

The hermeticists were the original alchemists, astrologers and psychologists, and Hermes was the founder of these schools of thought. Modern astronomy grew out of astrology, modern chemistry sprang from alchemy and modern psychology from the mystic psychology of the ancients.

The first of the great Hermetic principles is known as the Principle of Mentalism. It embodies the truth that "All is Mind". It explains that the All is the "Substantial Reality underlying all the outward manifestations and appearances which we know under terms of The Material Universe, the Phenomena of Life, Matter, Energy and, in short, all that is apparent to our material senses. It is called "Spirit" and is assumed to be unknowable and undefinable, but may be considered and thought of as An Universal, Infinite Living Mind. It states that "all the phenomenal world or universe is simply a Mental Creation of The All, subject to the Laws of Created Things, and that the universe, as a whole, and in its parts or units, has its existence in the Mind of The All in which Mind we "live and move and have our being". It was stated in this book that "This Principle, by establishing the Mental Nature of the Universe, *easily* explains all of the various mental and psychic phenomena . . . and without such explanation, are non-understandable and defy scientific treatment". This is among the first of the flaws appearing in this book. Until this treatise, *The Awesome Life Force*, was conceived, none of the Hermeticists or any of the teachers of esoteric subjects have ever presented a satisfactory explanation of any psychic phenomena! They are correct in assuming this First Principle provides the basis for explaining such things, but have been incapable of applying Hermetic principles to this end.

The All is defined in the following manner (1) "The All must be All that really is. There can be nothing existing outside of the All else the All would not be the All". (2) "The All must be infinite, for there is nothing else to define, confine, bound, limit or restrict the All. It must be infinite in time or eternal, it must have always continuously existed for there is nothing else to have ever created it and something can never evolve from nothing . . . it must continuously exist forever, for there is nothing to destroy it. It must be infinite in space — it must be everywhere for there is no place outside of the All". [Unquote; this last statement borders on the dogmatic and is contrary to principles outlined in Chapter 24 on The Pyramid of Life. The previous statements concerning the All do not necessarily demand that the last statement be valid. There is the great black void of infinite space outside the universe in which there is no creation and apparently where the All does not operate. This will be discussed in more detail shortly.] (3) "The All must be immutable and not subject to change in its real nature, for there is nothing to work changes upon it. . . . The All being infinite, absolute, eternal and unchangeable it must follow that anything finite changeable, finite, changeable, fleeting and conditioned cannot be the All. And as there is nothing outside of the All, in reality, then any and all such finite things must be as nothing in reality. . . . There is a reconciliation of this apparently contradictory state of affairs." Here is another of the flaws in the teaching of Hermetic principles which have been made evident by the concepts introduced in *The Awesome Life Force*. The above mentioned "contradictory state of affairs" was *not* reconciled. It was further stated that "The All cannot be mere energy or force for if it were there would be no such thing as life and mind in existence". This is faulty reasoning, since it has been shown that energy and force are an embodiment of life and mind and are inseparable from it. Only partial truths were employed to resolve the difficulty and the writers of the Kybalion progressed no further along this line with the statement, "The All is infinite Living Mind — the Illumined call it Spirit. . . . But what is Spirit? This question cannot be answered for the reason that its definition is practically that of The All, which cannot be explained or defined." Here is another statement that is somewhat dogmatic.

In the consideration of the nature of the universe the Kybalion deals with the question in the following manner: "The universe cannot be the All because it seems to be made up of many and is constantly changing and in others ways does not measure up to the ideas regarding the All. The All could not have created the universe from itself for the All cannot be subtracted from nor divided. If this were true then each particle in the universe would be aware of its being the All which is absurd". Such an absurdity is often carried to dogmatic extremes by people who, realizing that the All is indeed All and that they exist, jump to the conclusion that they and the All are identical and claim they are God. This is identical in principle to the corpuscle claiming that it is Man. This type of thinking has fostered such statements as "All men are created equal".

Hermeticists have coped with this question by applying the second Hermetic axiom or the Principle of Correspondence. We get a glimpse of what is happening on a higher plane by examining what is occuring on this one. Man creates without using materials or begetting by creating mentally. He creates mental images and thought forms. The All creates the universe mentally in a manner similar to the process by which Man creates mental images. The universe and all that it contains is a mental creation of the All. The principle of gender, or the 7th axiom, is manifested in all planes of life — material, mental and spiritual. Whenever anything is generated or created on any plane, the Principle of Gender must be manifested, and this is true even in the creation of universes.

Following the above elaboration on the creation of universes, the writers of the Kybalion are quick to add that the All, in itself, is above Gender, as it is above every other law, including those of time and space! It is indeed amazing that such a statement or belief has never been challenged by any Hermeticist, initiate or master, from the time of Hermes. This is a product of very faulty reasoning and is a direct violation of the Principle of Correspondence! This fallacy is followed with the statement that when the All manifests on the plane of generation or creation, then it acts according to Law and Principle, for it is moving on a lower plane of being. This is a contradiction since it was previously stated that these principles operate on all planes. This is equivalent to stating that the All can declare any principle, such as immutable laws of simple geometry, null and void if it so chooses.

With such a demonstration of bad logic, it is to be expected that other fallacies in Hermetic and esoteric teachings can be exposed. This will be accomplished in the pages to follow. It is universally accepted that "from an absolute viewpoint, the universe is in the nature of an illusion or a dream as compared to the All itself. According to Hermetic teachings, anything that has a beginning and an ending must be, in a sense, unreal and untrue, and the universe comes under the rule, in all schools of thought. From the absolute point of view, there is nothing real except the All. It is unsubstantial, nonenduring, a thing of time, space and change''. This type of thinking is consistent with the faulty logic already mentioned. It is carried still further when it is stated that ''Absolute truth has been defined as things as the mind as God knows them'' while relative truth is ''Things as the highest reason of man understands them''. ''While to the All the universe must be unreal and illusionary, a mere dream or the result of meditation — nevertheless, to the finite minds forming a part of that universe and viewing it through mortal faculties the universe is very real.'' This is contradictory and even laughable. These ''authorities'' admit that with their finite minds they are unable to comprehend the All, yet at the same time they claim to know how the All views things, and are thus elevating themselves to the level of the All. This is a form of doublethink. It is small wonder that, despite their broader views of the universe, none of them have ever come any closer to explaining or understanding natural phenomena than have the academic scientists.

Another indication of the faulty reasoning of the Hermeticists is the conclusion that, since the universe in its outer aspect is changing, everflowing and transitory, it is therefore devoid of substantiality and reality, even though we are compelled to act and live as if the fleeting things were real and substantial. A rational look at these statements shows that they violate most of the Hermetic principles. The nature of a cause can be determined by the effects and the effects are as real as the causes. Since everything follows a cyclic pattern, it must be concluded that this is the basic nature of the All in accordance with the 2nd Hermetic axiom and the law of cause and effect. The fact that thought forms or mental creations can have very tangible effects on their creator confutes this aspect of Hermetic teachings, especially when the Principle of Correspondence is considered. This conception is invalidated still further by another conception, which seems to have been overlooked by the Hermeticists. It is the entwining of the 3rd Hermetic axiom, The Principle of Rhythm and the 6th axiom, the Principle of Cause and Effect. During the workings of cause and effect relationships there are cyclic reversals of these two aspects. There is a period when one aspect functions as a cause and the other the effect. Later, what was the effect becomes the cause and what was the cause becomes the effect. In other words, the cause is changed by the effect it produces. All growth, progression and changes follow this pattern.

The second Hermetic Principle is basically defined in the following manner: All is in the All and the All is in All. Although at first glance it may seem paradoxical, it is not when viewed from the proper perspective. It merely indicates that the same basic laws and principles govern all aspects of the universe, including the All itself.

Another misconception of mammoth proportions that is a part of Hermetic teaching is the pattern of growth and progression. According to the Hermeticists, the creative process consists of the lowering of Vibrations until a very low degree of vibratory energy is reached, at which point the grossest possible form of matter is manifested. This is called the stage of involution, or the outpouring of the divine energy. After the lowest stage is reached, the evolutionary process begins, like the swing of a pendulum, in the opposite direction. During this part of the cycle, everything is supposed to move Spiritward. Matter becomes less gross; Life appears and manifests in higher and higher forms, the vibrations constantly becoming higher. In other words, All is withdrawn into the All from which it emerged. This is supposed to be the report of the Illumined. Evidently the Illumined need further illumination and can profit from studying *The Awesome Life Force.* The only truth contained in the above concept is in the so-called involution process. As clearly shown in Chapter 24 on The Pyramid of Life, the creative process is deeply involved in the creation of lower frequency matter, as in accordance with the law which states that energy can only flow from a high potential to a lower one. There is no swing backward. The so-called evolutionary or refining process consists in the establishment of perfect rapport of the lower realms with the higher, such that they function as a unit. The creation of the lower ethers, and subsequently the so-called "grosser matter", is actually a step upward in the creative process. The "Grosser matter" actually contains within itself the essence of all of the higher frequency or supposedly more refined matter. It has already been shown quite conclusively that the lower ethers are actually comprised of the higher ethers.

One enigmatic question which has always been in the minds of Hermeticists and other thinkers is: Why does the All create universes? Supposedly there have never been any satisfactory answers to this question. According to legend, Hermes himself was asked this question by his advanced students. He answered by pressing his lips tightly together and not saying a word. More than one conclusion can be derived from this, but they are all speculation. The best answer given so far is that the All creates by reason of its own "internal nature". Hermeticists do not accept this, since they do not believe the All is "compelled" by anything. Nevertheless, it is close to the truth and will be discussed in more detail shortly when the fuzzy thinking of Hermeticists is brought into sharper focus.

As mentioned before, the 3rd Hermetic axiom is the Principle of Vibration. It embodies the fact that everything vibrates; nothing is at rest. By the misapplication of this principle and the first two axioms, Hermeticists have developed a concept of the various realms of matter and the ether that differs considerably from that presented in this treatise. The author will not clutter up the reader's mind with a detailed presentation of the teachings along these lines, except to state that they consist of a nebulous comglomerate of a few truths mixed with half and quarter truths and a mish mash of fallacies. In answer to any Hermeticist who might want to challenge the author on this issue, the old maxim, "The proof of the pudding is in the eating," can be cited. The concepts outlined in this treatise fit all the known facts in every detail all along the line and have had a success in prediction that is unparallelled. Compare this to any of the esoteric teachings that have held the stage for thousands of years. In none of them can be found any that even remotely approaches the success of this new teaching. Yet, paradoxically, it embodies the same principles that are a part of the old teachings. It is also significant that the new teachings have far greater simplicity than do the old. This, of course, gives them still more credibility.

The 4th Hermetic axiom is the Principle of Polarity, which states that all manifested things have two sides or two aspects. The Hermetic teachings indicate that the difference between things seemingly diametrically opposed to each other is merely a matter of degree. Also, that pairs of opposites may be reconciled by the recognition of the Principle of Polarity. For example, the differences between heat and cold, the high and low points of a cycle, love and hate, etc. One can be transmuted into the other. However, things belonging to different classes cannot be transmuted into each other, but those belonging to the same class can.

The 5th Hermetic axiom is the Principle of Rhythm, which essentially means that in everything there is manifested a measured motion, a swing forward and backward or a flow and inflow. The Principle of Rhythm is closely connected with the Principle of Polarity. Rhythm manifests between the two poles established by the Principle of Polarity. This does not mean that the pendulum of rhythm swings to extreme poles. This seldom occurs. There is always an action and reaction. This pattern is evident in all aspects of our existence and therefore there is little need to give examples, except to state that everything is involved in a cyclic pattern.

The 6th great Hermetic axiom is the Principle of cause and effect, which means that law pervades the universe and that nothing happens by chance. Chance is a term indicating a cause existing but not perceived. It, of course, underlies nearly all scientific thought, shallow as it may be. To a rational thinker, this is a self-evident fact. However, many of today's theorists are anything but rational, as has been shown repeatedly throughout this treatise. Consequently, causation is fading into the background as far as a modern theory is concerned. There is no place in the universe for anything outside of and independent of law. If true, such a condition would render all natural law ineffective and chaos would reign throughout the universe. A close examination of reality will show there is no such thing as chance. There are always preceding events, and in some cases very subtle ones, in an orderly chain of events which are connected to any event which is claimed to have happened by chance, all of which flow from the All.

The 7th Hermetic axiom is the Principle of Gender, which states that Gender is manifested in everything, and the Masculine and Feminine principles are always present and active in all phases of phenomena on each and every plane of life. It should be stated that Gender, in the Hermetic sense, and Sex, in the ordinary accepted use of the term, are not the same. Sex is merely a manifestation of Gender in the realm of organic life. Gender is solely that of creating, producing and generating, etc., and its works are visible on every plane of phenomena. It is an integral part of the Principle of Polarity or the law of duality. In fact, all of the seven Hermetic principles are closely interlocked. It couldn't be otherwise. If this were not true, law could not prevail throughout the universe.

The above is an outline of Hermetic philosophy as it has been taught in various mystery schools and handed down from master to student throughout the planet for thousands of years. It has also been indicated that misapplication of these principles has led to deviations from reality which have also been a part of the teachings. It is time for such misconceptions to be replaced with infinitely better ideas.

One of the major flaws in Hermetic teachings is the belief that the All can transcend all known laws. This is a crass violation of Hermetic principles. One important thing Hermeticists have failed to recognize is that there are two main classifications of reality, which are: that which is a creation and that which is not a creation. This is in conformity with the

Principle of Polarity or dualtiy, but with this distinction: the two opposite poles are so far removed from each other they can never be reconciled. As shown previously in this treatise, created things are dependent on time, while things which are not creations are independent of time. This is an entirely new concept which, as far as the author has been able to determine, has never been presented before. There are two things which fall under the latter classification. One is space, which is formless and without substance and consequently independent of time. The other are laws and principles such as a theorem in geometry. Such things are discoveries and not creations. In no way can any of them be changed or declared null and void. The All must function in a manner that is in harmony with laws. It cannot do otherwise, and thus the All's activities must remain within the confines of time and space.

The above conclusions open up what may seem to be a colossal paradox. The universe occupies a finite volume of space. Information has filtered down from advanced civilizations to the effect that space travelers have penetrated to the outer limits of the universe. Beyond it is a great black void which is devoid of energy, and, of course, matter, in any form. Anything venturing into this void will automatically disintegrate into nothingness. All of the ethers and, consequently, energies or particles comprising the body would all disperse in the manner of a gas released into a limitless vacuum. This is the true nature of a unoccupied space, or one in which the All has not as yet directed its activities.

How can the All, with infinite power and energy, be confined to a space that is finite? Some of the findings of mathematics come to the rescue. Despite the limitations of academic mathematics, it does have aspects that are highly useful. There are infinite series the sum of which increases without limit, although the individual terms approach zero. The total quantity of energy can be likened to the sum of such a series. The individual terms can represent units or particles with which the All creates universes. There is an infinite number. As indicated earlier, all ether particles are universes of infinite complexity. It has yet to be shown how this infinitude of units with a total energy content of infinity can occupy a finite volume of space. There are also infinite series whose individual terms approach zero, but whose sum is finite. The sum of such a series can represent the total volume of space occupied by this infinitude of units. As we go down the scale of size, the amount of space occupied follows a pattern that conforms with an infinite series. The converging series represents the volume of space occupied, while the diverging series corresponds to the energy content. As the universe expands according to the pattern described in Chapter 24, The Pyramid of Life, the All has an infinite source of energy at its disposal with which to continue the expansion of universes indefinitely. Therefore, there is no limit to the amount of space the All can occupy during its creative process over an infinitude of cycles. As previously stated, "When we look at the microcosm we see infinity. When viewing the macrocosm we see the finite".

The picture just presented is in harmony with Hermetic principles, although it is an advance over previous teachings. The converging and diverging series as applied to the universe are in accordance with the principle of polarity. Also, when applying the principle of Polarity to the All, we see it as consisting of two aspects of that which is created and is in the process of continuous creation and that which is not a creation and is thus changeless. In other words, the two aspects of the All are that which is changing and that which cannot be changed, or that which is dependent upon time and that which is independent of time.

The question of why the All creates universes arises again. The answer is that it has no choice in the matter. An infinite quantity of energy in a finite space is going to expand outward indefinitely. But it can only do so in accordance with laws and principles which cannot be changed, and these laws encompass the Hermetic principles. Since the process of expansion has been proceeding for an infinite time, there was no beginning, nor will there be any end. According to the 2nd Hermetic Principle, the smallest units of energy are replicas of the entire universe. A similar pattern exists in the hologram. From a minute portion of the hologram, the entire object from which the hologram was produced can be replicated.

Another question is: Why haven't masters and initiates down through the ages, including Hermes, presented a better understanding of the nature of the universe than has been made available to students? It seems that a proper application of the 2nd Hermetic axiom should have accomplished this. In the case of Hermes, it was undoubtedly due to a lack of certain scientific facts regarding the physical universe. During the development of concepts outlined in this treatise, the author applied the 2nd axiom to discovered facts, which may be unique in the history of scientific pursuits on this planet. Although past civilizations have acquired technologies far in advance of that existing at the present time, scientific research in the past more than likely took different paths and thus bypassed certain things that have been uncovered during the past 300 years by this so-called civilization. There are a number of different ways of defining such things as velocity, inertia, force, energy, etc., which would be entirely foreign to those with which we are familiar, and somewhat clumsy compared to conventional methods. As to the reasons others since the time of Hermes have not done any better than they have toward explaining the universe, the author will be merciful and refrain from any comments.

The following is the most important article the author has ever submitted to any publication and categorically states is also the most important anyone has ever presented to any publication. The reasons will become apparent by the time the reader finishes it. Is it possible that a simple device which can be easily and cheaply mass produced and also easily constructed by any backyard handyman with no special tools, can put free energy within the reach of everyone? The answer is an unqualified yes! Incredibly this can be accomplished without any changes in our present technology. In a nutshell, it is a device that can be attached to any internal combustion engine which will obviate the need for fuel. No changes or alterations of any kind on the engine are required. One standard device of the correct size will work on any engine, at the same time the engine will perform better than it would on any fuel. Another dividend is that the exhaust, instead of being toxic, will be highly beneficial. It will contain a much higher neg ion content than ordinary air. Interestingly enough, the old outmoded gasoline engine, long condemned by free energy advocates including the author, can turn out to be perhaps our greatest and most practical source of free energy. The ramifications are staggering. Conventional engines can be used to operate conventional generators, heat homes by its exhaust and at the same time improve air quality along with many other uses. The only malefactors directly affected by such changes would be the oil and utility companies. Ironically the internal combustion engine, ruthlessly preserved by the establishment for nearly a century can finally be its downfall.

An early clue as to this possibility was revealed to the author several decades ago by an associate who had witnessed an incredible demonstration. For a period of several months, an old farmer gave public demonstrations of an ordinary gasoline engine running on air alone. This was accomplished by passing the air, which eventually went into the manifold, through a mass of ground up vegetable matter. The engine could be made to run for weeks on one batch. No doubt, he periodically added water to keep it from drying out. The reader has guessed it. He finally disappeared under mysterious circumstances.

Later another clue was revealed when it was learned that the engine of diesel trucks often run wild when they run out of fuel during operation. A former acquaintance of the author personally witnessed such an event. To remedy this effect some manufacturers have installed special valve lifters to cut compression when this occurs. In view of the science of soft particle physics developed by the author and thoroughly explained in his new book "The Awesome Life Force," the explanation of the above phenomena becomes self-evident.

As mentioned in previous articles, orgone (or soft electrons) which permeates all known space is the direct source of all our energy and also electricity. Heat is produced when soft electrons, which are relatively unstable, disintegrate and release the harder electrons they camouflage. The released harder electrons produce thermal agitation of atoms and molecules before they are recaptured. All living things including vegetable matter concentrate soft electrons. When the air passed through the the vegetable matter it picked up high concentrations of soft electrons before it entered the manifold. The high concentration of soft electrons in the super charged air became sufficiently agitated during compression and sparking to disintegrate which resulted in the production of much heat.

In the case of diesel engines, the situation was different but the results were identical. Diesel engines have ultra high compression ratios and this, coupled with the heat already built up in the engines during operation, enabled even a lower orgone concentration to disintegrate. This didn't occur when the engine was receiving fuel because the atomized fuel absorbed most of the orgone normally present in the air. This prevented excessive agitation and the only heat released was that due to the burning of the fuel. With this in mind the solution to the problem of obtaining energy directly from the air without fuel becomes almost self-evident.

A properly constructed orgone accumulator is the greatest concentrator of orgone energy known. The author is not thinking in terms of just a few alternate layers of metallic and non metallic substances as has been done in the past but as many as 40 layers! The more layers, the higher the concentration of orgone resulting. This means that air passing through an orgone accumulator with this number of layers will be supercharged sufficiently after it leaves the accumulator to operate an engine. The size of such an accumulator is also critical. If it is too small it cannot supply enough orgone to operate a large engine continuously. Orgone is not concentrated in an accumulator instantaneously after it is exhausted.

The picture is now complete. A box of sufficient size is covered with 40 alternate layers of aluminum foil and paper. Two thicknesses of newspaper to each layer of foil will be just fine. In other words, there is one thickness of aluminum foil and the paper to each of the 40 layers. Except for the openings for the air intake and air outlet, the box is completely encased. The inside of the box should contain a network of non metallic baffles to disperse the air and cause it to circulate throughout the entire volume. This enables it to pick up more of the orgone before it enters the outlet tube. It must also be kept in mind that the outside layer should be *non metallic*.

To accommodate the larger automotive engines, the inside volume of the box should be about 1½ cubic feet. A one-inch outside diameter flex tube will suffice for the outlet line to the carburetor. A box of this size will not fit under the hood of most cars. It can be placed anywhere in the car and the flex line from the outlet can be routed to the engine. It should also be apparent to the reader that despite what it can do it is also the epitome of simplicity.

The author was recently introduced to a mineral processor who is also a top douser. He uses his dousing ability to pick out the chemicals he needs for any specific purpose and to determine other things he needs to know with uncanny accuracy. He doused out questions put to him concerning this new device and the answers he received closely parallels the author's own determinations. His conclusions were as follows: Yes, the device will definitely work; 30 alternate layers of aluminum foil and paper or 26 using copper foil will do the job. The volume of the box should be at least 1.25 cubic feet. The input and output lines can be one-half inch inside diameter. The author neglected to ask if this would suffice under all conditions; however, to insure top performance under the worst of conditions when the orgone concentration in the atmosphere is relatively low, the author recommends the specs he originally laid down.

The author has demonstrated the potency of a multi-layered accumulator by covering a water jug with 18 alternate layers of copper foil and newspaper. The water from this jug is unique. It is vastly superior to water treated in any other way, including water placed under a pyramid. It has a sweet taste and has proven to be completely free of all impurities. Impurities settle to the bottom of the container and those who drink the water can cut down drastically on food intake. For treating water, copper should be used instead of aluminum since it has a more beneficial radiation which is absorbed by the water. The author now plans to cover a one-gallon glass jug with 30 layers of copper foil and paper.

If the reader plans to build either or both of the above devices, he will find that ordinary masking tape is effective for securing each layer.

Joseph H. Cater

Cross Section of Device

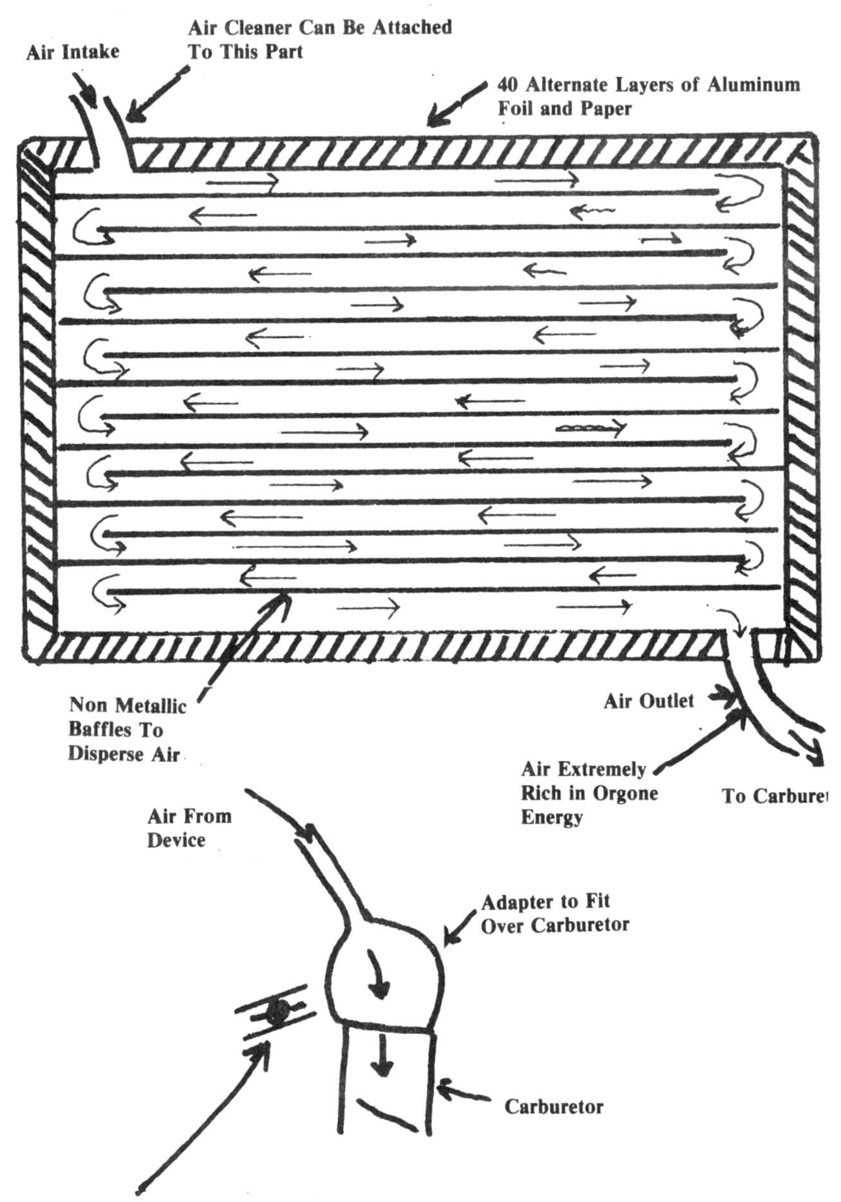

Butterfly Assembly to allow outside air to flow into manifold in case orgone concentration becomes too high and produces an effect similar to that which occurs when diesel engines run out of fuel during operation.

Enclosed is the latest on this device. The new design has been dowsed out as better than the original. I expect to have a sensational announcement to make soon. A close friend is starting the construction of one. What this could do for the book is staggering.

I covered the glass jug with 30 layers of copper and paper. The water from it is amazing. Even a stainless steel knife blade placed in a cup of the water from it soon becomes magnetized! It has also been dowsed out that the regular use of this water can rejuvenate one.

* * *

To those who wish to build the device analyzed in my article showing how to derive free energy directly from the atmosphere and want 'more' detail, a step by step description will now be given. In the author's article, he had neglected to mention the number of baffles required. For a unit 12 inches by 12 inches and 18 inches long at least 40 baffles would be needed for efficient operation. However, since then the author has devised a greatly improved version which will also be much easier to build.

The box housing the device can be constructed of heavy plexiglass. For a unit 12″ × 12″ × 18″ use four thick sheets of plexiglass 12″ × 18″ and two 12″ × 12″. For the pieces to fit properly the two 12 × 12 ends should be twice the thickness of the plexiglass less than 12 inches on a side. The box can be put together with epoxy glue. It must be sturdy to withstand stresses resulting from the partial vacuum produced by suction of engine. Before the top sheet is glued on, a perforated baffle is inserted ¼ inch from bottom of box producing a false bottom. (¼ inch spacers can be placed on bottom of box). It is completely sealed along all four sides to the sides of the box. This baffle has 250 to 300 $\frac{1}{16}$ inch diameter holes drilled into it, equally distributed throughout its area. When all of this is accomplished, the box is filled with fiber glass wool and packed in the manner of ordinary insulation. It must be pushed tightly against the sides of the box so incoming air won't find an easy outlet. The fiberglass fills the box to within ¼ inch from the top. Another perforated sheet identical to the bottom one is now placed over the wool and completely sealed on all four sides to the inside of the box. The heavy plexiglass top is now attached to the box. Both the top and bottom plates have one inch diameter holes to which are attached one inch diameter tubes for the input and outlet flow of air.

The 40 layers of aluminum foil and paper can be most easily applied to the outside in the following manner.

Four 12 × 18 sheets and two 12 × 12 sheets of plexiglass are cut. On these separate sheets are placed the 40 layers of aluminum foil and paper. However, it is done in the following manner. If two thicknesses of newspaper to each layer of aluminum foil is to be used then 80 thicknesses of newspaper and 40 layers of aluminum foil are laid out and then cut to the right dimensions. For two of the 12 × 18 sheets these layers will overlap on all four sides by an amount equal to the thickness of 40 layers of paper and aluminum. The other two 12 × 18 sheets will be overlapped only on the 12 inch ends. There will be no overlapping on the 12 × 12 sheets. With the layers of paper and aluminum cut to the right dimensions, they can be quickly applied to the sheets. Each layer is secured with a spot of ordinary glue in three or four places. When all six sheets are covered, they are then fitted and glued to the box and then secured with a generous amount of masking tape. The top and bottom portions of course have one inch holes drilled in them so they will fit over the inlet and outlet tubes.

When in operation, the inlet and outlet air must pass through all the small holes in the perforated baffles. This insures a uniform distribution of air flow throughout the fiberglass wool which is loose enough to insure the passage of the air without excessive restriction.

There shouldn't be any problem in stopping the motor. In case such a problem did arise, and shutting off the ignition didn't do it, a hand choke could be installed to completely shut off the air. Of course the throttle would obviously control RPM as it does with fuel. In the case of Diesel engines running wild, enough air got around the 'closed' throttle to power the engine. Once again a choke that would completely close off the air would have done the job.

In the above construction it must be emphasized that the proper packing of the glass is of paramount importance. It must be packed to the extent that the passage of air begins to be seriously restricted. Up to this point the tighter it is packed the better. The more wool, the greater the surface area of highly concentrated orgone exposed to the air flow and at the same time the greater the dispersion of air which is vital. If this is not followed, failure will more than likely result. The orgone box should be constructed so that the top can be easily removed or put back on.

The above method of construction can be followed by those who wish to use the box for converting otherwise impotent electric generators or free energy devices into highly potent ones. The box can also be used for energizing and purifying water or preserving food. In the latter case it will be more effective than any refrigerator.

The author covered a gallon glass jug with 30 alternate layers of copper foil and paper. The water from it is phenomenal. Even a stainless steel blade placed in a cup of this water soon becomes magnetized! It has dowsed out that this water has the power to rejuvenate if used regularly. The bottle is filled once a day and should be cleaned out once a month because of impurities that precipitate out and settle to the bottom.

Joseph H. Cater

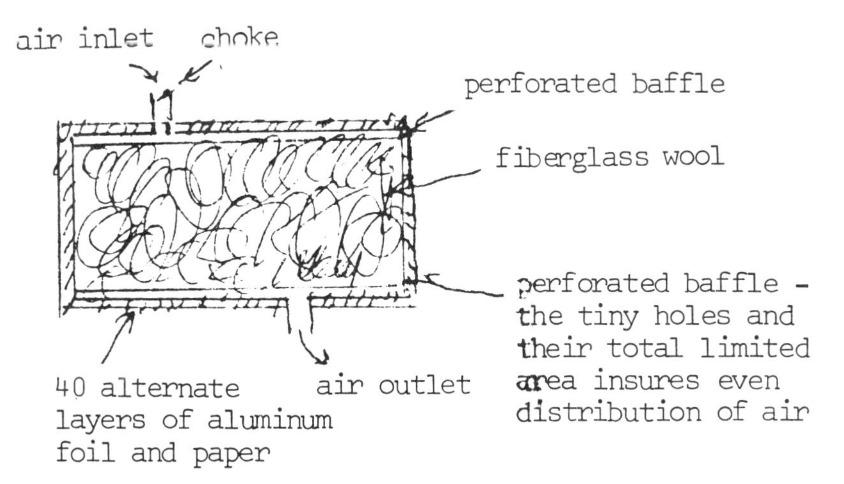

Library of Congress Card No. 84-081389